THE CITY & GUILDS TEXTBOOK

LEVEL 2 DIPLOMA IN
PAINTING AND
DECORATING

GW00671483

THE CITY & GUILDS TEXTBOOK

LEVEL 2 DIPLOMA IN
PAINTING AND DECORATING

ANN COOK

COLIN FEARN

STEVE WALTER

BARRIE YARDE

SERIES TECHNICAL EDITOR
MARTIN BURDFIELD

About City & Guilds

City & Guilds is the UK's leading provider of vocational qualifications, offering over 500 awards across a wide range of industries, and progressing from entry level to the highest levels of professional achievement. With over 8500 centres in 100 countries, City & Guilds is recognised by employers worldwide for providing qualifications that offer proof of the skills they need to get the job done.

Equal opportunities

City & Guilds fully supports the principle of equal opportunities and we are committed to satisfying this principle in all our activities and published material. A copy of our equal opportunities policy statement is available on the City & Guilds website.

Copyright

First edition 2014

ISBN 978-0-85193-296-5

Publisher: Fiona McGlade
Development Editors: Ellie Wheeler and Frankie Jones
Production Editor: Lauren Cubbage

Cover design by Design Deluxe
Illustrations by Barking Dog Art and Saxon Graphics Ltd
Typeset by Saxon Graphics Ltd, Derby
Printed in Croatia by Zrinski

British Library Cataloguing in Publication Data

A catalogue record for this book is available from the British Library.

Publications

For information about or to order City & Guilds support materials, contact 0844 534 0000 or centresupport@cityandguilds.com. You can find more information about the materials we have available at www.cityandguilds.com/publications.

Every effort has been made to ensure that the information contained in this publication is true and correct at the time of going to press. However, City & Guilds' products and services are subject to continuous development and improvement and the right is reserved to change products and services from time to time. City & Guilds cannot accept liability for loss or damage arising from the use of information in this publication.

City & Guilds
1 Giltspur Street
London EC1A 9DD

T 0844 543 0033

www.cityandguilds.com

publishingfeedback@cityandguilds.com

CONTENTS

FOREWORD

Whether in good times or in a difficult job market, I think one of the most important things for young people is to learn a skill. There will always be a demand for talented and skilled individuals who have knowledge and experience. That's why I'm such an avid supporter of vocational training. Vocational courses provide a unique opportunity for young people to learn from people in the industry, who know their trade inside out.

Careers rarely turn out as you plan them. You never know what opportunity is going to come your way. However, my personal experience has shown that if you haven't rigorously learned skills and gained knowledge, you are unlikely to be best placed to capitalise on opportunities that do come your way.

When I left school, I went straight to work in a butcher's shop, which was a fantastic experience. It may not be the industry I ended up making my career in, but being in the butcher's shop, working my way up to management level and learning from the people around me was something that taught me a lot about business and about the working environment.

Later, once I trained in the construction industry and was embarking on my career as a builder, these commercial principles were vital in my success and helped me to go on to set up my own business. The skills I had learned gave me an advantage and I was therefore able to make the most of my opportunities.

Later still, I could never have imagined that my career would take another turn into television. Of course, I recognise that I have had lucky breaks in my career, but when people say you make your own luck, I think there is definitely more than a grain of truth in that. People often ask me what my most life-changing moment has been, expecting me to say winning the first series of *Big Brother*. However, I always answer that my most life-changing moment was deciding to make the effort to learn the construction skills that I still use every day. That's why I was passionate about helping to set up a construction academy in the North West, helping other people to acquire skills and experience that will stay with them for their whole lives.

After all, an appearance on a reality TV show might have given me a degree of celebrity, but it is the skills that I learned as a builder that have kept me in demand as a presenter of DIY and building shows, and I have always continued to run my construction business. The truth is, you can never predict the way your life will turn out, but if you have learned a skill from experts in the field, you'll always be able to take advantage of the opportunities that come your way.

Craig Phillips

City & Guilds qualified bricklayer, owner of a successful construction business and television presenter of numerous construction and DIY shows

ABOUT THE AUTHORS

ANN COOK

CHAPTER 6

I started my painting and decorating career as a mature student, achieving the City & Guilds Bronze Medal for Advanced Craft, and progressed from self-employment to teaching between 1989 and 1998. I then became a City & Guilds External Verifier for Construction.

In 2002 I started my own assessment centre, delivering NVQs for experienced practitioners and CPD for college lecturers. I have also developed NVQ portfolios for 18 construction occupations, used by centres across the UK.

I am a member and past president of the Association of Painting Craft Teachers, and was a member of the committee for the Young Decorator of the Year competition for a number of years.

Since 2003, I have been a member of the National Working Group for Painting and Decorating, setting the National Occupational Standards. I have also written training programmes for apprentices, and I deliver training and assessment in the painting and decorating heritage sector.

COLIN FEARN

CHAPTERS 1 AND 2

I was born, grew up and continue to live in Cornwall with my wife, three children and Staffordshire bull terrier.

As a qualified carpenter and joiner, I have worked for many years on sites and in several joinery shops.

I won the National Wood Award for joinery work and am also a Fellow of the Institute of Carpenters, holder of the Master Craft certificate and have a BA in Education and Training.

I was until recently a full-time lecturer at Cornwall College, teaching both full-time students and apprentices.

I now work full-time as a writer for construction qualifications, practical assessments, questions and teaching materials for UK and Caribbean qualifications.

In my spare time I enjoy walks, small antiques and 'keeping my hand in' with various building projects.

STEVE WALTER

CHAPTERS 3 AND 4

I was born in London and on leaving school in 1967 was apprenticed to a large decorating company, attending Brixton School of Building part time.

In those days the apprenticeship lasted for five years, with an extra two years as an improver. I specialised in decorative finishes and wall coverings and worked in prestigious buildings for the rich and famous all over London.

I took a break from decorating for three years to train and work as a steeplejack, before returning to my first love to set up my own decorating firm.

I moved to the Sussex coast in 1995, and was soon employed full time while also studying to gain an educational qualification and degree. By 2012 I was head of department and lead Internal Verifier for Sussex Downs College. I am now semi-retired, but I still do consultancy work, building and painting of stage sets and enjoy keeping up with the decorating at home.

BARRIE YARDE

CHAPTERS 5, 7 AND 8

I have been very fortunate to have had a long career in construction, and in particular as a painter and decorator. I was trained as an apprentice by an 'old master', who helped me gain the skills that have given me such a wonderful career.

It was very much a case of practice and more practice, until I was able to demonstrate mastery of the skills that I had been shown.

I later went into teaching, and the years spent teaching in college have, I believe, delivered the right result – many of my learners have developed into fine craftspeople themselves.

I hope I can continue to encourage others to follow a worthwhile career in construction. I have been inspired by many others – too numerous to mention – and so I hope that this textbook will provide inspiration for you, encouraging you to study and learn the skills of painting and decorating.

MARTIN BURDFIELD

SERIES TECHNICAL EDITOR

I come from a long line of builders and strongly believe that you will find a career in the construction industry a very rewarding one. Be proud of the work you produce; it will be there for others to admire for many years.

As an apprentice I enjoyed acquiring new knowledge and learning new skills. I achieved the C&G Silver Medal for the highest marks in the Advanced Craft Certificate and won the UK's first Gold Medal in Joinery at the World Skills Competition. My career took me on from foreman, to estimator and then works manager with a number of large joinery companies, where I had the privilege of working on some prestigious projects.

Concurrent with this I began working in education. I have now worked in further education for over 35 years enjoying watching learners' skills improve during their training. For 10 years I ran the Skillbuild Joinery competitions and was the UK Training Manager and Chief Expert Elect at the World Skills Competition, training the UK's second Gold Medallist in Joinery.

Working with City & Guilds in various roles over the past 25 years has been very rewarding.

I believe that if you work and study hard anything is possible.

HOW TO USE THIS TEXTBOOK

Welcome to your City & Guilds Level 2 Diploma in Painting and Decorating textbook. It is designed to guide you through your Level 2 qualification and be a useful reference for you throughout your career. Each chapter covers a unit from the 6707 Level 2 qualification, and covers everything you will need to understand in order to complete your written or online tests and prepare for your practical assessments.

Please note that not all of the chapters will cover the learning outcomes in order. They have been put into a logical sequence as used within the industry and to cover all skills and techniques required.

Throughout this textbook you will see the following features:

Scumble

A glaze (semi-transparent product which will retain a design), to which a colourant has been added

Useful words – Words in bold in the text are explained in the margin to help your understanding.

INDUSTRY TIP

Do not confuse slow-drying paint with anti-theft paint. This is a specially formulated paint that remains tacky and is used on exterior surfaces, such as drainpipes, to prevent burglary.

Industry tips – Useful hints and tips related to working in the painting and decorating industry.

ACTIVITY

Study the list of defects and answer the following questions.

■ How are overlaps caused?
■ What causes flattening of embossed patterns?
■ What causes delamination of embossed papers?

Activities – These are suggested activities for you to complete.

FUNCTIONAL SKILLS

Visit a DIY store or builders' merchant and find out the cost of the above primers. Find out:

1 How much does each of the primers cost per litre? (They may be in different-sized bottles.)
2 Which is the most expensive?
3 Which is the cheapest? What is the mean price per litre?

Work on this activity can support FM1 (C1.13).

Functional Skills – These are activities that are tied to learning outcomes for the Functional Skills Maths, English and ICT qualifications.

Step-by-steps – These steps illustrate techniques and procedures that you will need to learn in order to carry out painting and decorating tasks.

STEP 1 Place the stencil plate accurately on the surface, lining up registration marks with the chalked lines, and secure with low-tack tape or a proprietary spray adhesive.

STEP 2 Before applying any paint, check whether a chalk line passes through the area to be stencilled. If so, remove it with a dry cloth, otherwise it will absorb the paint and create bittiness and uneven colour.

Case Study: Greg and Angelo

Greg and Angelo were in the middle of hanging a patterned paper to a lounge. This had been a bit of rush job, as they were behind on this contract. As Angelo looked back over the work they had done so far he noticed that some lengths appeared to be different in colour. The difference was quite noticeable now that he looked more closely at what they had done. Some lengths appeared darker than others.

Case Studies – Each chapter ends with a case study of an operative who has faced a common problem in the industry. Some of these will reveal the solution and others provide you with the opportunity to solve the problem.

Access equipment

Equipment that will enable you to gain access to work at a higher level than you can reach from the floor.

Trade dictionary – This feature lists key terms and tools that you will pick up from reading this book.

At the end of every chapter are some 'Test your knowledge' questions. These questions are designed to test your understanding of what you have learnt in that chapter. This can help with identifying further training or revision needed. You will find the answers at the end of the book.

INTRODUCTION

This book has been written to support students studying painting and decorating at Level 2. By studying this book, you should receive a thorough grounding in the skills and knowledge you will need to complete your course and either progress to Level 3, or enter the workforce. You will learn about the wider construction industry and how it works, as well as the skills and techniques you will need in order to work as a painter and decorator. You will be able to work safely on site and in domestic settings, using the correct tools and equipment to prepare, paint and wallpaper surfaces to produce a professional finish.

The features mentioned on the previous page are there to help you retain the information you will need to become a painter and decorator. The large trade dictionary included in this textbook is a list of important industry terms, techniques and tools. Use this for reference in class and in the workshop. Become familiar with the terms and techniques, and pay attention to the skills you need to master. If you put in the effort, you will be rewarded with a satisfying and successful career in painting and decorating.

ACKNOWLEDGEMENTS

I wish to thank my family and colleagues, particularly Tom Little, for their support and encouragement during the writing of this book.

Ann Cook

I would like to thank my dear wife Helen for her support in writing for this book. I dedicate my work to Matt, Tasha and Daisy, and not forgetting Floyd and Mrs Dusty.

Colin Fearn

I dedicate this to the trade I have been passionate about since I first held a paint brush and I hope that this will inspire future generations of decorators to have pride in their work. I would like to thank my partner, Wendy Dovey, for her support as proofreader, scribe and computer wizard! She taught me grown-up words and political correctness.

Steve Walter

I would like to thank in particular my wife, Becky, for her patience and understanding throughout this project. I would like also to pay tribute to Dick Fouracre, who set me on the way as a decorator; and to Albert Allen, my great friend and teaching mentor who set me on my way into teaching. We have all shared a passion for the craft of decoration and it has served us well.

Barrie Yarde

To my gorgeous wife Clare, without whose constant support, understanding and patience I would not have been able to continue. To Matthew and Eleanor, for not being there on too many occasions; normal service will be resumed. Finally, my parents, to whom I will always be grateful.

Martin Burdfield

City & Guilds would like to sincerely thank the following:

For invaluable painting and decorating expertise

Stephen Jones, Stephen Olsen and Elaine Bentley.

For their help with photoshoots

Jules Selmes (photographer), Adam Giles (photographer's assistant), Steve Lammas, Gary Thoirs, Casie Bedwell, Hamed Bamba, Lee Farrell, Luke Kalavashoti, Jade Keen, Stefan Kuhl, Andrew Maughan, Ismail Mohamud, Kris O'Neill, Abdul Qaffar, Mohammed Sanusi-Omosanya, Alan Saxton, James Shiels and Billy Snowball.

For supplying pictures for the book cover

Jules Selmes: © City & Guilds

TRADE DICTIONARY

Industry term	Definition and regional variations
Abrade 	To scratch the surface with a coarse material to provide a 'key', which will help coatings adhere.
Absorbent	An absorbent surface that soaks up liquids, eg bare plaster, bare timber. The more liquid a material can soak up, the more absorbent it is.
Absorption	The process of fluid disappearing and being incorporated into a material – highly absorbent surfaces such as softwoods suck up primers and paints, impairing the finish.
Accent	In colour terminology, using a small amount of contrast colour will enhance the other colour(s) and add excitement to a scheme.
Access equipment 	Equipment that will enable you to gain access to work at a higher level than you can reach from the floor.
Adhere 	To stick to a substance or surface.

Industry term	Definition and regional variations
Adhesive	In decorating and particularly paperhanging terms, adhesive is a material sometimes referred to as paste that can stick paper to ceiling and wall surfaces.
Alkaline	A substance that has a pH greater than 7. Alkalis form a caustic or corrosive solution when mixed with water. Examples include lime and caustic soda.
Approved Code of Practice (ACoP)	An ACoP gives practical advice for those involved in the construction industry on complying with health and safety legislation, such as using machinery safely. It has a special legal status and employers and employees are expected to work within its guidelines.
Architect	A trained professional who designs a structure and represents the client who wants the structure built. They are responsible for the production of the working drawings. They supervise the construction of buildings or other large structures.
Architectural technician	A draftsperson who works in an architectural practice. They usually prepare the drawings for a building.
Architraves	The moulded frames around doors or windows.

Industry term	Definition and regional variations
Arris	A sharp external edge, such as the edge of a door.
Asbestos	A naturally occurring mineral that was commonly used for a variety of purposes, including: insulation, fire protection, roofing and guttering. It is extremely hazardous and can cause a serious lung disease known as asbestosis.
Barrier cream	Cream used to protect hands from contaminants such as solvents, which may cause dermatitis and irritation, some brands are also water repellant. It is advisable to use before carrying out most painting and decorating tasks.
Batch	The wallpaper batch is shown by an identification number, or code, that denotes when it was produced and the print details. Codes should be the same on all rolls to avoid colour differences.
Belt sander	This is a sanding machine with a continuous belt of abrasive paper that has a flat sanding action.
Bill of quantities	Produced by a quantity surveyor and describes everything that is required for a job based on the drawings, specification and schedules. It is sent out to contractors and ensures that all the contractors are pricing for the job using the same information.
Bituminous	A word to describe a sticky black or brown substance made from petroleum, often known simply as 'tar'.
Block brush	Useful for brushing down rough surfaces such as cement rendering and brickwork and for applying cement-based paints. *Regional variation: cement paint brush*

Industry term	Definition and regional variations
British Standards Institute (BSI)	The organisation that develops and publishes standards in the UK.
Brush marks	A defect in the paint finish where visible heavy brush marks are left by the brush filling/bristles, even after laying off has been completed. *Regional variation: ladders*
Buckle	To bend, warp or bulge.
Building Regulations	A series of documents that set out legal requirements for the standards of building work.
Butt joint	Edges of lengths of paper that touch without a gap or overlap.
Capillarity	The rate at which liquid is drawn into a material through pores or small tubes.
Caulking	Caulking is a process of covering joints in dry lining. After the joints between the boards or at the angles have been filled, paper tape is sandwiched between a thin layer of filler. This work is carried out with the use of a caulking tool (shown left).
Centring	Setting out a wall to create a balanced or even effect for the pattern. Working out from the centre should enable this.
Chalk and line	A tool for marking chalk lines when setting out for paperhanging, and for marking lines in design setting out. The image on the left is of the self-chalking type of line, although it is possible to use a piece of string and chalk sticks.

Industry term	Definition and regional variations
Check/tick roller 	A small roller made of serrated zinc metal discs which revolve independently and take scumble off a 'mottler' (positioned above the discs and clipped in place) and then deposit a random series of dark 'tick' marks to simulate the darker, open pores of oak grain.
Cherry pickers 	A motor vehicle which has an extendable boom with a cage that operatives can stand in when painting high points/areas on buildings/bridges, etc.
Chisel knife 	A narrow bladed scraper, usually of 25mm width, used to access areas into which a normal scraper cannot reach.
Chroma	The degree of intensity, saturation, purity and brilliance of a colour.
Cissing 	This occurs when an applied material does not form a continuous film, separating to form surface globules, which leaves some areas of the surface to which it is applied uncoated.
Claw hammer 	A hammer used mainly for removing projecting nails from a surface. It can be used in conjunction with a nail punch to drive in projecting nails in new joinery.
Coalesce	In painting and decorating terms, where particles merge to form a film, particularly in water-borne coatings – the drying process is also known as coalescence.

Industry term	Definition and regional variations
Combs 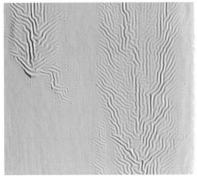	Made from metal (steel), rubber or card (improvised) and used mainly in producing the graining of oak.
Concrete	Material made up of cement, sand and stones of varying sizes and in varying proportions. It is mixed with water.
Consistency	Related directly to the viscosity of a coating, which can be altered by the addition of thinners or solvents.
Contact dermititis	A type of eczema that can cause red, itchy and scaly skin, and sometimes burning and stinging. It leads to skin becoming blistered, dry and cracked, and can affect any part of the body, but most commonly the hands.
Contrast/contrasting	In colour terminology this usually relates to colours opposite on the colour wheel. They will naturally go well together – you can use one to accentuate the other.
Creep	Where masking tape has not been securely fixed to a surface and some scumble or paint seeps beneath it – this will result in there not being a sharp edge to the broken colour effect.
Curtains	Heavy build-up of paint/coating sliding down a surface.

Industry term	Definition and regional variations
Cutting in 	The process of producing a sharp neat paint line between two structural components in a room, such as a wall/ceiling, architrave/wall, etc.
Dado 	An area of wall immediately above the skirting in a room, and separated from the wall filling by a timber, plaster or plastic strip secured to the wall.
Dado rail 	A rail secured to the wall that produces two individual areas in a room; the upper walls are normally much larger in area.
Damp proof course (DPC) 	A layer or strip of watertight material placed in a joint of a wall to prevent the passage of water. Fixed at a minimum of 150mm above finished ground level.
Datum point 	A fixed point or height from which to take reference levels. It may be a permanent Ordnance bench mark (OBM) or a temporary bench mark (TBM, pictured here). The datum point is used to transfer levels across a building site. It represents the finished floor level (FFL) on a dwelling.
Decant	To transfer a liquid by pouring from one container into another.
Denatured timber 	Timber that has been exposed to UV light and become grey and friable.

Industry term	Definition and regional variations
Distillate	A product which has been separated from a mixture by boiling it, and then cooling the vapour, in a process known as distillation.
Door furniture 	Anything attached to the door, eg handles, knobs, locks, letterboxes, fingerplates and hinges. *Regional variation: ironmongery*
Drop sheets 	Most commonly these large sheets are made from cotton twill (although they can also be plastic), which are designed to prevent preparation debris and paint from causing damage to the floor and/or furnishings.
Dusting brush 	A dusting brush is used to remove dust, debris and other particles from a surface before painting.
Efflorescence 	A white crystalline deposit which may form on the surface of plaster, cement or new bricks if the substrate contains a high proportion of soluble mineral salts.
Epidiascope	An opaque projector which has a strong light shining onto an opaque or transparent object and, by the use of its internal mirrors/prisms and/or lenses, projects the 'enlarged' object onto a screen (or wall).

Industry term	Definition and regional variations
Extension pole 	An extension pole can be fitted to a roller frame to reach high walls and ceilings. Using one may reduce the need for scaffolding.
Fall arrest 	A system of restraint that stops a person from hitting the ground.
Fall protection system 	Safety equipment designed to prevent or arrest falls. Examples include guard-rail systems, safety net systems, positioning-device systems and personal fall-restraint systems (PFASs).
Ferrous 	Containing iron.
Figurework/figure graining	The main design or pattern of a wood grain, which differs between tree species and according to the method of conversion.

Industry term	Definition and regional variations
Filling board	A filling board is used for transferring filler from where it is mixed to the workstation. A decorator may make their own to suit their needs. It is very similar to a plasterer's hawk.
Filling knife	A knife used to apply filler to open-grain work on timber, holes, cracks or any defect on a surface. It looks very much like a stripping knife but the blade is more flexible as it is made of a thinner-gauge metal.
First fix	The main elements of construction. First fix carpentry relates to fixing roofing timbers, building frames, etc.
Fitch brush	Used for fine detailed work in areas that are difficult to reach with a paint brush. They are available with pure bristle or synthetic filling, which is usually white and set in a round or flat ferrule.
Flashing	A defect that occurs in flat and eggshell finishes and looks like glossy streaks or patches. One cause is losing the wet edge during application.
Flash point	The temperature at which a material gives off a vapour that will ignite if exposed to flame. Chemicals with a low flash point are labelled as highly flammable.
Flat wall brush	Used to apply emulsion to large flat areas such as ceilings and walls, and may also be used to apply adhesive to wallpaper. Available in a wide range of varying qualities, and may be either man made or pure bristle.
Flush filling	Filling that is level with the rest of the surface.
Folding rule	Used for measuring lengths of wallpaper before cutting and widths of cuts. It is typically 1m long. It folds into four to make it easy to store in the pocket of overalls.

Industry term	Definition and regional variations
Foundation	Used to spread the load of a building to the subsoil.
Fugitive colours	Colours that fade when exposed to light. Some colours that are reasonably stable when used at full strength develop fugitive tendencies when mixed with white to create a lighter shade.
Fungicidal wash	When preparing a surface for decoration, this product is used to treat a surface that has become infected with mould, mildew or other kind of fungal growth. If it isn't used, the stains will show through the final finish and the fungi will continue to grow.
Graining	Applying and manipulating an appropriately coloured scumble to simulate the appearance of a specific timber.
Grounding out	Applying the ground coat for painted decorative work.
Hacking knife	Used to remove old putty from a window frame.

Industry term	Definition and regional variations
Hair stipple brush 	Used to remove all traces of brush marks and leave a smooth, even finish. *Regional variations: hair stippler, stippler*
Handrail 	Used with access equipment to reduce the risk of falling.
Hard dry 	Describing paint film that is hard enough to be worked on without damaging its finish.
Harmony/harmonious 	Terms often used in the description of colour schemes to express that something is pleasing to look at.
Hatchings 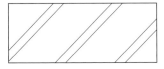 Brickwork	Patterns used on a drawing to identify different materials to meet the standard BS 1192.
Health and Safety Executive (HSE)	The national independent watchdog for work-related health, safety and illness. Its mission is to prevent death, injury and ill health in Great Britain's workplaces.

Industry term	Definition and regional variations
Hop-up	Small podium scaffold which can be collapsed down when not in use.
Hot air gun	A hot air gun is used to remove paint from a surface by heating the coating to a temperature where it softens; it can then be removed by using a scraper, shavehook, etc. *Regional variation: stripper*
Improvement notice	Issued by an HSE or local authority inspector to formally notify a company that improvements are needed to the way it is working.
Incandescent lighting	This is used to refer to tungsten lighting in particular. A wire filament is heated by electricity which then glows white hot and emits light.
Industrial Standards	Minimum standards of quality of completed work universally adopted within an industry.
Inertia-operated anchor device	A safety device attached to a safety line that operates in the same way as car seat belts.
Key	The condition of a surface to receive paint which will help adhesion of the coating. A 'key' can be provided by natural porosity, or by abrading the surface.

Industry term	Definition and regional variations
Kinetic lifting	This is a method of lifting items where the main force is provided by the operative's own muscular strength. Using the recognised technique will avoid injury.
Kitemark 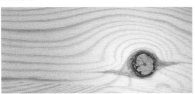	Confirms that the product that carries it conforms to the relevant British Standards.
Knot 	A natural defect in timber, which occurs where branches formed during the growth of a tree. Most often very resinous, and require the application of knotting to seal them.
Knotting brush 	Used to apply shellac knotting to knots on a timber surface before priming.
Knotting solution 	A quick drying spirit-based sealer, used to prevent the resin in knots causing discolouration of applied paint. It can also be used to seal small areas of other surface contaminants, eg felt-tip pen, during preparation.
Laser level	Using a laser level can be an extremely accurate method of producing both vertical and horizontal lines, eg for paperhanging, etc. Accuracy of lines will depend on correctly setting up the equipment.

Industry term	Definition and regional variations
Ladders	Ladders can be made from wood, aluminium, steel or fibreglass. Ladder types include pole ladders, standing ladders, double and treble extending ladders and roof ladders.
Laying off	Finishing off an area of paintwork with very light strokes of the brush in order to eliminate brush marks.
LED	An LED (light-emitting diode) is an electronic device that emits light when an electrical current is passed through it. Halogen and LED lights come closest to daylight in terms of how colours are affected – however, because bright light is cast on specific areas there may well be areas of deep shadow where colours will look less bright.
Lightfast	Describes colours that are resistant to fading – unaffected by light.
Liquid paint remover (LPR)	A chemical-based type of paint stripper for removing old paint systems.
Making good	Typically to fill holes and defects in the surface. Repairing a defective area to produce a sound, level finish.

Industry term	Definition and regional variations
Manufacturer's instructions 	Guidelines given by the manufacturer on conditions of use.
Masking tape 	A self-adhesive paper which comes in 55m lengths and 12mm, 19mm, 25mm, 38mm or 75mm widths. Interior tape is used mainly for masking items that cannot be removed and stored, for taping down dust sheets to wooden floors or carpets to stop them moving and to protect narrow surfaces from paint or paint remover. Waterproof masking tape can be used for exterior work, such as masking up door furniture, window frames or fascia boards, and particularly to cover surrounding areas when painting rendered, brick or pebbledashed walls.
Medium	The liquid ingredient that enables a glaze to be spread over a surface and dry as a film. A medium binds the colourant particles together and provides good adhesion to the substrate.
Method of conversion Through-and-through	The way a newly felled tree is sawn up into usable-sized pieces of timber, using two main methods: through-and-through or quarter-sawn.
Method statement	A description of the intended method of carrying out a task, often linked to a risk assessment.
Micro-porous paint	A paint that leaves a breathable film that allows moisture and air to be released but prevents moisture, like rain, getting in.
Mildew 	Sometimes referred to as mould. A fungus that produces a superficial growth on various kinds of damp surface. It can be whitish in colour or black spots that multiply.
Mill	A paper mill is a factory for manufacturing paper.

Industry term	Definition and regional variations
Mould growth	Mould is a general term for types of fungi, made up of airborne spores that can multiply and feed on organic matter, for example in pastes (starch pastes contain organic products such as wheat). It may vary in colour depending on the species of fungus, ie black, green, pink etc.
Nail punch	This is a metal tool used with a hammer, to set protruding nails below a timber surface.
Natural paint brush	Pure bristle brushes are made from animal hair and are used mainly for applying solvent-borne surface coatings.
Needle de-scaling gun	This consists of an outer body containing a number of hardened steel needles which are propelled forward by a spring loaded piston. On hitting the surface, the needles rebound and are forced forward by the piston in a continuous action. The individual needles are self-adjusting making it ideal for preparing uneven metal surfaces and around awkward areas such as nuts and bolts.
Nibs	Small particles of foreign matter, such as paint skin or grit, that have dried in the film of a coating and which cause it to feel rough.
Niche	A shallow recess in a wall intended to hold a statue, vase, etc.
Opacity	The ability of the pigment in paint to obliterate or hide the existing surface colour.

Industry term	Definition and regional variations
Opaque	Not transmitting light – the opposite of transparent.
Orbital sander	This sander consists of a rectangular flexible platform pad on to which various types of abrasive paper are fixed. The sander moves in a small circular or orbital motion to abrade the surface.
Outrigger	Stabilisers on mobile tower scaffolds.
Overalls	Protective clothing worn when painting and decorating. If the overalls have a bib they will enable you to carry a small number of tools, particularly a hanging brush and shears, in the pockets, making them efficient and easy to use.
Paint kettle	These are made from either plastic or metal and are used to decant paint for use. Plastic is generally used for water-borne paint and metal for solvent-borne paint. *Regional variation: paint pot*
Paint stirrer	These are used to ensure that all the ingredients in a paint container are dispersed evenly and that the coating is of a smooth consistency.

Industry term	Definition and regional variations
Paint strainer 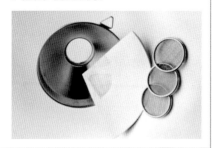	Paint strainers are useful for removing contaminants from those surface coatings whose viscosity will allow them to pass through the gauze. Straining paint from containers to which unused material has been returned is the main use for this piece of equipment, but even new unused materials can contain 'bits'.
Palette 	A rectangular timber or plastic board (sometimes with a hole to place the thumb through) on which a quantity of paint is placed.
Paperhanging brush 	This is used to apply papers to walls to ensure that all air pockets are removed and that the paper lies flat without creases. *Regional variation: smoothing brush*
Paperhanging shears 	These are used to cut lengths of wallpaper, and also for trimming around obstacles. *Regional variations: scissors, paperhanging scissors*
PASMA 	The Prefabricated Access Suppliers' & Manufacturers' Association – the lead trade association for the mobile access tower industry.
Paste brush 	This is a 125mm or 150mm flat wall brush used to apply paste or adhesive to wall or surface coverings. It is also used to apply size to absorbent wall and ceiling surfaces before hanging papers.

Industry term	Definition and regional variations
Paste table 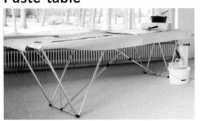	This is used to lay out wallpapers for measuring, cutting, matching and pasting. It is usually made from wood or plastic, and is typically 1.8m long and 560mm wide.
Pasting machine 	This is used to apply paste to papers. This method can be extremely quick and ensures that the correct amount of paste is applied when correctly set up.
Pattern match Straight match symbol	This helps you identify where the pattern at the edge of one piece of wallpaper fits together with another roll. This could be an offset match, such as a half-drop or random match, or a straight match. The type of pattern match is given by the symbol on the packet.
Pattern repeat 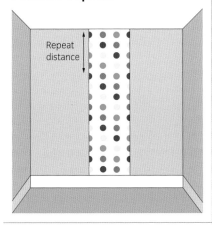	This is the distance between a single point on a pattern and the next point where it is repeated on the pattern.
Perimeter 	The distance around an object or room. In this instance: 2.2 2.2 4.2 4.2 ——— 12.8m

Industry term	Definition and regional variations
Personal protective equipment (PPE) 	This is defined in the Personal Protective Equipment (PPE) at Work Regulations 1992 as 'all equipment (including clothing affording protection against the weather) which is intended to be worn or held by a person at work and which protects against one or more risks to a person's health or safety.' For example, safety helmets, gloves, eye protection, high-visibility clothing, safety footwear and safety harnesses.
Pin hammer 	Small hand-held hammer used with nail punches and when placing sprigs in window frames, etc.
Plumb bob 	This is used for ensuring that first and subsequent lengths of wallpaper are hung vertically. It is a small weight, usually made from steel, suspended from a length of cord.
Podium steps 	A low-level access platform with adjustable height and guard rail. The steps may be tubular, self-erecting or folded prior to erection, to enable them to pass through standard doors and corridors.
Porosity	The state of being porous – when small spaces or voids in a solid material mean that it can absorb liquids.

Industry term	Definition and regional variations
Pounce bag 	A small bag of coarsely woven or thin fabric (eg cheesecloth) filled with a fine powder (eg crushed chalk or charcoal) – used to transfer pounced designs.
Pounce wheel 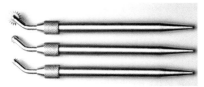	A toothed wheel that perforates paper with evenly spaced fine holes – varying sizes are available to produce different-sized holes.
Pouncing	Chalk is pounced through the holes made by a pounce wheel. The chalk marks leave an outline of the design prior to applying paint.
Preparatory 	In the context of paperhanging, this refers to the preparation of a surface for further treatment.
Primary 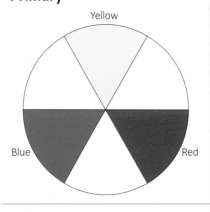	First in a sequence. In the case of primary colours, red, yellow and blue are deemed primary as from these first colours many others can be mixed.
Prime 	To apply the first coat of paint to a surface. Most often the paint will be thinned to increase absorption, which will provide increased adhesion, particularly on a porous surface.
Programme of work	A series of events where the order of activities and the amount of time involved has been planned out. This is usually shown in the form of a bar or Gantt chart. *Regional variation: work schedule*

Industry term	Definition and regional variations
Prohibition notice	Issued by an HSE or local authority inspector when there is an immediate risk of personal injury. Receiving one means you are breaking health and safety regulations.
Proud filling 	Filling that projects above the surface and will need to be rubbed down when dry to make it level with the rest of the surface.
Putty knife 	Used to fill small nail holes and cracks and also for applying putty to traditional wood and metal windows when replacing glass. *Regional variation: stopping knife*
PVA 	PVA stands for polyvinyl acetate, a resin used in both adhesives and paints to provide a hard, strong film – in the case of adhesives, the film is clear and does not stain.
Radiator brush 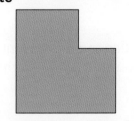	Used to apply paint to areas that are difficult to reach with a paint brush, particularly behind pipes, radiators and columns. These have a bristle filling attached to a long wooden handle, or a wire handle that can be bent to fit into awkward areas.
Rebate	A rectangular area removed from the corner of a timber section. Used to locate a pane of glass while a frame rebate locates a window sash.

Industry term	Definition and regional variations
Registration marks 	Marks (or a very small cut-out section) made on a stencil which are lined up with chalk lines on the surface, and/or part of a previously applied stencil if using a multi-plate stencil, to ensure correct positioning before applying paint.
Rendering 	A sand and cement mix covering to brickwork.
Risk assessment 	An assessment of the hazards and risks associated with an activity and the reduction and monitoring of them.
Roller 	The standard type of roller used by decorators is a cylinder roller, which consists of a straight cylinder with a fabric cover called a sleeve. The choice of roller will depend on the type of coating being used and the type of substrate to be painted. There are many types, including very smooth rollers for applying finishing paints to flat doors and lambswool rollers for applying paint to a textured surface such as pebbledash.
Roller tray	A flat-bottomed container with a 'reservoir' which holds only small quantities of paint. It is used to charge the roller before application.
Ropiness 	Another surface finish defect similar to brush marks, but where the marks are much heavier and coarser; being more pronounced, they are highly visible and unsightly. Usually due to poor brush application because paint has thickened and has not been adequately brushed out or laid off. *Regional variations: ribbiness, tramlines*

Industry term	Definition and regional variations
Rotary disc sander 	A sander where the backing support for the abrasive is a regular disc made from a flexible material. The disc rotates only in a circular motion.
Rotary wire brush 	A fitting that can be attached to an electric drill, used for the preparation of ferrous metal surfaces.
Rubbing block 	A tool used when abrading surfaces, particularly applied filler. Rubber types can be used when rubbing down wet, and have pins which can be used to hold the abrasive in place whilst the block is in use. *Regional variation: sanding block*
Saponification	A defect which is a soft sticky paint film caused by alkali contamination. It sometimes exudes a brown soapy liquid.
Scaffold boards 	Planks used to provide a working platform on trestles and tubular scaffolds.
Scale Scale: 1:1250	This is the ratio in size of an item in a drawing in relation to its actual size. On site, scale rulers are used to determine the actual size of the item in a structure.
Scumble 	A glaze (translucent product that will retain a design), to which a colourant has been added.

Industry term	Definition and regional variations
Scuttle	A type of bucket used with a roller and filled with paste to speed up the process of pasting papers on the paste table. They are also useful for the types of papers that require the wall to be pasted instead of the back of the paper.
Seam roller	A small roller made from boxwood or plastic, used to apply localised pressure to wallpaper seams and/or internal corners that may not be adhering well. Care should be taken in their use.
Secondary	Second, or the second stage (after primary).
Second fix	The final finish, the construction work following plastering, ie when a carpenter fixes architraves, skirtings, doors, etc.
Services	The energy and water facilities that are supplied to properties from the 'mains' supplies, and also the drainage systems to remove waste from a building.
Set out	To put in a specified position or location – following a drawing, written specification or verbal instructions.
Shading	A process normally associated with paperhanging where the operative visually checks every roll to ensure that all rolls to be used are of the same colour and tone.
Shavehooks	These are hand tools used when removing coatings in conjunction with hot air or paint removers, particularly from surfaces that have intricate mouldings. They can have triangular, combination, or pear-shaped heads.

Industry term	Definition and regional variations
Shellac 	A natural resin found mainly in India, made of secretions from insects. When dissolved in spirit it forms the basis of French polish, knotting and sealers.
Sinking 	Reduction in the sheen of a paint film. This may occur where a section of making good has not been spot-primed and the film former has been partly absorbed by the porous filler.
Sizing	Applying a thin coat of glue size or thinned paste to an absorbent surface before hanging wallpaper.
Skeleton gun 	Sealants, caulk and mastic tubes are inserted into a metal frame called a skeleton gun in order to dispense them directly onto a surface. *Regional variation: cage, mastic gun, caulking gun, caulk gun*
Skid marks 	This is a defect caused by poor application techniques, normally occurring when applying too much pressure during the roller application of paint or the production of broken colour effects. It leaves marks which appear as 'streaks' on the surface.
Specification	A contract document that gives information about the quality of materials and standards of workmanship required.
Spirit level 	A tool used to make sure the work is level (horizontal) and plumb (vertical).

Industry term	Definition and regional variations
Spot-prime	To apply appropriate primer to sections of surface area that have been made good, to prevent the next coat from sinking into the filler.
Stencil brush	A round brush with a filling of short, stiff bristles set in a metal ferrule on a short handle. Stencil brushes are available in a range of sizes from 6 to 38mm.
Straight edge	Used by some decorators, particularly for trimming waste paper when up against straight edges such as skirtings, door frames and ceiling edges. They can come with a handle or without and are typically 600mm in length.
Stripping knife	Knife used to remove wallpaper, loose or flaking paint and other debris or nibs in the making good process. *Regional variation: scraper*
Substrate	The building material (eg plaster, timber) or surface on which decorative materials are applied.
Surface tension	Simply explained, this is the tendency of the surface of a liquid/solid to resist an external force.
Sustainability	Materials that can be 'replaced' by regrowth in the future will be sustainable.

Industry term	Definition and regional variations
Swatch 	A collection of paint, wallpaper, or fabric samples, usually collected into a book form.
Swingback 	This is the name given to the rear frame of a pair of swingback steps. A framed back support is hinged to the back of the steps to provide support and to enable the steps to be set at the correct angle.
Synthetic paint brush 	Paint brush with man-made fibres and mainly used for water-based paints (emulsion).
Tack rag 	A cotton gauze textile, impregnated with a non-drying resin which makes it 'sticky'. It is used to remove fine residual dust from a surface before any paint is applied.
Tape measure 	A measuring tool used to set out and check dimensions. A range of tape measures in various sizes is required when setting out a structure or for the application of decorative finishes. Tape measures vary in range from 3m to 30m.
Tertiary	Third, or the third stage (after secondary).

Industry term	Definition and regional variations
Toe board	Attached to access equipment for extra safety and to stop items being kicked off the platform.
Tonal balance	You can achieve tonal balance by manipulating your use of colour. For example, a small amount of colour can offset the visual weight of a large area of neutral values. Similarly, a small area of warm colour can balance a large area of cool colour.
Tower scaffold	A static or mobile working platform.
Translucent	Allows light to pass through, but prevents images from being seen clearly.
Transparent	Easily seen through, like clear glass.
Trestle	A type of working platform. Used with scaffold boards or lightweight stagings to form a working platform.
Trimming knife	Some decorators like to use trimming knives when wallpapering, when they need to cut around obstacles.

Industry term	Definition and regional variations
Trowel	This is used by a painter mainly for making good defective plasterwork.
Two-knot brush	Used to apply water-thinned paints to rough surfaces such as cement, rendering and brickwork. They are also used to apply cement-based paints, as the bristles are not attacked by the alkali in the cement, and for washing down surfaces when using a cleaning agent such as sugar soap.
UV light	Ultraviolet rays from the sun, which can cause health problems (for example with the skin or eyes) and damage to materials.
Value	Relating to the amount of light which will be reflected from a colour on a surface and, to the eye, makes them look 'light' or 'dark'.
Varnish brush	Normally well-worn brushes, capable of producing a high quality finish which is free from brush marks. They should be stored carefully, and used only for the application of these types of coating.
Viscosity	The ability of a liquid or coating to flow; the more viscous it is, the slower it flows.
Visible spectrum	The colours of a rainbow: red, orange, yellow, green, blue, indigo and violet.

Industry term	Definition and regional variations
Volatile organic compound (VOC) 	Materials that evaporate readily from many sources; an example of which is the solvents used in the manufacture of many coatings. The measurement of volatile organic compounds shows how much pollution a product will emit into the air when in use.
Washing-down brush 	These are relatively cheap two-knot or flat brushes, available in one size only, and used for washing down with sugar soap or detergent.
Wet and dry (abrasive paper) 	A type of abrasive where silicon carbide abrasive particles are bonded to a backing paper using a waterproof resin. This makes it suitable for use in both preparation situations, with wet abrading providing a dust-free atmosphere and less clogging of the material, making it last longer.
Whiting 	Chalk (calcium carbonate) prepared by drying and grinding, as used in whitewash and sometimes as an extender in paint. Also rubbed over oil-painted grounds to stop cissing. This is done before applying watercolour during the graining process.
Wire brush 	Used for removing loose rust and corrosion from metalwork.

Industry term	Definition and regional variations
Wood ingrain	Wood ingrain paper is a pulp paper made up of two layers between which small chips of wood are sandwiched. It usually comes in 10m long by 530mm wide rolls and can be supplied in different grades of texture: fine, medium or coarse. Wood ingrain is usually coated with water-borne paints, or sometimes oil based paints, after hanging. It tends to mask irregularities in the underlying surface due to the pronounced texture of the woodchip appearance. *Regional variation: woodchip*
Work at height	Any work that, without the proper precautions in place, could result in a fall. This can include work at ground level with the risk of falling into an opening in a floor or hole in the ground.
Work restraint	A device used to prevent people climbing out of a mobile elevating work platform (MEWP).
Worked up	Re-activated, or made workable, by rubbing with a brush containing a small quantity of the material, or a suitable thinner.

Chapter 1
Unit 201: Health, safety and welfare in construction

A career in the building industry can be a very rewarding one, both personally and financially. However, building sites and workshops are potentially very dangerous places; there are many potential hazards in the construction industry. Many construction operatives (workers) are injured each year, some fatally. Regulations have been brought in over the years to reduce accidents and improve working conditions.

By reading this chapter you will know about:

1 The health and safety regulations, roles and responsibilities.
2 Accident and emergency reporting procedures and documentation.
3 Identifying hazards in the workplace.
4 Health and welfare in the workplace.
5 Handling materials and equipment safely.
6 Access equipment and working at heights.
7 Working with electrical equipment in the workplace.
8 Using personal protective equipment (PPE).
9 The cause of fire and fire emergency procedures.

HEALTH AND SAFETY LEGISLATION

According to the Health and Safety Executive (HSE) figures, in 2011/12:

- Forty-nine construction operatives were fatally injured. Twenty-three of these operatives were self-employed. This compares with an average of 59 fatalities over the previous five years, of which an average of 19 fatally injured construction operatives were self-employed.

- The rate of fatal injury per 100,000 construction operatives was 2.3, compared with a five-year average of 2.5.

- Construction industry operatives were involved in 28% of fatal injuries across all industry sectors and it accounts for the greatest number of fatal injuries in any industry sector.

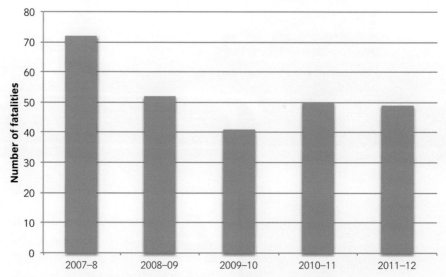

Number and rate of fatal injuries to workers in construction (RIDDOR)

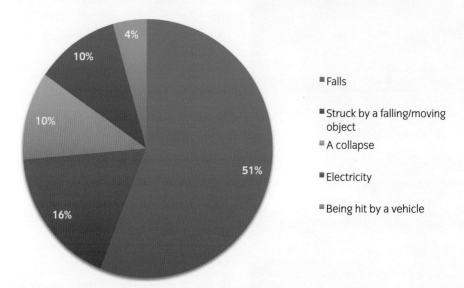

Proportion of fatalities in 2011/12 in construction

Health and safety legislation and great efforts made by the industry have made workplaces much safer in recent years. It is the responsibility of everyone involved in the building industry to continue to make it safer. Statistics are not just meaningless numbers – they represent injuries to real people. Many people believe that an accident will never happen to them, but it can. Accidents can:

■ have a devastating effect on lives and families

■ cost a lot financially in injury claims

■ result in prosecution

■ lead to job loss if an employee broke their company's safety policy.

Employers have an additional duty to ensure operatives have access to welfare facilities, eg drinking water, first aid and toilets, which will be discussed later in this chapter.

If everyone who works in the building industry pays close attention to health, safety and welfare, all operatives – including you – have every chance of enjoying a long, injury-free career.

UK HEALTH AND SAFETY REGULATIONS, ROLES AND RESPONSIBILITIES

In the UK there are many laws (legislation) that have been put into place to make sure that those working on construction sites, and members of the public, are kept healthy and safe. If these laws and regulations are not obeyed then prosecutions can take place. Worse still, there is a greater risk of injury and damage to your health and the health of those around you.

The principal legislation which relates to health, safety and welfare in construction is:

■ Health and Safety at Work Act (HASAWA) 1974

■ Control of Substances Hazardous to Health (COSHH) Regulations 2002

■ Reporting of Injuries, Diseases and Dangerous Occurrences Regulations (RIDDOR) 2013

■ Construction, Design and Management (CDM) Regulations 2007

■ Provision and Use of Work Equipment Regulations (PUWER) 1998

■ Manual Handling Operations Regulations 1992

■ Personal Protective Equipment (PPE) at Work Regulations 1992

Standard construction safety equipment

- Work at Height Regulations 2005 (as amended)
- Lifting Operations and Lifting Equipment Regulations (LOLER) 1998
- Control of Noise at Work Regulations 2005
- Control of Vibration at Work Regulations 2005.

HEALTH AND SAFETY AT WORK ACT (HASAWA) 1974

The Health and Safety at Work Act (HASAWA) 1974 applies to all workplaces. Everyone who works on a building site or in a workshop is covered by this legislation. This includes employed and self-employed operatives, subcontractors, the employer and those delivering goods to the site. It not only protects those working, it also ensures the safety of anyone else who might be nearby.

KEY EMPLOYER RESPONSIBILITIES

The key employer health and safety responsibilities under HASAWA are to:

- provide a safe working environment
- provide safe access (entrance) and egress (exit) to the work area
- provide adequate staff training
- have a written health and safety policy in place
- provide health and safety information and display the appropriate signs
- carry out risk assessments
- provide safe machinery and equipment and to ensure it is well-maintained and in a safe condition
- provide adequate supervision to ensure safe practices are carried out
- involve trade union safety representatives, where appointed, in matters relating to health and safety
- provide personal protective equipment (**PPE**) free of charge, ensure the appropriate PPE is used whenever needed, and that operatives are properly supervised
- ensure materials and substances are transported, used and stored safely.

PPE

This is defined in the Personal Protective Equipment at Work Regulations 1992 as 'all equipment (including clothing affording protection against the weather) which is intended to be worn or held by a person at work and which protects against one or more risks to a person's health or safety.'

Risk assessments and method statements

The HASAWA requires that employers must carry out regular **risk assessments** to make sure that there are minimal dangers to their employees in a workplace.

Risk assessment

An assessment of the hazards and risks associated with an activity and the reduction and monitoring of them

---

Risk Assessment

Activity / Workplace assessed: Return to work after accident
Persons consulted / involved in risk assessment
Date:
Reviewed on:

Location:
Risk assessment reference number:
Review date:
Review by:

Significant hazard	People at risk and what is the risk Describe the harm that is likely to result from the hazard (eg cut, broken leg, chemical burn etc) and who could be harmed (eg employees, contractors, visitors etc)	Existing control measure What is currently in place to control the risk?	Risk rating Use matrix identified in guidance note Likelihood (L) Severity (S) Multiply (L) * (S) to produce risk rating (RR)				Further action required What is required to bring the risk down to an acceptable level? Use hierarchy of control described in guidance note when considering the controls needed	Actioned to: Who will complete the action?	Due date: When will the action be completed by?	Completion date: Initial and date once the action has been completed
			L	S	RR	L/M/H				
Uneven floors	Operatives	Verbal warning and supervision	2	1	2	M	None applicable	Site supervisor	Active now	Ongoing
Steps	Operatives	Verbal warning	2	1	2	M	None applicable	Site supervisor	Active now	Ongoing
Staircases	Operatives	Verbal warning	2	2	4	M	None applicable	Site supervisor	Active now	Ongoing

Likelihood
3 – Very likely
2 – Possible
1 – Unlikely

Severity
3 – Major injury/extensive damage
2 – Medium injury/significant damage
1 – Slight/minor damage

1   – Low risk, action should be taken to reduce the risk if reasonably practicable
2, 3, 4 – Medium risk, is a significant risk and would require an appropriate level of resource
6 & 9   – High risk, may require considerable resource to mitigate. Control should focus on elimination of risk, if not possible control should be obtained by following the hierarchy of control

123 type risk assessment

A risk assessment is a legally required tool used by employers to:

- identify work hazards

- assess the risk of harm arising from these hazards

- adequately control the risk.

Risk assessments are carried out as follows:

1 Identify the hazards. Consider the environment in which the job will be done. Which tools and materials will be used?

2 Identify who might be at risk. Think about operatives, visitors and members of the public.

3 Evaluate the risk. How severe is the potential injury? How likely is it to happen? A severe injury may be possible but may also be very improbable. On the other hand a minor injury might be very likely.

4 If there is an unacceptable risk, can the job be changed? Could different tools or materials be used instead?

5 If the risk is acceptable, what measures can be taken to reduce the risk? This could be training, special equipment and using PPE.

6 Keep good records. Explain the findings of the risk assessment to the operatives involved. Update the risk assessment as required – there may be new machinery, materials or staff. Even adverse weather can bring additional risks.

A **method statement** is required by law and is a useful way of recording the hazards involved in a specific task. It is used to communicate the risk and precautions required to all those involved in the work. It should be clear, uncomplicated and easy to understand as it is for the benefit of those carrying out the work (and their immediate supervisors).

Inductions and tool box talks

Any new visitors to and operatives on a site will be given an induction. This will explain:

- the layout of the site

- any hazards of which they need to be aware

- the location of welfare facilities

- the assembly areas in case of emergency

- site rules.

Tool box talks are short talks given at regular intervals. They give timely safety reminders and outline any new hazards that may have arisen because construction sites change as they develop. Weather conditions such as extreme heat, wind or rain may create new hazards.

KEY EMPLOYEE RESPONSIBILITIES

The HASAWA covers the responsibilities of employees and subcontractors:

- You must work in a safe manner and take care at all times.

- You must make sure you do not put yourself or others at risk by your actions or inactions.

Method statement

A description of the intended method of carrying out a task, often linked to a risk assessment

INDUSTRY TIP

The Construction Skills Certification Scheme (CSCS) was set up in the mid-'90s with the aim of improving site operatives' competence to reduce accidents and drive up on-site efficiency. Card holders must take a health and safety test. The colour of card depends on level of qualification held and job role. For more information see www.cscs.uk.com

ACTIVITY

Think back to your induction. Write down what was discussed. Did you understand everything? Do you need any further information? If you have not had an induction, write a list of the things you think you need to know.

INDUSTRY TIP

Remember, if you are unsure about any health and safety issue always seek help and advice.

- You must co-operate with your employer in regard to health and safety. If you do not you risk injury (to yourself or others), prosecution, a fine and loss of employment. Do not take part in practical jokes and horseplay.

- You must use any equipment and safeguards provided by your employer. For example, you must wear, look after and report any damage to the PPE that your employer provides.

- You must not interfere or tamper with any safety equipment.

- You must not misuse or interfere with anything that is provided for employees' safety.

FIRST AID AND FIRST-AID KITS

First aid should only be applied by someone trained in first aid. Even a minor injury could become infected and therefore should be cleaned and a dressing applied. If any cut or injury shows signs of infection, becomes inflamed or painful seek medical attention. An employer's first-aid needs should be assessed to indicate whether a first-aider (someone trained in first aid) is necessary. The minimum requirement is to appoint a person to take charge of first-aid arrangements. The role of this appointed person includes looking after the first-aid equipment and facilities and calling the emergency services when required.

First-aid kits vary according to the size of the workforce. First-aid boxes should not contain tablets or medicines.

INDUSTRY TIP

The key employee health and safety responsibilities are to:
- work safely
- work in partnership with your employer
- report hazards and accidents as per company policy.

INDUSTRY TIP

Employees must not be charged for anything given to them or done for them by the employer in relation to safety.

INDUSTRY TIP

In the event of an accident, first aid will be carried out by a qualified first aider. First aid is designed to stabilise a patient for later treatment if required. The casualty may be taken to hospital or an ambulance may be called. In the event of an emergency you should raise the alarm.

ACTIVITY

Your place of work or training will have an appointed first-aider who deals with first aid. Find out who they are and how to make contact with them.

ACTIVITY

Find the first-aid kit in your workplace or place of training. What is inside it? Is there anything missing?

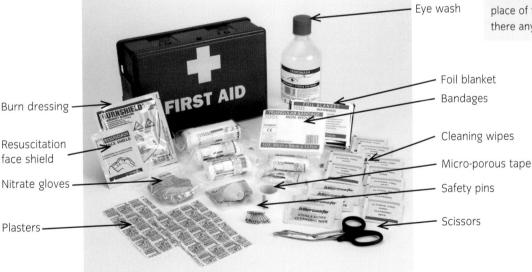

Eye wash

Burn dressing

Resuscitation face shield

Nitrate gloves

Plasters

Foil blanket

Bandages

Cleaning wipes

Micro-porous tape

Safety pins

Scissors

First-aid kit

SOURCES OF HEALTH AND SAFETY INFORMATION

Source	How they can help
Health and Safety Executive (HSE)	A government body that oversees health and safety in the workplace. It produces health and safety literature such as the **Approved Code of Practice** (ACoP).
Construction Skills	The construction industry training body produces literature and is directly involved with construction training.
The Royal Society for the Prevention of Accidents (ROSPA)	It produces literature and gives advice.
The Royal Society for Public Health	An independent, multi-disciplinary charity that is dedicated to the promotion and protection of collective human health and wellbeing.
Institution of Occupational Safety and Health (IOSH)	A chartered body for health and safety practitioners. The world's largest health and safety professional membership organisation.
The British Safety Council	It helps businesses with their health, safety and environmental management.

Approved Code of Practice

ACoP gives practical advice for those in the construction industry in relation to using machinery

INDUSTRY TIP

There are many other trade organisations, eg the Timber Research and Development Association (TRADA), which also offer advice on safe practices.

ACTIVITY

You have been asked to give a tool box talk because of several minor injuries involving tripping on site. What topics would you include in this talk?

INDUSTRY TIP

To find out more information on the sources in the table, enter their names into a search engine on the internet.

HEALTH AND SAFETY EXECUTIVE (HSE)

The HSE is a body set up by the government. The HSE ensures that the law is carried out correctly and has extensive powers to ensure that it can do its job. It can make spot checks in the workplace, bring the police, examine anything on the premises and take things away to be examined.

If the HSE finds a health and safety problem that breaks health and safety law it might issue an **improvement notice** giving the employer a set amount of time to correct the problem. For serious health and safety risks where there is a risk of immediate major injury, it can issue a **prohibition notice** which will stop all work on site until the health and safety issues are rectified. It may take an employer, employee, self-employed person (subcontractor) or anyone else

Improvement notice

Issued by an HSE or local authority inspector to formally notify a company that improvements are needed to the way it is working

Prohibition notice

Issued by an HSE or local authority inspector when there is an immediate risk of personal injury. They are not issued lightly and if you are on the receiving end of one, you are clearly breaking a health and safety regulation

involved with the building process to court for breaking health and safety legislation.

The HSE provides a lot of advice on safety and publishes numerous booklets and information sheets. One example of this is the Approved Code of Practice (ACoP) which applies to wood working machinery. The ACoP has a special legal status and employers and employees are expected to work within its guidelines.

The duties of the HSE are to:

■ give advice

■ issue improvement and prohibition notices

■ caution

■ prosecute

■ investigate.

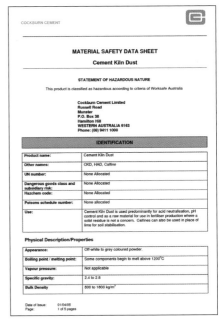

The Approved Code of Practice booklet is available free online

CONTROL OF SUBSTANCES HAZARDOUS TO HEALTH (COSHH) REGULATIONS 2002

The Control of Substances Hazardous to Health (COSHH) Regulations 2002 control the use of dangerous substances, eg preservatives, fuels, solvents, adhesives, cement and oil based paint. These have to be moved, stored and used safely without polluting the environment. It also covers hazardous substances produced while working, eg wood dust produced when sanding or drilling.

Hazardous substances may be discovered during the building process, eg lead-based paint or asbestos. These are covered by separate regulations.

When considering substances and materials that may be hazardous to health an employer should do the following to comply with COSHH:

■ Read and check the COSHH safety data sheet that comes with the product. It will outline any hazards associated with the product and the safety measures to be taken.

■ Check with the supplier if there are any known risks to health.

■ Use the trade press to find out if there is any information about this substance or material.

Example of COSHH data sheet

■ Use the HSE website, or other websites, to check any known issues with the substance or material.

When assessing the risk of a potentially dangerous substance or material it is important to consider how operatives could be exposed to it. For example:

- by breathing in gas or mist

- by swallowing it

- by getting it into their eyes

- through their skin, either by contact or through cuts.

Safety data sheets

Products you use may be 'dangerous for supply'. If so, they will have a label that has one or more hazard symbols. Some examples are given here.

These products include common substances in everyday use such as paint, bleach, solvent or fillers. When a product is 'dangerous for supply', by law, the supplier must provide you with a safety data sheet. Note: medicines, pesticides and cosmetic products have different legislation and don't have a safety data sheet. Ask the supplier how the product can be used safely.

Safety data sheets can be hard to understand, with little information on measures for control. However, to find out about health risks and emergency situations, concentrate on:

- Sections 2 and 16 of the sheet, which tell you what the dangers are;
- Sections 4-8, which tell you about emergencies, storage and handling.

Since 2009, new international symbols have been gradually replacing the European symbols. Some of them are similar to the European symbols, but there is no single word describing the hazard. Read the hazard statement on the packaging and the safety data sheet from the supplier.

European symbols

Toxic · Very toxic · Harmful · Irritant

Highly flammable · Extremely flammable · Explosive · Dangerous to the environment

Oxidising · Corrosive

New International symbols

Hazard checklist

☐ Does any product you use have a danger label?
☐ Does your process produce gas, fume, dust, mist or vapour?
☐ Is the substance harmful to breathe in?
☐ Can the substance harm your skin?
☐ Is it likely that harm could arise because of the way you use or produce it?
☐ What are you going to do about it?
   - Use something else?
   - Use it in another, safer way?
   - Control it to stop harm being caused?

CONTROL MEASURES

The control measures below are in order of importance.

1 Eliminate the use of the harmful substance and use a safer one. For instance, swap high **VOC** oil based paint for a lower VOC water-based paint.

2 Use a safer form of the product. Is the product available ready-mixed? Is there a lower strength option that will still do the job?

VOC

The volatile organic compounds measure shows how much pollution a product will emit into the air when in use

INDUSTRY TIP

Product data sheets are free and have to be produced by the supplier of the product.

3 Change the work method to emit less of the substance. For instance, applying paint with a brush releases fewer VOCs into the air than spraying paint. Wet grinding produces less dust than dry grinding.

4 Enclose the work area so that the substance does not escape. This can mean setting up a tented area or closing doors.

5 Use extraction or filtration (eg a dust bag) in the work area.

6 Keep operatives in the area to a minimum.

7 Employers must provide appropriate PPE.

Paint with high VOC content

European symbols

New International symbols

COSHH symbols. The international symbols will replace the European symbols in 2015.

INDUSTRY TIP

For more detailed information on RIDDOR visit the HSE webpage at www.hse.gov.uk/riddor.

REPORTING OF INJURIES, DISEASES AND DANGEROUS OCCURRENCES REGULATIONS (RIDDOR) 2013

Despite all the efforts put into health and safety, incidents still happen. The Reporting of Injuries, Diseases and Dangerous Occurrences Regulations (RIDDOR) 2013 state that employers must report to the HSE all accidents that result in an employee needing more than seven days off work. Diseases and dangerous occurrences must also be reported. A serious occurrence that has not caused an injury (a near miss) should still be reported because next time it happens things might not work out as well.

Below are some examples of injuries, diseases and dangerous occurrences that would need to be reported:

- A joiner cuts off a finger while using a circular saw.

- A plumber takes a week off after a splinter in her hand becomes infected.

- A ground operative contracts **leptospirosis**.

- A labourer contracts dermatitis (a serious skin problem) after contact with an irritant substance.

- A scaffold suffers a collapse following severe weather, unauthorised alteration or overloading but no one is injured.

Leptospirosis

Also known as Weil's disease, this is a serious disease spread by rats and cattle

The purpose of RIDDOR is to enable the HSE to investigate serious incidents and collate statistical data. This information is used to help reduce the number of similar accidents happening in future and to make the workplace safer.

INDUSTRY TIP

Accidents do not just affect the person who has the accident. Work colleagues or members of the public might be affected and so will the employer. The consequences may include:
- a poor company image (this may put potential customers off)
- loss of production
- insurance costs increasing
- closure of the site
- having to pay sick pay
- other additional costs.

New HSE guidelines require employers to pay an hourly rate for time taken by the HSE to investigate an accident. This is potentially very costly.

An F2508 injury report form

Although minor accidents and injuries are not reported to HSE, records must be kept. Accidents must be recorded in the accident book. This provides a record of what happened and is useful for future reference. Trends may become apparent and the employer may take action to try to prevent that particular type of accident occurring again.

ACTIVITY

You have identified a potential risk. What action should you take? Make notes.

CONSTRUCTION, DESIGN AND MANAGEMENT (CDM) REGULATIONS 2007

The Construction, Design and Management (CDM) Regulations 2007 focus attention on the effective planning and management of construction projects, from the design concept through to maintenance and repair. The aim is for health and safety considerations to be integrated into a project's development, rather than be an inconvenient afterthought. The CDM Regulations reduce the risk of harm to those that have to work on or use the structure throughout its life, from construction through to **demolition**.

The CDM Regulations play a role in safety during demolition

Demolition

When something, often a building, is completely torn down and destroyed

CDM Regulations protect workers from the construction to demolition of large and complex structures

The CDM Regulations apply to all projects except for those arranged by private clients, ie work that isn't in furtherance of a business interest. Property developers need to follow the CDM Regulations.

Under the CDM Regulations, the HSE must be notified where the construction work will take:

- more than 30 working days or

- 500 working days in total, ie if 100 people work for 5 days (500 working days) the HSE will have to be notified.

DUTY HOLDERS

Under the CDM Regulations there are several duty holders, each with a specific role.

Duty holder	Role
Client	This is the person or organisation who wishes to have the work done. The client will check that: - all the team members are competent - the management is suitable - sufficient time is allowed for all stages of the project - welfare facilities are in place before construction starts. HSE notifiable projects require that the client appoints a CDM co-ordinator and principal contractor, and provides access to a health and safety file.
CDM co-ordinator	Appointed by the client, the co-ordinator advises and assists the client with CDM duties. The co-ordinator notifies the HSE before work starts. This role involves the co-ordination of the health and safety aspects of the design of the building and ensures good communication between the client, designers and contractors.
Designer	At the design stages the designer removes hazards and reduces risks. The designer provides information about the risks that cannot be eliminated. Notifiable projects require that the designer checks that the client is aware of their CDM duties and that a CDM co-ordinator has been appointed. The designer will also supply information for the health and safety file.
Principal contractor	The principal contractor will plan, manage and monitor the construction in liaison with any other involved contractors. This involves developing a written plan and site rules before the construction begins. The principal contractor ensures that the site is made secure and suitable welfare facilities are provided from the start and maintained throughout construction. The principal contractor will also make sure that all operatives have site inductions and any further training that might be required to make sure the workforce is competent.
Contractor	Subcontractors and self-employed operatives will plan, manage and monitor their own work and employees, co-operating with any main contractor in relation to site rules. Contractors will make sure that all operatives have any further training that might be required to make sure they are competent. A contractor also reports any incidents under RIDDOR to the principal contractor.
Operatives	Operatives need to check their own competence: Can you carry out the task you have been asked to do safely? Have you been trained to do this type of activity? Do you have the correct equipment to carry out this activity? You must follow all the site health and safety rules and procedures and fully co-operate with the rest of the team to ensure the health and safety of other operatives and others who may be affected by the work. Any health and safety issues must be reported.

A client, a contractor and an operative looking over building plans ahead of construction

WELFARE FACILITIES REQUIRED ON SITE UNDER THE CDM REGULATIONS

The table below shows the welfare facilities that must be available on site.

Facility	Site requirement
Sanitary conveniences (toilets) 	■ Suitable and sufficient toilets should be provided or made available. ■ Toilets should be adequately ventilated and lit and should be clean. ■ Separate toilet facilities should be provided for men and women.
Washing facilities 	■ Sufficient facilities must be available, and include showers if required by the nature of the work. ■ They should be in the same place as the toilets and near any changing rooms. ■ There must be a supply of clean hot (or warm) and cold running water, soap and towels. ■ There must be separate washing facilities provided for men and women unless the area is for washing hands and the face only.

Facility	Site requirement
Clean drinking water 	■ This must be provided or made available. ■ It should be clearly marked by an appropriate sign. ■ Cups should be provided unless the supply of drinking water is from a water fountain.
Changing rooms and lockers 	■ Changing rooms must be provided or made available if operatives have to wear special clothing and if they cannot be expected to change elsewhere. ■ There must be separate rooms for, or separate use of rooms by, men and women where necessary. ■ The rooms must have seating and include, where necessary, facilities to enable operatives to dry their special clothing and their own clothing and personal effects. ■ Lockers should also be provided.
Rest rooms or rest areas 	■ They should have enough tables and seating with backs for the number of operatives likely to use them at any one time. ■ Where necessary, rest rooms should include suitable facilities for pregnant women or nursing mothers to rest lying down. ■ Arrangements must be made to ensure that meals can be prepared, heated and eaten. It must also be possible to boil water.

ACTIVITY

What facilities are provided at your workplace or place of training?

PROVISION AND USE OF WORK EQUIPMENT REGULATIONS (PUWER) 1998

The Provision and Use of Work Equipment Regulations (PUWER) 1998 place duties on:

■ people and companies who own, operate or have control over work equipment

■ employers whose employees use work equipment.

Work equipment can be defined as any machinery, appliance, apparatus, tool or installation for use at work (whether exclusively or not). This includes equipment that employees provide for their own use at work. The scope of work equipment is therefore extremely wide. The use of work equipment is also very widely interpreted and, according to the HSE, means 'any activity involving work equipment and includes starting, stopping, programming, setting, transporting, repairing, modifying, maintaining, servicing and cleaning.' It includes equipment such as diggers, electric planers, stepladders, hammers or wheelbarrows.

Under PUWER, work equipment must be:

- suitable for the intended use

- safe to use

- well maintained

- inspected regularly.

Regular inspection is important as a tool that was safe when it was new may no longer be safe after considerable use.

Additionally, work equipment must only be used by people who have received adequate instruction and training. Information regarding the use of the equipment must be given to the operator and must only be used for what it was designed to do.

Protective devices, eg emergency stops, must be used. Brakes must be fitted where appropriate to slow down moving parts to bring the equipment to a safe condition when turned off or stopped. Equipment must have adequate means of isolation. Warnings, either by signs or other means such as sounds or lights, must be used as appropriate. Access to dangerous parts of the machinery must be controlled. Some work equipment is subject to additional health and safety legislation which must also be followed.

Employers who use work equipment must manage the risks. ACoPs (see page 9) have been developed in line with PUWER. The ACoPs have a special legal status, as outlined in the introduction to the PUWER ACoP:

> *Following the guidance is not compulsory and you are free to take other action. But if you do follow the guidance you will normally be doing enough to comply with the law. Health and safety inspectors seek to secure compliance with the law and may refer to this guidance as illustrating good practice.*

> **INDUSTRY TIP**
>
> Abrasive wheels are used for grinding. Under PUWER these wheels can only be changed by someone who has received training to do this. Wrongly fitted wheels can explode!

> **ACTIVITY**
>
> All the tools you use for your work are covered by PUWER. They must be well maintained and suitable for the task. A damaged head on a bolster chisel must be reshaped. A split shaft on a joiner's wood chisel must be repaired. Why would these tools be dangerous in a damaged condition? List the reasons.

MANUAL HANDLING OPERATIONS REGULATIONS 1992

Employers must try to avoid manual handling within reason if there is a possibility of injury. If manual handling cannot be avoided then they must reduce the risk of injury by means of a risk assessment.

An operative lifting heavy bricks

LIFTING AND HANDLING

Incorrect lifting and handling is a serious risk to your health. It is very easy to injure your back – just ask any experienced builder. An injured back can be very unpleasant, so it's best to look after it.

Here are a few things to consider when lifting:

- Assess the load. Is it too heavy? Do you need assistance or additional training? Is it an awkward shape?

- Can a lifting aid be used, such as any of the below?

Wheelbarrow

Gin lift

Scissor lift

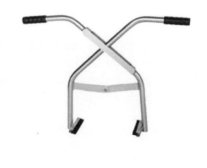

Kerb lifter

- Does the lift involve twisting or reaching?

- Where is the load going to end up? Is there a clear path? Is the place it's going to be taken to cleared and ready?

How to lift and place an item correctly

If you cannot use a machine, it is important that you keep the correct posture when lifting any load. The correct technique to do this is known as **kinetic lifting**. Always lift with your back straight, elbows in, knees bent and your feet slightly apart.

Kinetic lifting

A method of lifting that ensures that the risk of injury is reduced

Safe kinetic lifting technique

ACTIVITY

Try it out. Place a box on the floor and lift it using the technique shown.

ACTIVITY

Consider this list of materials: plywood, cement, aggregates, sawn timber joists, glass, drainage pipes, and kerbs. Make a table to show how you would transport and stack them around your place of work.

INDUSTRY TIP

Most workplace injuries are a result of manual handling. Remember pushing or pulling an object still comes under the Manual Handling Operations Regulations.

When placing the item, again be sure to use your knees and beware of trapping your fingers. If stacking materials, be sure that they are on a sound level base and on bearers if required.

Heavy objects that cannot easily be lifted by mechanical methods can be lifted by several people. It is important that one person in the team is in charge, and that lifting is done in a co-operative way. It has been known for one person to fall down and the others to then drop the item!

CONTROL OF NOISE AT WORK REGULATIONS 2005

Under the Control of Noise at Work Regulations 2005, duties are placed on employers and employees to reduce the risk of hearing damage to the lowest reasonable level practicable. Hearing loss caused by work is preventable. Hearing damage is permanent and cannot be restored once lost.

ACTIVITY

Watch this link to find out more about hearing loss and damage: www.hse.gov.uk/noise/video/hearingvideo.htm

EMPLOYER'S DUTIES UNDER THE REGULATIONS

An employer's duties are:

- to carry out a risk assessment and identify who is at risk

- to eliminate or control its employees' exposure to noise at the workplace and to reduce the noise as far as practicable

- to provide suitable hearing protection

- to provide health surveillance to those identified as at risk by the risk assessment

■ to provide information and training about the risks to their employees as identified by the risk assessment.

EMPLOYEES' DUTIES UNDER THE REGULATIONS

Employees must:

■ make full and proper use of personal hearing protectors provided to them by their employer

■ report to their employer any defect in any personal hearing protectors or other control measures as soon as is practicable.

NOISE LEVELS

Under the Regulations, specific actions are triggered at specific noise levels. Noise is measured in decibels and shown as dB (a). The two main action levels are 80dB (a) and 85dB (a).

Requirements at 80dB (a) to 85dB (a):

■ Assess the risk to operatives' health and provide them with information and training.

■ Provide suitable ear protection free of charge to those who request ear protection.

Requirements above 85dB (a):

■ Reduce noise exposure as far as practicable by means other than ear protection.

■ Set up an ear protection zone using suitable signage and segregation.

■ Provide suitable ear protection free of charge to those affected and ensure they are worn.

PERSONAL PROTECTIVE EQUIPMENT (PPE) AT WORK REGULATIONS 1992

Employees and subcontractors must work in a safe manner. Not only must they wear the PPE that their employers provide but they must also look after it and report any damage to it. Importantly, employees must not be charged for anything given to them or done for them by the employer in relation to safety.

Ear defenders

Ear plugs

INDUSTRY TIP

The typical noise level for a hammer drill and a concrete mixer is 90 to 100dB (a).

ACTIVITY

Think about your place of work or training. What PPE do you think you should use when working with cement or using a powered planer?

The hearing and respiratory PPE provided for most work situations is not covered by these Regulations because other regulations apply to it. However, these items need to be compatible with any other PPE provided.

The main requirement of the Regulations is that PPE must be supplied and used at work wherever there are risks to health and safety that cannot be adequately controlled in other ways.

The Regulations also require that PPE is:

- included in the method statement

- properly assessed before use to ensure it is suitable

- maintained and stored properly

- provided to employees with instructions on how they can use it safely

- used correctly by employees.

An employer cannot ask for money from an employee for PPE, whether it is returnable or not. This includes agency workers if they are legally regarded as employees. If employment has been terminated and the employee keeps the PPE without the employer's permission, then, as long as it has been made clear in the contract of employment, the employer may be able to deduct the cost of the replacement from any wages owed.

Using PPE is a very important part of staying safe. For it to do its job properly it must be kept in good condition and used correctly. If any damage does occur to an article of PPE it is important that this is reported and it is replaced. It must also be remembered that PPE is a last line of defence and should not be used in place of a good safety policy!

A site safety sign showing the PPE required to work there

The following table shows the type of PPE used in the workplace and explains why it is important to store, maintain and use PPE correctly. It also shows why it is important to check and report damage to PPE.

PPE	Correct use
Hard hat/safety helmet 	Hard hats must be worn when there is danger of hitting your head or danger of falling objects. They often prevent a wide variety of head injuries. Most sites insist on hard hats being worn. They must be adjusted to fit your head correctly and must not be worn back to front! Check the date of manufacture as plastic can become brittle over time. Solvents, pens and paints can damage the plastic too.
Toe-cap boots or shoes  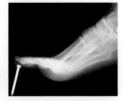 Safety boots A nail in a construction worker's foot	Toe-cap boots or shoes are worn on most sites as a matter of course and protect the feet from heavy falling objects. Some safety footwear has additional insole protection to help prevent nails going up through the foot. Toe caps can be made of steel or lighter plastic.
Ear defenders and plugs   Ear defenders Ear plugs	Your ears can be very easily damaged by loud noise. Ear protection will help prevent hearing loss while using loud tools or if there is a lot of noise going on around you. When using earplugs always ensure your hands are clean before handling the plugs as this reduces the risk of infection. If your ear defenders are damaged or fail to make a good seal around your ears have them replaced.
High-visibility (hi-viz) jacket 	This makes it much easier for other people to see you. This is especially important when there is plant or vehicles moving in the vicinity.
Goggles and safety glasses   Safety goggles Safety glasses	These protect the eyes from dust and flying debris while you are working. It has been known for casualties to be taken to hospital after dust has blown up from a dry mud road. You only get one pair of eyes: look after them!

PPE	Correct use
Dust masks and respirators   Dust mask Respirator	Dust is produced during most construction work and it can be hazardous to your lungs. It can cause all sorts of ailments from asthma through to cancer. Wear a dust mask to filter this dust out. You must ensure it is well fitted. Another hazard is dangerous gases such as solvents. A respirator will filter out hazardous gases but a dust mask will not! Respirators are rated P1, P2 and P3, with P3 giving the highest protection.
Gloves  Latex glove Nitrile glove  Gauntlet gloves Leather gloves	Gloves protect your hands. Hazards include cuts, abrasions, dermatitis, chemical burns or splinters. Latex and nitrile gloves are good for fine work, although some people are allergic to latex. Gauntlets provide protection from strong chemicals. Other types of gloves provide good grip and protect the fingers.  A chemical burn as a result of not wearing safety gloves
Sunscreen   Suncream Melanoma	Another risk, especially in the summer months, is sunburn. Although a good tan is sometimes considered desirable, over-exposure to the sun can cause skin cancer such as melanoma. When out in the sun, cover up and use sunscreen (ie suncream) on exposed areas of your body to prevent burning.
Preventing HAVS 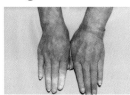	Hand–arm vibration syndrome (HAVS), also known as vibration white finger (VWF), is an industrial injury caused by using vibrating power tools (such as a hammer drill, vibrating poker and vibrating plate) for a long time. This injury is controlled by limiting the time such power tools are used. For more information see page 31.

You are working on a site and a brick falls on your head. Luckily, you are doing as you have been instructed and you are wearing a helmet. You notice that the helmet has a small crack in it. What do you do?

1 Carry on using it as your employer will charge you for a new one; after all it is only a small crack.

2 Take it to your supervisor as it will no longer offer you full protection and it will need replacing.

3 Buy a new helmet because the old one no longer looks very nice.

WORK AT HEIGHT REGULATIONS 2005 (AS AMENDED)

The Work at Height Regulations 2005 (as amended by the Work at Height (Amendment) Regulations 2007) put several duties upon employers:

- Working at height should be avoided if possible.

- If working at height cannot be avoided, the work must be properly organised with risk assessments carried out.

- Risk assessments should be regularly updated.

- Those working at height must be trained and competent.

- A method statement must be provided.

Workers wearing safety harnesses on an aerial access platform

Several points should be considered when working at height:

- How long is the job expected to take?

- What type of work will it be? It could be anything from fitting a single light bulb, through to removing a chimney or installing a roof.
  - □ How is the access platform going to be reached? By how many people?
  - □ Will people be able to get on and off the structure safely? Could there be overcrowding?

- What are the risks to passers-by? Could debris or dust blow off and injure anyone on the road below?

- What are the conditions like? Extreme weather, unstable buildings and poor ground conditions need to be taken into account.

A cherry picker can assist you when working at height

ACCESS EQUIPMENT AND SAFE METHODS OF USE

The means of access should only be chosen after a risk assessment has been carried out. There are various types of access.

Ladders

Ladders are normally used for access onto an access platform. They are not designed for working from except for light, short-duration work. A ladder should lean at an angle of 75°, ie one unit out for every four units up.

Strong upper resting point

Adequate lap on extension ladders

Ground back slope not exceeding 6°

Ground side slope not exceeding 16°, clean and free of slippery algae and moss

Using a ladder correctly

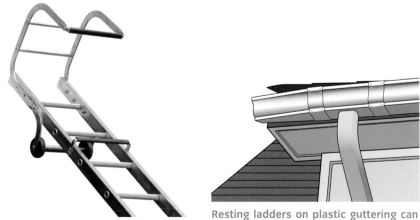

Roof ladder

Resting ladders on plastic guttering can cause it to bend and break

The following images show how to use a ladder or stepladder safely.

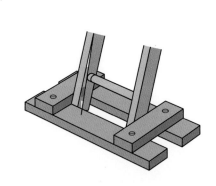

A ladder secured at the base.

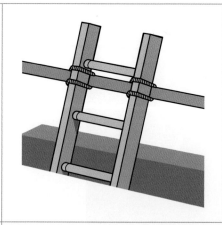

A ladder secured at the top of a platform for working from.

Access ladders should extend 1m above the landing point to provide a strong handhold.

Certain stepladders are unsafe to work from the top three rungs.

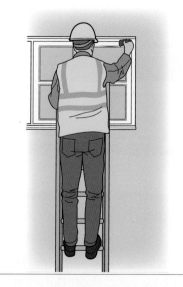

Don't overreach, and stay on the same rung.

Grip the ladder when climbing and remember to keep three points of contact.

INDUSTRY TIP

Always complete ladder pre-checks. Check the stiles (the two uprights) and rungs for damage such as splits or cracks. Do not use painted ladders because the paint could be hiding damage! Check all of the equipment including any stays and feet.

Stepladders

Stepladders are designed for light, short-term work.

Working from the side can make stepladders unstable. Do not overreach

Don't stand on the top three steps

Stepladder is fully open

Locked open firm and level on the ground

Using a stepladder correctly

Trestles

This is a working platform used for work of a slightly longer duration.

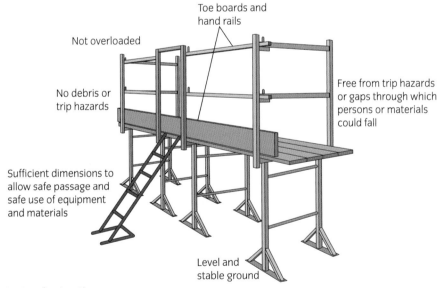

Not overloaded

Toe boards and hand rails

No debris or trip hazards

Free from trip hazards or gaps through which persons or materials could fall

Sufficient dimensions to allow safe passage and safe use of equipment and materials

Level and stable ground

Parts of a trestle

Tower scaffold

These are usually proprietary (manufactured) and are made from galvanised steel or lightweight aluminium alloy. They must be erected by someone competent in the erection and dismantling of mobile scaffolds.

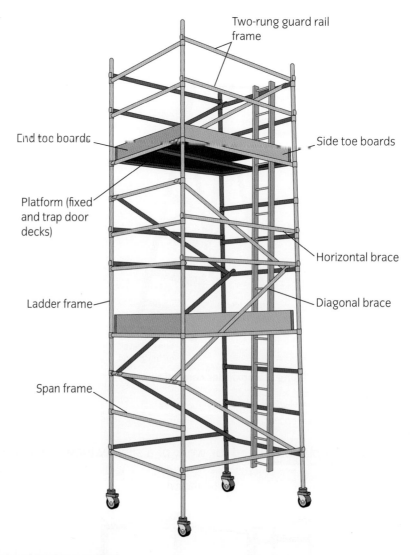

Two-rung guard rail frame

End toe boards

Side toe boards

Platform (fixed and trap door decks)

Horizontal brace

Ladder frame

Diagonal brace

Span frame

Parts of a tower scaffold

To use a tower scaffold safely:

- Always read and follow the manufacturer's instruction manual.

- Only use the equipment for what it is designed for.

- The wheels or feet of the tower must be in contact with a firm surface.

- Outriggers should be used to increase stability. The maximum height given in the manufacturer's instructions must not be exceeded.

- The platform must not be overloaded.

- The platform should be unloaded (and reduced in height if required) before it is moved.

- Never move a platform, even a small distance, if it is occupied.

INDUSTRY TIP

Remember, even a mobile access tower should have toe boards and guard rails fitted at all times when in use.

Tubular scaffold

This comes in two types:

- independent scaffold has two sets of standards or uprights

- putlog scaffold is built into the brickwork.

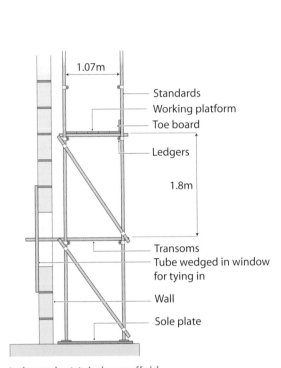

Independent tubular scaffold

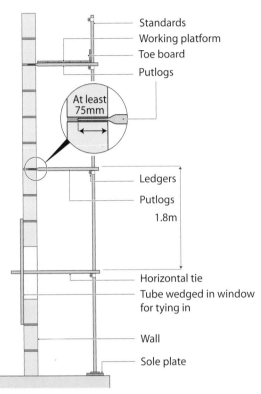

Putlog tubular scaffold

Tubular scaffold is erected by specialist scaffolding companies and often requires structural calculations. Only trained and competent scaffold erectors should alter scaffolding. Access to a scaffold is usually via a tied ladder with three rungs projecting above the step off at platform level.

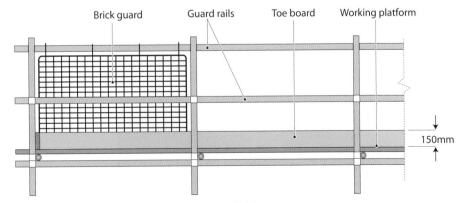

A safe working platform on a tubular scaffold

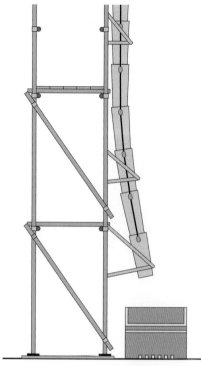

A debris chute for scaffolding

All scaffolding must:

- not have any gaps in the handrail or toe boards
- have a safe system for lifting any materials up to the working height
- have a safe system of debris removal.

Fall protection devices include:

- harnesses and lanyards
- safety netting
- air bags.

A harness and lanyard or safety netting will stop a person falling too far, leaving them suspended in the air. Air bags (commonly known as 'bouncy castles') are set up on the ground and inflated. If a person falls, they will have a soft landing. Air bags have fallen out of favour somewhat as some operatives use them as an easy way to get off the working platform – not the purpose they were intended for!

LIFTING OPERATIONS AND LIFTING EQUIPMENT REGULATIONS (LOLER) 1998

The Lifting Operations and Lifting Equipment Regulations (LOLER) 1998 put responsibility upon employers to ensure that the lifting equipment provided for use at work is:

- strong and stable enough for the particular use and marked to indicate safe working loads
- positioned and installed to minimise any risks
- used safely, ie the work is planned, organised and performed by competent people
- subject to on-going thorough examination and, where appropriate, inspection by competent people.

Using a scissor lift at height

THE CONTROL OF VIBRATION AT WORK REGULATIONS 2005

Vibration white finger or hand-arm vibration syndrome (HAVS) (see page 23), is caused by using vibrating tools such as hammer drills, vibrating pokers or hand held breakers over a long period of time. The most efficient and effective way of controlling exposure to hand–arm vibration is to look for new or alternative work methods that remove or reduce exposure to vibration.

Follow these steps to reduce the effects of HAVS:

▪ Always use the right tool for each job.

▪ Check tools before using them to make sure they have been properly maintained and repaired to avoid increased vibration caused by faults or general wear.

▪ Make sure cutting tools are kept sharp so that they remain efficient.

▪ Reduce the amount of time you use a tool in one go, by doing other jobs in between.

▪ Avoid gripping or forcing a tool or work piece more than you have to.

▪ Encourage good blood circulation by:
  ☐ keeping warm and dry (when necessary, wear gloves, a hat, waterproofs and use heating pads if available)
  ☐ giving up or cutting down on smoking because smoking reduces blood flow
  ☐ massaging and exercising your fingers during work breaks.

Damage from HAVS can include the inability to do fine work and cold can trigger painful finger blanching attacks (when the ends of your fingers go white).

An operative taking a rest from using a power tool

Don't use power tools for longer than you need to

CONSTRUCTION SITE HAZARDS

DANGERS ON CONSTRUCTION SITES

Study the drawing of a building site. There is some demolition taking place, as well as construction. How many hazards can you find? Discuss your answers.

Dangers	Discussion points
Head protection	The operatives are not wearing safety helmets, which would prevent them from hitting their head or from falling objects.
Poor housekeeping	The site is very untidy. This can result in slips, trips and falls and can pollute the environment. An untidy site gives a poor company image. Offcuts and debris should be regularly removed and disposed of according to site policy and recycled if possible.
Fire	There is a fire near a building; this is hazardous. Fires can easily become uncontrollable and spread. There is a risk to the structure and, more importantly, a risk of operatives being burned. Fires can also pollute the environment.

Dangers	Discussion points
Trip hazards	Notice the tools and debris on the floor. The scaffold has been poorly constructed. There is a trip hazard where the scaffold boards overlap.
Chemical spills	There is a drum leaking onto the ground. This should be stored properly – upright and in a lockable metal shed or cupboard. The leak poses a risk of pollution and of chemical burns to operatives.
Falls from height	The scaffold has handrails missing. The trestle working platform has not been fitted with guard rails. None of the operatives are wearing hard hats for protection either.
Noise	An operative is using noisy machinery with other people nearby. The operative should be wearing ear PPE, as should those working nearby. Better still, they should be working elsewhere if at all possible, isolating themselves from the noise.
Electrical	Some of the wiring is 240V as there is no transformer, it's in poor repair and it's also dragging through liquid. This not only increases the risk of electrocution but is also a trip hazard.
Asbestos or other hazardous substances	Some old buildings contain **asbestos** roofing which can become a hazard when being demolished or removed. Other potential hazards include lead paint or mould spores. If a potentially hazardous material is discovered a supervisor must be notified immediately and work must stop until the hazard is dealt with appropriately.

Asbestos

A naturally occurring mineral that was commonly used for a variety of purposes including: **insulation**, fire protection, roofing and guttering. It is extremely hazardous and can cause a serious lung disease known as asbestosis

Insulation

A material that reduces or prevents the transmission of heat

Cables can be a trip hazard on site

FUNCTIONAL SKILLS

Using the data you collected in the Functional Skills task on page 3, produce a pie chart to show the proportion of occupational cancer that is caused by asbestosis.

Work on this activity can support FM L2.3.1 and C2.4.

Boiler suit

Hand cleaner

PERSONAL HYGIENE

Working in the construction industry can be very physical, and it's likely to be quite dirty at times. Therefore you should take good care with your personal hygiene. This involves washing well after work. If contaminants are present, then wearing a protective suit, such as a boiler suit, that you can take off before you go home will prevent contaminants being taken home with you.

You should also wash your hands after going to the toilet and before eating. This makes it safer to eat and more pleasant for others around you. The following steps show a safe and hygienic way to wash your hands.

STEP 1 Apply soap to hands from the dispenser.

STEP 2 Rub the soap into a lather and cover your hands with it, including between your fingers.

STEP 3 Rinse hands under a running tap removing all of the soap from your hands.

STEP 4 Dry your hands using disposable towels. Put the towels in the bin once your hands are dry.

WORKING WITH ELECTRICITY

Electricity is a very useful energy resource but it can be very dangerous. Electricity must be handled with care! Only trained, competent people can work with electrical equipment.

THE DANGERS OF USING ELECTRICAL EQUIPMENT

The main dangers of electricity are:

■ shock and burns (a 230V shock can kill)

■ electrical faults which could cause a fire

■ an explosion where an electrical spark has ignited a flammable gas.

VOLTAGES

Generally speaking, the lower the voltage the safer it is. However, a low voltage is not necessarily suitable for some machines, so higher voltages can be found. On site, 110V (volts) is recommended and this is the voltage rating most commonly used in the building industry. This is converted from 230V by use of a transformer.

110V 1 phase – yellow

230V (commonly called 240V) domestic voltage is used on site as battery chargers usually require this voltage. Although 230V is often used in workshops, 110V is recommended.

400V (otherwise known as 3 phase) is used for large machinery, such as joinery shop equipment.

230V 1 phase – blue

Voltages are nominal, ie they can vary slightly.

BATTERY POWER

Battery power is much safer than mains power. Many power tools are now available in battery-powered versions. They are available in a wide variety of voltages from 3.6V for a small screwdriver all the way up to 36V for large masonry drills.

400V 3 phase – red

The following images are all examples of battery-powered tools you may come across in your workplace or place of training.

Battery drill   Battery-powered planer   Battery-powered jigsaw

WIRING

The wires inside a cable are made from copper, which conducts
electricity. The copper is surrounded by a plastic coating that is
colour coded. The three wires in a cable are the live (brown), which
works with the neutral (blue) to conduct electricity, making the
appliance work. The earth (green and yellow stripes) prevents
electrocution if the appliance is faulty or damaged.

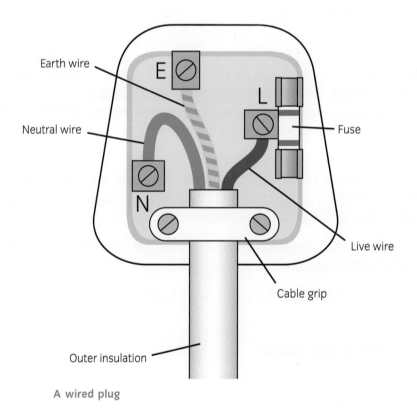

A wired plug

POWER TOOLS AND CHECKS

Power tools should always be checked before use. Always inform your supervisor if you find a fault. The tool will need to be repaired, and the tool needs to be kept out of use until then. The tool might be taken away, put in the site office and clearly labelled 'Do not use'.

Power tool checks include:

- *Look for the portable appliance testing (PAT) label*: PAT is a regular test carried out by a competent person (eg a qualified electrician) to ensure the tool is in a safe electrical condition. A sticker is placed on the tool after it has been tested. Tools that do not pass the PAT are taken out of use.

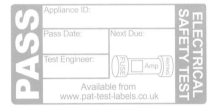

PAT testing labels

- *Cable*: Is it damaged? Is there a repair? Insulation tape may be hiding a damaged cable. Damaged cables must be replaced.

- *Casing*: Is the casing cracked? Plastic casings ensure the tool is double-insulated. This means the live parts inside are safely shielded from the user. A cracked casing will reduce the protection to the user and will require repair.

- *Guards and tooling*: Are guards in place? Is the tooling sharp?

- *Electricity supply leads*: Are they damaged? Are they creating a trip hazard? You need to place them in such a way that they do not make a trip hazard. Are they protected from damage? If they are lying on the floor with heavy traffic crossing them, they must be covered.

- *Use appropriate equipment for the size of the job*: For example, too many splitters can result in a web of cables.

- *Storage*: After use, power tools and equipment should be stored correctly. Tools must be returned to the boxes, including all the guards and parts. Cables need to be wound onto reels or neatly coiled as they can become tangled very easily.

Cable protection

Cable reel

INDUSTRY TIP

Remember, always fully unroll an extension lead before use because it could overheat and cause a fire.

FIRE

Fire needs three things to start; if just one of them is missing there will be no fire. If all are present then a fire is unavoidable:

1 *Oxygen*: A naturally occurring gas in the air that combines with flammable substances under certain circumstances.

2 *Heat*: A source of fire, such as a hot spark from a grinder or naked flame.

3 *Fuel*: Things that will burn such as acetone, timber, cardboard or paper.

The fire triangle

If you have heat, fuel and oxygen you will have a fire. Remove any of these and the fire will go out.

PREVENTING THE SPREAD OF FIRE

Being tidy will help prevent fires starting and spreading. For instance:

- Wood offcuts should not be left in big piles or standing up against a wall. Instead, useable offcuts should be stored in racks.

- Put waste into the allocated disposal bins or skips.

- Always replace the cap on unused fuel containers when you put them away. Otherwise they are a potential source of danger.

- Flammable liquids (not limited to fuel-flammable liquids) such as oil based paint, thinners and oil must be stored in a locked metal cupboard or shed.

- Smoking around flammable substances should be avoided.

- Dust can be explosive, so when doing work that produces wood dust it is important to use some form of extraction and have good ventilation.

FIRE EXTINGUISHERS AND THEIR USES

You need to know where the fire extinguishers and blankets are located and which fire extinguishers can be used on different fires. The table below shows the different classes of fire and which extinguisher to use in each case.

Class of fire	Materials	Type of extinguisher
A	Wood, paper, hair, textiles	Water, foam, dry powder, wet chemical
B	Flammable liquids	Foam, dry powder, CO_2
C	Flammable gases	Dry powder, CO_2
D	Flammable metals	Specially formulated dry powder
E	Electrical fires	CO_2, dry powder
F	Cooking oils	Wet chemical, fire blanket

Fire blanket

INDUSTRY TIP

Remember, although all fire extinguishers are red, they each have a different coloured label to identify their contents.

CO_2 extinguisher

Dry powder extinguisher

Water extinguisher

Foam extinguisher

It is important to use the correct extinguisher for the type of fire as using the wrong one could make the danger much worse, eg using water on an electrical fire could lead to the user being electrocuted!

EMERGENCY PROCEDURES

In an emergency, people tend to panic. If an emergency were to occur, such as fire, discovering a bomb or some other security problem, would you know what to do? It is vital to be prepared in case of an emergency.

It is your responsibility to know the emergency procedures on your work site:

- If you discover a fire or other emergency you will need to raise the alarm:
  - ☐ You will need to tell a nominated person. Who is this?
  - ☐ If you are first on the scene you will have to ring the emergency services on 999.

- Be aware of the alarm signal. Is it a bell, a voice or a siren?

- Where is the assembly point? You will have to proceed to this point in an orderly way. Leave all your belongings behind: they may slow you or others down.

- At the assembly point, there will be someone who will ensure everyone is out safely and will do so by taking a count. Do you know who this person is? If during a fire you are not accounted for, a firefighter may risk their life to go into the building to look for you.

- How do you know it's safe to re-enter the building? You will be told by the appointed person. It's very important that you do not re-enter the building until you are told to do so.

Emergency procedure sign

ACTIVITY

What is the fire evacuation procedure at your workplace or place of training?

SIGNS AND SAFETY NOTICES

The law sets out the types of safety signs needed on a construction site. Some signs that warn us about danger and others tell us what to do to stay safe.

The following table describes five basic types of sign.

Type of sign	Description
Prohibition	These signs are red and white. They are round. They signify something that must *not* be done.
Mandatory	These signs are blue. They are round. They signify something that *must* be done.

Type of sign	Description
Caution 	These signs are yellow and black. They are triangular. These give warning of hazards.
Safe condition 	These signs are green. They are usually square or rectangular. They tell you the safe way to go, or what to do in an emergency.
Supplementary 	These white signs are square or rectangular and give additional important information. They usually accompany the signs above.

Case Study: Miranda

A site has a small hut where tools are stored securely, and inside the hut there is a short bench that has some sharpening equipment including a grinding wheel.

Miranda wished to grind her plane blade, but before using it found that the grinding wheel was defective as the side of the wheel had been used, causing a deep groove.

She found another old grinding wheel beneath the bench which looked fine. She fitted it to the grinder and used it.

Afterwards, she wondered if she should have asked someone else to change the wheel for her.

- What health and safety issues are there with this scenario?

- What training could Miranda undertake?

Work through the following questions to check your learning.

1   Which one of the following must be filled out prior to carrying out a site task?

   a   Invoice.

   b   Bill of quantities.

   c   Risk assessment.

   d   Schedule.

2   Which one of the following signs shows you something you **must** do?

   a   Green circle.

   b   Yellow triangle.

   c   White square.

   d   Blue circle.

3   Two parts of the fire triangle are heat and fuel. What is the third?

   a   Nitrogen.

   b   Oxygen.

   c   Carbon dioxide.

   d   Hydrogen sulphite.

4   Which of the following types of fire extinguisher would **best** put out an electrical fire?

   a CO_2.

   b   Powder.

   c   Water.

   d   Foam.

5   Which piece of health and safety legislation is designed to protect an operative from ill health and injury when using solvents and adhesives?

   a   Manual Handling Operations Regulations 1992.

   b   Control of Substances Hazardous to Health (COSHH) Regulations 2002.

   c   Health and Safety (First Aid) Regulations 1981.

   d   Lifting Operations and Lifting Equipment Regulations (LOLER) 1998.

6   What is the correct angle at which to lean a ladder against a wall?

   a   70°.

   b   80°.

   c   75°.

   d   85°.

7   Which are the **most** important pieces of PPE to use when using a disc cutter?

   a   Overalls, gloves and boots.

   b   Boots, head protection and overalls.

   c   Glasses, hearing protection and dust mask.

   d   Gloves, head protection and boots.

8   Which one of the following is **not** a lifting aid?

   a   Wheelbarrow.

   b   Kerb lifter.

   c   Gin lift.

   d   Respirator.

9   Which one of the following is a 3 phase voltage?

   a   400V.

   b   230V.

   c   240V.

   d   110V.

10   Above what noise level must you wear ear protection?

   a   75dB (a).

   b   80dB (a).

   c   85dB (a).

   d   90dB (a).

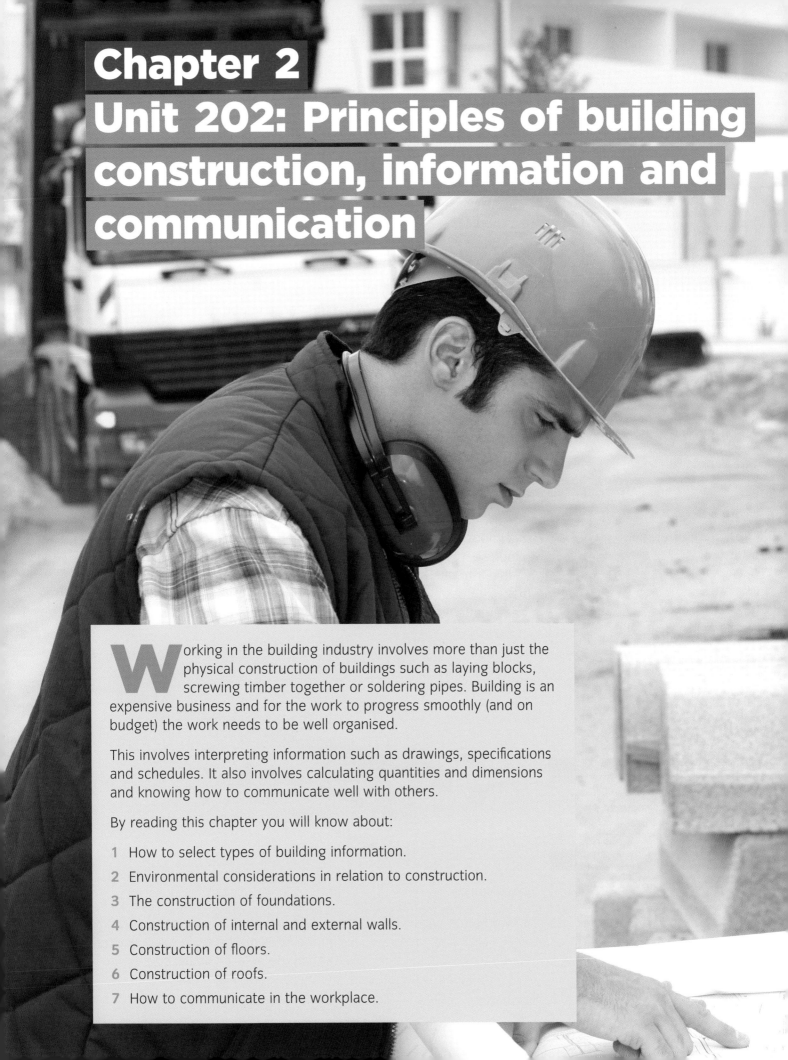

Chapter 2
Unit 202: Principles of building construction, information and communication

Working in the building industry involves more than just the physical construction of buildings such as laying blocks, screwing timber together or soldering pipes. Building is an expensive business and for the work to progress smoothly (and on budget) the work needs to be well organised.

This involves interpreting information such as drawings, specifications and schedules. It also involves calculating quantities and dimensions and knowing how to communicate well with others.

By reading this chapter you will know about:

1 How to select types of building information.
2 Environmental considerations in relation to construction.
3 The construction of foundations.
4 Construction of internal and external walls.
5 Construction of floors.
6 Construction of roofs.
7 How to communicate in the workplace.

TECHNICAL INFORMATION

This section will discuss the three main sources of technical information that are used when constructing buildings:

- working drawings and **specifications**
- schedules
- **bill of quantities**.

These are all essential information and form the contract documents (those that govern the construction of a building). All documentation needs to be correctly interpreted and correctly used. The contract documents need to be looked after and stored (filed) correctly and safely. If documents are left lying around they will become difficult to read and pages may be lost, leading to errors. The contract documents will need to be **archived** at the end of the contract, so they can be referred back to in case of any query or dispute over the work carried out or the materials used.

DRAWING SCALES

It is impossible to fit a full-sized drawing of a building onto a sheet of paper, so it is necessary to **scale** (shrink) the size of the building to enable it to fit. The building has to be shrunk in proportion; this makes it possible to convert measurements on the drawing into real measurements that can be used. Scale rules are made specifically for this purpose.

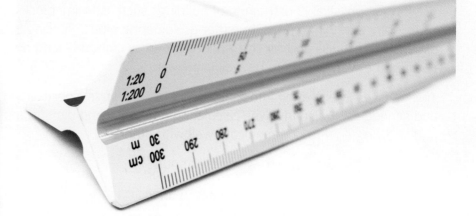

Triangular scale rule

How do scale rules work? Let's say we are using a scale of 1:5. That means that what we draw – using the sizes on the scale rule – will be five times smaller on the drawing than the object's actual size. So, a line 30mm long will represent an object 150mm long (30 × 5 = 150).

Specification

A contract document that gives information about the quality of materials and standards of workmanship required

Bill of quantities

A document containing quantities, descriptions and cost of works and resources

Archived

Kept in storage

Scale

The ratio of the size on a drawing to the size of the real thing that it represents

Dimension

A measurement

The British Standards Institute's BS 1192 (Drawing office practice) gives a range of standard scales that are used for various drawing types and scale rules are manufactured to meet this purpose.

British Standards Institute

The British Standards Institute (BSI) is the UK organisation which develops and publishes standards in the UK

SCALES IN COMMON USE

Scale	Use
1:1	Full size (used for rods)
1:2 1:5 1:10	Building details
1:20 1:50 1:100 1:200	Plans, elevations and sections
1:200 1:500 1:1250	Site plans
1:1250 1:2500	Location plans

The documents these scales are used for are described on pages 49–51.

The documents these scales are used for are described on pages 49–51.

FUNCTIONAL SKILLS

Work out the following:

Scale size	Scale	Actual size
10mm	1:10	100mm
25mm	1:20	a)
b)	1:50	300mm
50mm	1:200	c)

Work on this activity can support FM L2.3.2 and C2.3.

Answers: a) 500mm, b) 6mm, c) 10m

DATUM POINTS

Heights of buildings and the relative heights of components within the building are calculated from a common **datum point**. Datum points are determined by transferring a known fixed height from a bench mark. There are two types of datum point:

- A permanent Ordnance bench mark (OBM) is a given height on an Ordnance Survey map. This fixed height is described as a value, eg so many metres above sea level (as calculated from the average sea height at Newlyn, Cornwall).

- A temporary bench mark (TBM) is set up on site.

Datum point

A fixed point or height from which reference levels can be taken. The datum point is used to transfer levels across a building site. It represents the finished floor level (FFL) on a dwelling

Ordnance and temporary bench marks

ACTIVITY

Find your local OBM or your site TBM. What is the height of your OBM or TBM?

BASIC DRAWING SYMBOLS (HATCHINGS)

Standard symbols, also known as hatching symbols, are used on drawings as a means of passing on information simply. If all the parts of a building were labelled in writing, the drawing would soon become very crowded. Additionally, it is important to use standard symbols so that everyone can read them and they mean the same to everyone. The following images are just some of the standard symbols used.

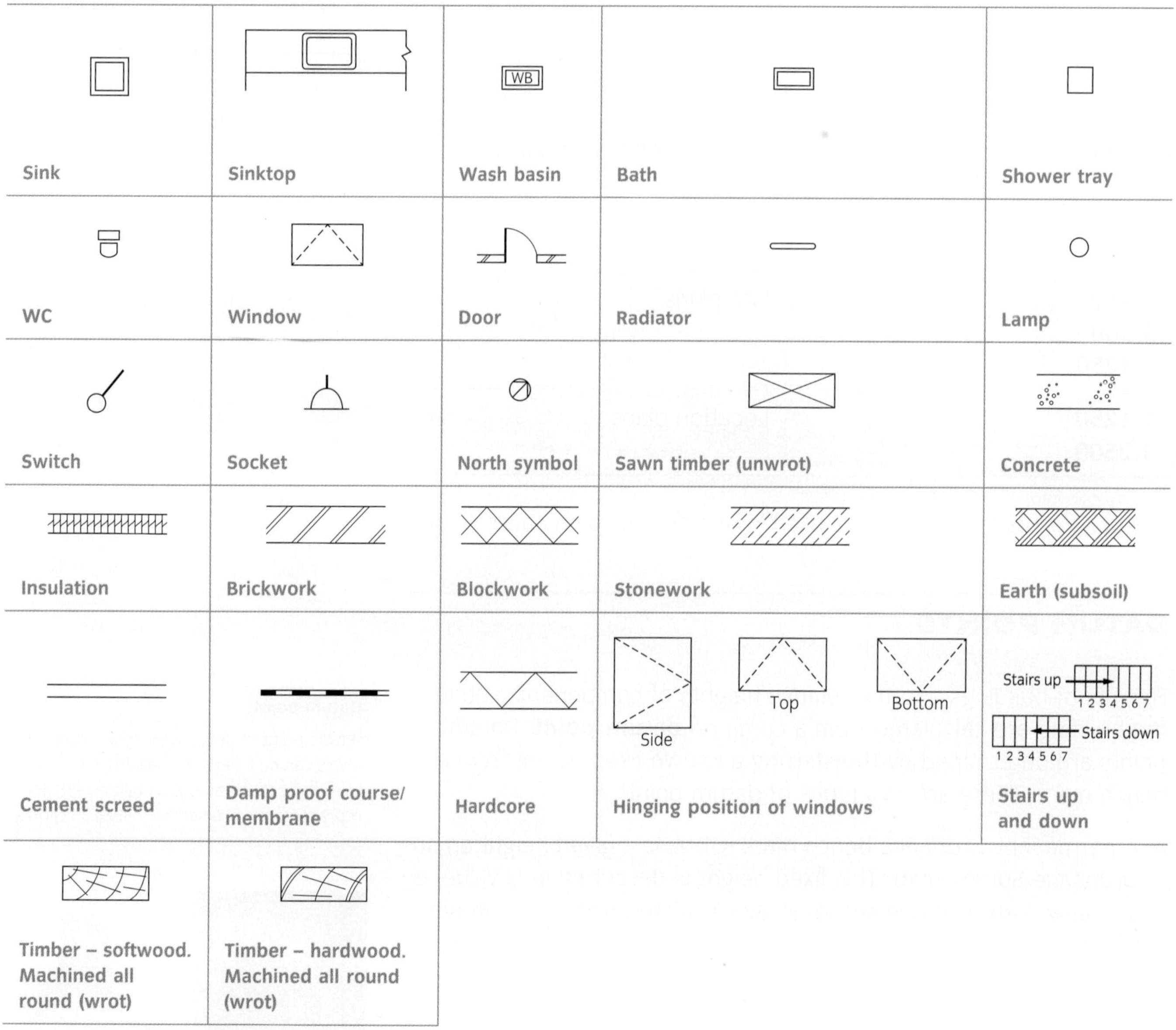

Sink
Sinktop
WB
Wash basin
Bath
Shower tray
WC
Window
Door
Radiator
Lamp
Switch
Socket
North symbol
Sawn timber (unwrot)
Concrete
Insulation
Brickwork
Blockwork
Stonework
Earth (subsoil)
Cement screed
Damp proof course/ membrane
Hardcore
Side
Top
Bottom
Hinging position of windows
Stairs up
1 2 3 4 5 6 7
Stairs down
1 2 3 4 5 6 7
Stairs up and down
Timber – softwood. Machined all round (wrot)
Timber – hardwood. Machined all round (wrot)

INFORMATION SOURCES

Type of drawing	Description
Location drawings	Usually prepared by an **architect** or **architectural technician**. Show the location of the building plot, position of the building and areas within the building. The term location drawings covers all of the drawings in this table.
Block plans 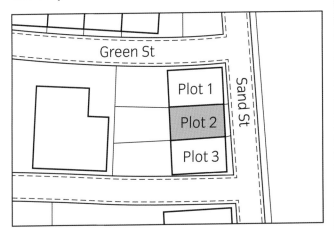	Show the proposed development in relation to its surrounding properties. The scales used are 1:1250 or 1:2500. Very little detail is available from this type of plan. The direction North is usually shown.
Site plans 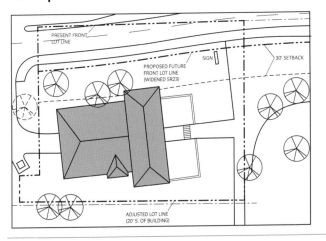	Show the plot in more detail, with drain runs, road layouts and the size and position of the existing building (and any extensions proposed) in relation to the property boundary. A scale of 1:200 or 1:500 is used. The Planning Portal sometimes refers to site plans as block plans, but the two types of plan have been distinguished in this book.

Architect

A trained professional who designs a structure and represents the client who wants the structure built. They are responsible for the production of the working drawings. They supervise the construction of buildings or other large structures

Architectural technician

A draftsperson who works in an architectural practice

Type of drawing	Description
Floor plans 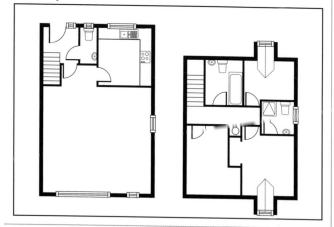	Show the positioning of walls, size of rooms along with the positioning of elements within the building such as units.
Elevations 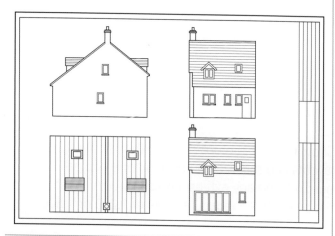	Show a building from a particular side and show the positioning of features such as doors and windows.
Sections 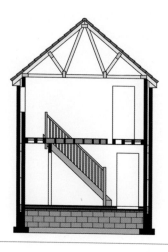	Show in greater detail what the section of a component looks like and how it might fit in relation to another component. A typical example would be a cross-section of a window showing the size of the features and how they fit together. Using these drawings it is possible to determine the positions of rooms, windows, doors, kitchen units and so on. Elevations are shown. These drawings are more detailed, and are often scaled to provide construction measurements. Some of the scales used are 1:200, 1:100, 1:50, 1:10, 1:5 and 1:1. A scale of 1:1 is full size.

Type of drawing	Description
Construction drawings (detail drawings) 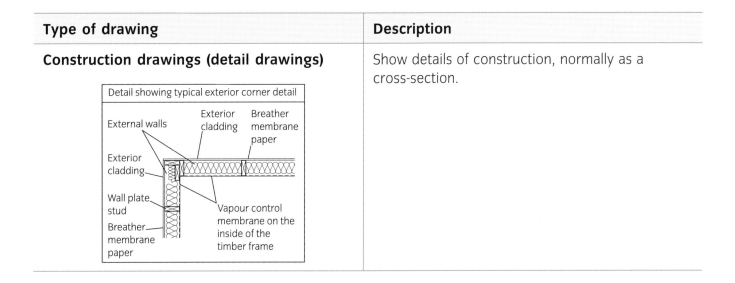	Show details of construction, normally as a cross-section.

PERMITS TO WORK

The permit to work is a documented procedure that gives authorisation for certain people to carry out specific work within a specified time frame. It sets out the precautions required to complete the work safely, based on a risk assessment. The following is an example of permit-to-work documentation that must be filled out.

PERMIT TO WORK

1. Area	2. Date
3. Work to be Done	4. Valid From
	5. Valid To
6. Company	
7. Man in Charge	8. No of Men
9. Safety Precautions	

10. Safety Planning Certificate (cancelled if alarm sounds)

I have inspected the above job which has been safely prepared according to requirements of a safety planning certificate

Signed ....

11. Approval of Permit to Work

I am satisfied that this permit is properly authorised, that safe access is provided, and that all persons affected by this job have been informed

Signed ....

12. Electrical Equipment

All power has been isolated/locked/tagged/tried*
Circuits are live for troubleshooting only

Signed ....

13. Acceptance of Permit to Work

I/we* have read and understood the above precautions and will observe them. All equipment complies with relevant standards. I understand the site emergency plan.

Signed ....

14. Completion of Permit to Work

I/we* certify that this job is complete/incomplete*, all guards have been replaced and secured and all equipment has been removed. The job site has been left clean and tidy.

Permit to work

SIGNS AND NOTICES

As mentioned in Chapter 1, signs are used to keep operatives safe, and the law sets out the types of safety signs needed on a construction site. Some signs warn us about danger and others tell us what to do to stay safe. There are five basic types of sign on a site: prohibition, mandatory, caution, safe condition and supplementary. For more information on the colour, shape and use of these signs, see Chapter 1, pages 41–42.

Examples of safe condition and caution signs

Prohibition notice

Notices are also used on construction sites, and again these are covered in Chapter 1, page 8. Two that you need to know are improvement notices and prohibition notices, both of which are issued by the HSE. An improvement notice is issued by an HSE or local authority inspector to formally notify a company that improvements are needed to the way it is working. A prohibition notice is issued by an HSE or local authority inspector when there is an immediate risk of personal injury. They are not issued lightly and if you receive one, you are clearly breaking a health and safety regulation. The HASAWA workplace notice is also important.

SPECIFICATIONS

A specification accompanies the working drawings. It gives further information that cannot be shown on the drawings because the drawings need to be clear and not covered in notes. A specification would include information such as:

- the colour of paint required
- a specific timber species
- the brick type required
- the plaster finish required.

It is prepared by construction professionals such as architects and building services engineers. They can be produced from previous project specifications, in-house documents or master specifications such as the National Building Specification (NBS). The NBS is owned by the Royal Institute of British Architects (RIBA).

INDUSTRY TIP

Operatives need to refer to the specification before, during and on completion of a project to make sure all criteria have been met.

System Outline

102 External cavity walling

✗ • ~~Drawing references:~~

✗ • ~~Parameters:~~

• Walling below ground:

- Type:	Cavity walling, concrete filled.
- Masonry units:	Common bricks.
- Mortar:	Class M6 mortar.

• Dpc at ground floor: Flexible cavity trays.

• Walling above ground:

- External leaf above ground:

Masonry units:	Facing bricks.
Bond or coursing:	Flemish bond.

- Internal leaf above ground:

Masonry units:	Aerated concrete blocks.

- Mortar:

Type:	Class M4 mortar.
Joint profile to external faces:	Bucket handle.

- Wall ties:	Insulation retaining wall ties.
- Cavity insulation:	Full fill cavity insulation.
- Ventilation components:	Air bricks and sub-floor ventilation ducts.

✗ - ~~Items supplied by others:~~

• Openings:

- Lintels:

Type:	Manufactured stone lintels.
Cavity tray over:	Flexible cavity trays.
- Cavity closers:	Flexible insulated dpcs.

- Sills:

Type:	
Dpc below:	Manufactured stone sills.

Natural stone sills.

Precast concrete sills.

As drawings.

• Abutments:

- Cavity trays and dpcs:

- Flashings built into masonry:

Example of a specification

COMPONENT RANGE DRAWINGS

A component range drawing shows the range of components available from a manufacturer. It includes:

- sizes available

- coding for ordering purposes

- availability (whether it can be bought off-the-shelf or whether pre-ordering is required).

Availability is particularly important when planning delivery dates. Schedules reference this type of drawing.

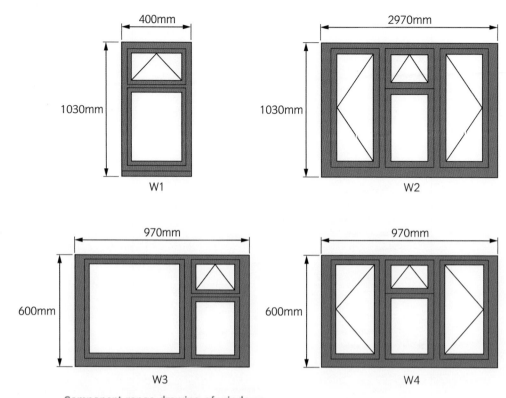

Component range drawing of windows

SCHEDULES

A schedule is used to record repeated design information that applies to a range of components or fittings, such as:

- windows

- doors

- kitchen units

- joinery fittings.

A schedule is mainly used on bigger sites where there are multiples of several designs of houses, with each type having different components and fittings. It avoids a house being given the wrong component or fitting.

A schedule is usually used in conjunction with a component range drawing, a detail drawing and a floor plan.

A detail drawing shows just that – a detail of a particular part of a building and how it is constructed.

In a typical plan, the doors and windows are labelled D1, D2, W1, W2 etc. These components would be included in the schedule, which would provide additional information on them. For example, see the following schedule.

Master Internal Door Schedule							
Ref:	Door size	S.O. width	S.O. height	Lintel type	FD30	Self closing	Floor level
D1	838 × 1981	900	2040	BOX	Yes	Yes	GROUND FLOOR
D2	838 × 1981	900	2040	BOX	Yes	Yes	GROUND FLOOR
D3	762 × 1981	824	2040	BOX	No	No	GROUND FLOOR
D4	838 × 1981	900	2040	N/A	Yes	No	GROUND FLOOR
D5	838 × 1981	900	2040	BOX	Yes	Yes	GROUND FLOOR
D6	762 × 1981	824	2040	BOX	Yes	Yes	FIRST FLOOR
D7	762 × 1981	824	2040	BOX	Yes	Yes	FIRST FLOOR
D8	762 × 1981	824	2040	N/A	Yes	No	FIRST FLOOR
D9	762 × 1981	824	2040	BOX	Yes	Yes	FIRST FLOOR
D10	762 × 1981	824	2040	N/A	No	No	FIRST FLOOR
D11	686 × 1981	748	2040	N/A	Yes	No	SECOND FLOOR
D12	762 × 1981	824	2040	BOX	Yes	Yes	SECOND FLOOR
D13	762 × 1981	824	2040	100 HD BOX	Yes	Yes	SECOND FLOOR
D14	686 × 1981	748	2040	N/A	No	No	SECOND FLOOR

Example of a schedule

BILLS OF QUANTITIES

A bill of quantities is produced by the quantity surveyor and describes everything that is required for the job based on the drawings, specification and schedules. A bill of quantities contains the following information:

- *Preliminaries*: General information including the names of the client and architect, details of the work and descriptions of the site.

- *Preambles*: Like the specification, this outlines the quality and description of materials and workmanship, etc.

- *Measured quantities*: A description of how each task and material is to be measured, with measurements in metres (linear and square), hours, litres, kilogrammes and the number of components required.

The completed document is sent out to contractors who then price the work and enter the costs into the blank spaces. The bill of quantities ensures that all the contractors are pricing for the job using the same information.

BILL OF QUANTITIES

Number	Item Description	Unit	Quantity	Rate	Amount	
					£	p
	CLASS A: GENERAL ITEMS					
	Specified Requirements					
	Testing of Materials					
A250	Testing of recycled and secondary aggregates	sum				
	Information to be provided by the Contractor					
A290	Production of Materials Management Plan	sum				
	Method Related Charges					
	Recycling Plant/Equipment					
A339.01	Mobilise; Fixed	sum				
A339.02	Operate; Time-Related	sum				
A339.03	De-mobilise; Fixed	sum				
	CLASS D: DEMOLITION AND SITE CLEARANCE					
	Other Structures					
D522.01	Other structures; Concrete	sum				
D522.02	Grading/processing of demolition material to produce recycled and secondary aggregates	m^3	70			
D522.03	Disposal of demolition material offsite	m^3	30			
	CLASS E: EARTHWORKS					
	Excavation Ancillaries					
E542	Double handling of recycled and secondary aggregates produced from demolition material	m^3	70			
	Filling					
E615	Importing primary aggregates for filling to structures	m^3	15			
E619.1	Importing recycled and secondary aggregates for filling to structures	m^3	15			

WORK SCHEDULES

It is very important indeed that the progress of work is planned out. A work schedule or programme of work is an easy way of showing what work is to be carried out and when. This is usually shown in the form of a bar chart called a Gantt chart. The chart lists the tasks that need to be done on the left-hand side and shows a timeline across the top. The site manager or trade supervisors can quickly tell from looking at this chart:

- if work is keeping to schedule

- what materials, equipment and labour are required

- when they are required.

Materials very often have a **lead-in time** and so cannot be delivered immediately. These need to be ordered and delivered at the correct time. Labour planning is also required otherwise the trades may be working elsewhere when needed.

INDUSTRY TIP

Use of a planning document such as a Gantt chart will reduce waste and ensure effective use of labour.

Lead-in time

The time taken between ordering an item and it being delivered

	Time (days)						
Task	**1**	**2**	**3**	**4**	**5**	**6**	**7**
Prepare the ground							
Spread foundations							
Lay cables for services							
Build walls up to DPC							
	Proposed time in orange						

Gantt chart

CALCULATING QUANTITIES FOR MATERIALS

Calculations are required throughout the building process. It is important that these calculations are accurate, as mistakes can be very expensive. A company can lose a lot of money if it underestimates:

- the amount of materials required

- how much they cost

- how long it will take to complete a job.

It could also lead to the company gaining a bad reputation for not being able to complete a job on time and in budget.

Materials are usually better priced if bought in bulk, whereas a buy-as-you go approach can cost more.

FUNCTIONAL SKILLS

You have been asked to provide a quote for building a garage. Find the prices online for all the costs, and record them using a spreadsheet. Remember to include labour, plant costs and VAT. Don't forget to make a profit!

Work on this activity can support FICT 2.C and FM C2.9.

Consider these points when buying materials:

- Is there sufficient storage room for delivered materials?

- Is there a risk of the materials being damaged if there is nowhere suitable to store them or if they are delivered too early?

- Will it be a problem to obtain the same style, colour or quality of product if they are not all ordered at the same time?

- Will over-ordering cause lots of wastage?

These and many other considerations will help determine when and in what quantity materials are ordered.

Some wastage is unavoidable. Allowances must be made for wastage, eg cut bricks that cannot be re-used, short ends of timber, partly full paint cans. Up to 5% waste is allowed for bricks and blocks and 10% for timber and paint.

It may be that all the materials are ordered by the office or supervisory staff, but you still need to know how to recognise and calculate material requirements. Deliveries have to be checked before the delivery note is signed and the driver leaves. Any discrepancies in the type or quantity of materials, or any materials that have arrived damaged, must be recorded on the delivery note and reported to the supervisor. Any discrepancies will need to be followed up and new delivery times arranged.

You must be able to identify basic materials and carry out basic calculations. You will often have to collect sufficient materials to carry out a particular operation. Being able to measure accurately will mean you can make the most economic use of materials and therefore reduce waste.

Deliveries must be checked before signing the delivery note

UNITS OF MEASUREMENT

The construction industry uses metric units as standard; however, you may come across some older measures called imperial units.

Units for measuring	Metric units	Imperial units
Length	millimetre (mm) metre (m) kilometre (km)	inch (in) or " eg 6" (6 inches) foot (ft) or ' eg 8' (8 foot)
Liquid	millilitre (ml) litre (l)	pint (pt)
Weight	gramme (g) kilogramme (kg) tonne (t)	pound (lb)

Units for measuring	Quantities	Example
Length	There are 1,000mm in 1m There are 1,000m in 1km	1mm × 1,000 = 1m 1m × 1,000 = 1km 6,250mm can be shown as 6.250m 6,250m can be shown as 6.250km
Liquid	There are 1,000ml in 1l	1ml × 1,000 = 1l
Weight	There are 1,000g in 1kg There are 1,000kg in 1t	1g × 1,000 = 1kg 1kg × 1,000 = 1t

ACTIVITY

Look online to find out:
- What other imperial units are still commonly used?
- How many millimetres are there in an inch?
- How many litres are there in a gallon?

INDUSTRY TIP

Although everything supplied in the construction industry is measured in metric units, many materials still use the imperial equivalent. For example, a plywood sheet will be 1.22m × 2.44m. This is actually the equivalent of an 8ft by 4ft board. It is worth noting these differences as they can cause problems.

CALCULATIONS

Four basic mathematical operations are used in construction calculations.

ADDITION

The addition of two or more numbers is shown with a plus sign (**+**).

Example

A stack of bricks 3 bricks long and 2 bricks high contains 6 bricks.

$$3 + 3 = 6$$

More examples:

$$5 + 2 = 7$$

$$19 + 12 = 31$$

$$234 + 105 = 339$$

SUBTRACTION

The reduction of one number by another number is shown with a minus sign (**−**).

Pallet of bricks

Example

A pallet containing 100 bricks is delivered on site, but you need only 88 bricks. How many are left over?

$$100 − 88 = 12$$

More examples:

$$5 − 2 = 3$$

$$19 − 12 = 7$$

$$234 − 105 = 129$$

MULTIPLICATION

The scaling of one number by another number is shown with a multiplication sign (×).

Example

A stack of bricks is 3 bricks long and 2 bricks high. It contains 6 bricks.

$$3 \times 2 = 6$$

More examples:

$$19 \times 12 = 228$$

$$234 \times 10 = 2,340$$

$$234 \times 105 = 24,570$$

In the last two examples, the comma (,) is used to show we are in the thousands. In words we would say, twenty-four thousand, five hundred and seventy.

DIVISION

Sharing one number by another number in equal parts (how many times it goes into the number) is shown with a division sign (÷).

Example

$$4 \div 2 = 2$$

$$36 \div 12 = 3$$

$$600 \div 4 = 150$$

ACTIVITY

Try these sums:
1   29 + 51
2   79 – 23
3   54 × 76
4   23 ÷ 4

Answers: 1) 80, 2) 56, 3) 4,104, 4) 5.75

LINEAR MEASUREMENTS

Linear means how long a number of items would measure from end to end if laid in a straight line. Examples of things that are calculated in linear measurements are:

- skirting board

- lengths of timber

- rope

- building line

- wallpaper.

The quantity of skirting required is calculated using linear measurements

We use this form of measurement when working out how much of one of the materials listed above we need, eg to find out how much

A joiner measuring a room

Perimeter

The distance around an object or room

skirting board is required for a room. First, we need to measure the **perimeter** (sides) of a room. To find the linear length we add the length of all four sides together. This can be done in two ways: adding or multiplying.

Example 1

A site carpenter has been asked how many metres of skirting are required for the rooms below.

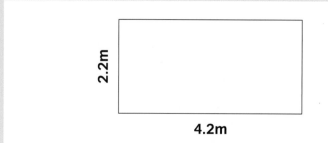

They can add all the sides together:
$$2.2 + 4.2 + 2.2 + 4.2 = 12.8m$$

Or, they can multiply each side by 2, and add them together:
$$(2.2 \times 2) + (4.2 \times 2) = 12.8m$$

Either way, **12.8m** is the correct answer.

Example 2

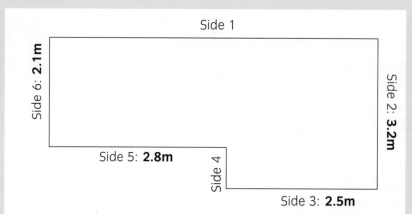

To work out the perimeter of this room we need to add all the sides together. In this example each side has been given a reference number, so all we need to do is add all the sides together, like this:

side 1 (side 3 + side 5) + side 2 + side 3 + side 4 (side 2 − side 6) + side 5 + side 6

Now, let's show the working out: $(2.8 + 2.5) + 3.2 + 2.5 + (3.2 − 2.1) + 2.8 + 2.1 = 17m$

The amount of skirting board required is **17m**.

Now let's put some door openings in. This symbol ←——→ represents an opening.

Example 3

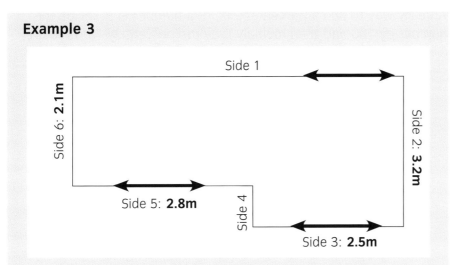

On side 1 there is an opening 0.9m wide, on side 3 there is an opening 1.5m wide and on side 5 there is an opening 2.1m wide.

We know from Example 2 that the perimeter of the room is 17m. We now need to remove the openings. Skirting board will not be needed for the openings.

Step 1

Add together the lengths of the three combined openings:

0.9 + 1.5 + 2.1 = 4.5m

Step 2

Deduct this from 17m:

17 − 4.5 = 12.5m

The linear length of skirting board required is 12.5m.

Step 3

However, this calculation does not take into account any waste. We would normally add 10% extra to allow for waste:

12.5 + 10% = 12.5 + 1.25 = 13.75m

The total amount of skirting board required is **13.75m**.

PERCENTAGES

An easy way to find a percentage (%) of a number is to divide the number by 100 and then multiply it by the percentage you require.

Example

Increase 19m by 12%

$19 \div 100 = 0.19$

$0.19 \times 12 = 2.28$

$19 + 2.28 = 21.28$m

Total required **21.28m**.

AREA

Floors

The structured layers of a building, eg ground floor, first floor, second floor

To find out how much material is required to cover a surface such as a **floor** or wall you need to calculate its area. Area is the measurements of a two-dimensional surface, eg the surface of floors, walls, glass or a roof.

To find the area of a surface you need to multiply its length by its width (L × W) or one side by the other. This will give you an answer which is expressed in square units (^{2}). For example, mm^2, m^2 or km^2.

Example 1

A bricklayer has been asked to work out the area of the floor below.

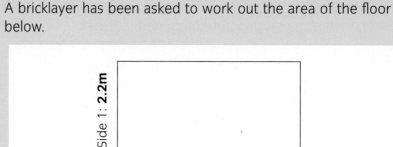

side 1 × side 2 = floor area

$2.2 \times 4.4 = 9.68$m^2

The total floor area is **9.68m²**.

Irregularly shaped areas can be calculated by breaking up the area into sections that can be worked out easily, and then adding them together.

Example 2

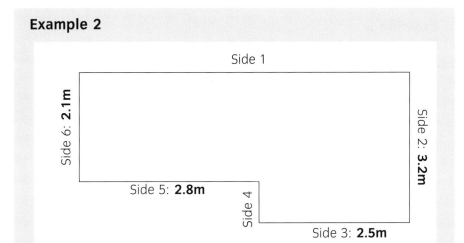

Irregularly shaped rooms can be split into sections to calculate the area

Step 1

Divide the area into two parts, and then calculate the area of each part. The easiest way to do this is to divide it into two smaller sections:

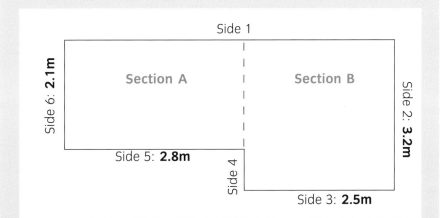

Step 2

Work out the areas of section A and section B:

section A = 2.1 × 2.8 = 5.88m²

section B = 2.5 × 3.2 = 8m²

Step 3

Add the areas of section A and section B together:

section A + section B = total floor area

5.88 + 8 = 13.88m²

The total floor area is **13.88m²**.

A tiler tiling a floor

INDUSTRY TIP

Remember, there are 1,000mm in a metre so we show the sum as 0.305m in Example 3.

ACTIVITY

Find the area of the following measurements:

1   2.1m × 2.4m
2   0.9m × 2.7m
3   250mm × 3.4m

Answers: 1) 5.04m², 2) 2.43m², 3) 0.85m²

Now let's say the floor requires tiling. The tiler needs to calculate the number of floor tiles required.

Example 3

The size of each floor tile is 305mm × 305mm. We can also show this as 0.305m × 0.305m.

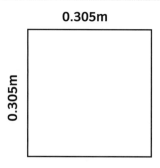

0.305m

0.305m

How many floor tiles are required for the floor area in Example 2? The total floor area is 13.88m².

Step 1

Calculate the area of one tile. As the floor area is given in m², we need to calculate the size of the tile in the same unit, ie m².

0.305 × 0.305 = 0.093m²

Step 2

Now you need to divide the total floor area by the area of one tile to find out the total number of tiles required.

total floor area ÷ area of one tile = total number of tiles

13.88 ÷ 0.093 = 149.247 tiles

This number is rounded up to the next full tile, so a total of 150 floor tiles are required.

Step 3

However, this total does not allow for any waste.

Add 5% to allow for waste:

150 + 5% = 158 tiles (to the next full tile)

Let's look at the working out:

150 ÷ 100 = 1.5 tiles (this is 1%)

1.5 × 5 = 7.5 tiles (this is 5%)

5% of 150 tiles, rounded up to the next full tile, is 8 tiles.

Therefore **158 tiles** are required.

AREA OF A TRIANGLE

Sometimes you will be required to work out an area that includes a triangle.

Example 1

A painter has been asked to work out how much paint will be needed to paint the front of this house.

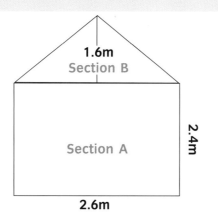

Step 1

Divide the area up into a rectangular section (section A) and a triangular section (section B).

Step 2

Find the area of section A:

2.4 × 2.6 = 6.24m²

The area of section A is 6.24m².

Step 3

Find the area of section B.

The area of a triangle can be found by multiplying the base by the height, then dividing by 2.

(base × height) ÷ 2 = area

2.6 × 1.6 = 4.16

4.16 ÷ 2 = 2.08m²

The area of section B is 2.08m².

Step 4

area of section A + area of section B = total wall area

6.24 + 2.08 = 8.32m²

The total wall area is **8.32m²**.

A decorator measuring the height of a room

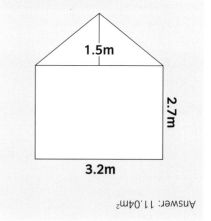

ACTIVITY

Look at the diagram. Work out the area of the wall in order to arrange the delivery of sufficient paint.

Answer: 11.04m²

RIGHT-ANGLED TRIANGLE

Now let's look at the right-angled triangle below. It has three sides, A, B and C. Pythagorean theorem tells us that in a right-angled triangle the **hypotenuse** is equal to the sum of the square of the lengths of the two other sides, in other words $a^2 + b^2 = c^2$. In this example the hypotenuse is side C.

Using the Pythagorean theorem we can work out the length of any side.

Hypotenuse

The longest side of a right-angled triangle. It is always opposite the right angle

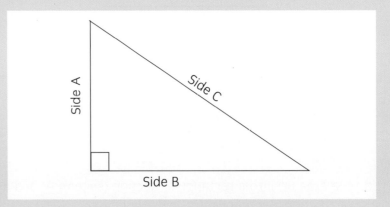

The hypotenuse

INDUSTRY TIP

If a triangle has a small square in the corner, this shows you the corner is a right angle.

Example 1

If side A is 3m long and side B is 4m long, what is the length of side C?

$3 \times 3 = 9$

$4 \times 4 = 16$

$9 + 16 = 25$

$\sqrt{25} = 5$

($\sqrt{}$ means square root. A square root of a number is the number that is multiplied by itself, in this case $5 \times 5 = 25$)

Side C is **5m** long.

Example 2

A joiner has been asked to work out the length of a roof (side C).

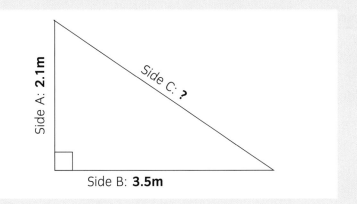

2.1×2.1 (side A) = 4.41

3.5×3.5 (side B) = 12.25

$4.41 + 12.25 = 16.66$

$\sqrt{16.66} = 4.08m$

The length of side C is **4.08m**.

Example 3

A bricklayer needs to find the rise of a roof (side A).

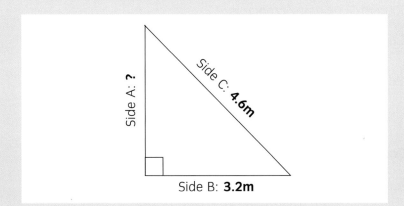

3.2×3.2 (side B) = 10.24

4.6×4.6 (side C) = 21.16

$21.16 - 10.24 = 10.92$

$\sqrt{10.92} = 3.30m$

The length of side A is **3.3m**.

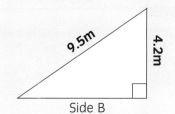
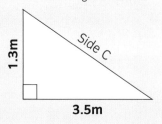

PERIMETERS AND AREAS OF CIRCLES

Circumference

The distance around the edge of a circle

Diameter

The length of a straight line going through the centre of a circle connecting two points on its circumference

Sometimes you are required to find the perimeter or **circumference** of a circle.

circumference of a circle = π × **diameter**

$$C = \pi d$$

π (or 'pi') is the number of times that the diameter of a circle will divide into the circumference.

π = 3.142

This is equal to the number of diameters in one revolution of a circle. It is the same for any sized circle.

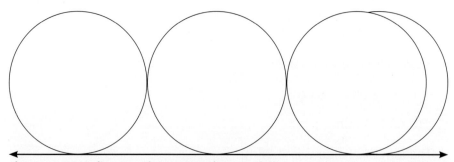

There are 3.142 diameters in one complete revolution

Example 1

A joiner is making a circular window that has a diameter of 600mm. Its circumference is:

0.600 × 3.142 = **1.885m**

The diameter of a circle from a given circumference is:

diameter = circumference ÷ π

Example 2

A window has a circumference of 2.250m. Its diameter is:

2.250 ÷ 3.142 = **0.716m** (or 716mm)

Radius

The length of a line from the centre to a point on the circumference of a circle. It is exactly half the length of the diameter

The area of a circle is found by:

area of a circle = π × **radius²** (radius is equal to half the diameter)

Example 3

A painter needs to paint a circle that is 1.2m in diameter and is required to find the area of the circle to enable them to order the correct quantity of paint.

1.2 ÷ 2 = **0.6m** (the radius)

3.142 × 0.6m² = **1.13m²**

VOLUME

The volume of an object is the total space it takes up, eg a tin of paint, a foundation for a wall or the capacity of a concrete mixer, and is shown as m³ (cubic metres). To find the volume of an object you must multiply length by width by height.

volume = length × width × height

Example 1

Each side of this cube is 1m. The total space it takes up is 1m³

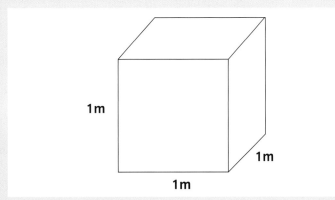

1m × 1m × 1m = **1m³**

Example 2

A bricklayer has been asked to work out how many m³ of **concrete** is required for a strip foundation. The size of the foundation is 3.2m long, 0.600m wide and 0.900m deep.

length × width × height = volume

3.2 × 0.600 × 0.900 = 1.728m³

The volume of concrete needed for the strip foundation is **1.728m³**.

A bricklayer taking levels

Concrete

Composed of cement, fine aggregate (sand) and course aggregate (stone) of varying sizes and in varying proportions

To work out the volume of a cylinder:

volume = πr²h (π × r² × h)

ACTIVITY

A bricklayer has been given two tasks:

1 Measure the volume of a strip foundation measuring 4.250m long, 1.1m wide and 1m deep.

2 Find the volume of four pile foundations (see page 83) each measuring 2.5m deep, with a diameter of 0.9m.

Work out the answers to the tasks.

Answers: 1) 4.675m³, 2) 6.36m²

Example 3

A joiner has a tin of preservative and needs to know its volume. The tin has a diameter of 250mm and a height of 700mm.

πr²h (π × r² × h) = volume

The radius (r) is half the diameter:

250 ÷ 2 = 125mm

3.142 × 0.125² × 0.700 = 0.034m³

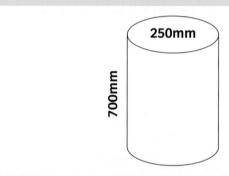

The volume of the tin of paint is **0.034m³**.

COMMUNICATION

Good communication is vital to the smooth running of any building project.

Communication involves sharing thoughts, information and ideas between people. For communication to be effective, information must be:

- given in a clear way

- received without misunderstanding.

It has been said that to be a good communicator it is just as important to be a good listener as it is to be a good speaker! Good communication leads to a safer and more efficient workplace, not to mention helping to maintain a pleasant working environment.

Most sites will have policies and procedures in place that govern the chain of command and communication between supervisory staff and workers.

INDUSTRY TIP

Before communicating something, it is good to gather your thoughts. Have relevant information to hand, eg a drawing, and take notes if required.

ACTIVITY

A customer has asked for the best steps to take before painting the skirting board in their new home. You have been asked to reply to the customer and give advice on the best way for them to do this.

Decide on the best form of communication and list all the information you should give along with the stages they should follow.

WRITTEN COMMUNICATION

There are many methods of communication within the building industry. In this chapter we have discussed drawings, schedules and specifications etc. The architect uses these methods to communicate details about the building to the team who will **tender** for and erect the building.

Communication is usually electronic via email (with or without attachments) or through intranet sites. Drawings are very commonly distributed in electronic formats which are printed on to paper when required. Messages are often given via text.

Sometimes communication will be via a memorandum (memo), a written form of communication.

Site rules, risk assessments and method statements (see Chapter 1) communicate safety information.

SITE PAPERWORK

Communication on site is aided by the use of paperwork and without it no building site could operate. It is an important method of communication between operatives and supervisory staff, builders, architects and clients.

Tender

To supply a client with a fixed quotation for work

INDUSTRY TIP

Messages that are passed on by word of mouth are open to interpretation, so written messages often can be more clear.

FUNCTIONAL SKILLS

Thinking about the garage that you worked out the costs for on page 57 and using a computer, write a letter to the client outlining the cost and other details such as when the work would start and any basic terms regarding payment.

Work on this activity can support FE 2.3.1.

Type of paperwork	Description
Timesheet **Timesheet** Employer: CPF Building Co. Employee Name: Louise Miranda Week starting: 17/6/14 Date: 21/6/13 (see timesheet table below) Employee's signature:_____ Supervisor's signature: _____	Used to record the hours completed each day, and is usually the basis on which pay is calculated. Timesheets also help to work out how much the job has cost in working hours, and can give information for future estimating work when working up a tender.

Day	Job/Job Number	Start Time	Finish Time	Total Hours	Overtime
Monday	Penburthy, Falmouth 0897	9am	6pm	8	
Tuesday	Penburthy, Falmouth 0897	9am	6pm	8	
Wednesday	Penburthy, Falmouth 0897	8.30am	5.30pm	8	
Thursday	Trelawney, Truro 0901	11am	8pm	8	2
Friday	Trelawney, Truro 0901	11am	7pm	7	1
Saturday	Trelawney, Truro 0901	9am	1pm	4	
Totals				43	3

Type of paperwork	Description
Job sheet **CPF Building Co** **Job sheet** **Customer name:** Henry Collins **Date:** 9/12/14 **Address:** 57 Green St Kirkham London **Work to be carried out** Finishing joint work to outer walls **Instructions** Use weather struck and half round	Gives details of a job to be carried out, sometimes with material requirements and hours given to complete the task.
Variation order **Confirmation notice** **Architect's instruction** **CPF Building Co** **Variation order** **Project Name:** Penburthy House, Falmouth, Cornwall **Reference Number:** 80475 **Date:** 14/11/14 **From: :** _____ **To:** _____ Reason for change: — Tick Customer requirements — ✔ Engineer requirements — ☐ Revised design — ☐ **Instruction:** Entrance door to be made from Utile hardwood with brushed chrome finished ironmongery (changed from previous detail, softwood with brass ironmongery). Signature _____	Sometimes alterations are made to the contract which changes the work to be completed, eg a client may wish to move a door position or request a different brick finish. This usually involves a variation to the cost. This work should not be carried out until a variation order and a confirmation notice have been issued. Architect's instructions are instructions given by an architect, first verbally and then in writing to a site agent as work progresses and questions inevitably arise over details and specifications.

Type of paperwork	Description
Requisition order	Filled out to order materials from a supplier or central store. These usually have to be authorised by a supervisor before they can be used.

CPF Building Co
Requisition order

Supplier Information: Construction Supplies Ltd　　　　**Date:** 9/12/14

Contract Address/Delivery Address: Penburthy House, Falmouth, Cornwall

Tel number: 0207294333

Order Number: 26213263CPF

Item number	Description	Quantity	Unit/Unit Price	Total
X22433	75mm 4mm gauge countersunk brass screws slotted	100	30p	£30
YK7334	Brass cups to suit	100	5p	£5
V23879	Sadikkens water based clear varnish	1 litre	£20.00	£20.00
Total:				£55.00

Authorised by:　Denzil Penburthy

Delivery note	Accompanies a delivery. Goods have to be checked for quantity and quality before the note is signed. Any discrepancies are recorded on the delivery note. Goods that are not suitable (because they are not as ordered or because they are of poor quality) can be refused and returned to the supplier.

Construction Supplies Ltd
Delivery note

Customer name and address: CPF Building Co Penburthy House Falmouth Cornwall	**Delivery Date:** 16/12/14 **Delivery time:** 9am **Order number:** 26213263CPF

Item number	Quantity	Description	Unit Price	Total
X22433	100	75mm 4mm gauge countersunk brass screws slotted	30p	£30
YK7334	100	Brass cups to suit	5p	£5
V23879	1 litre	Sadikkens water based clear varnish	£20	£20

Subtotal	£55.00
VAT	20%
Total	£66.00

Discrepancies: ....

Customer Signature: ....

Print name: ....

Date: ....

Type of paperwork	Description
Delivery record **Davids & Co** **Monthly delivery record** *Customer name and address:* CPF Building Co, Penburthy House, Falmouth, Cornwall *Customer order date:* 28th May 2014 (table: Item number / Quantity / Description / Unit Price / Date Delivered) BS3647 — 2 — 1 tonne bag of building sand — £60 — 3/6/14 CM4324 — 12 — 25kg bags of cement — £224 — 17/6/14 Customer Signature: .... Print name: .... Date:	Every month a supplier will issue a delivery record that lists all the materials or hire used for that month.
Invoice **Davids & Co** **Invoice** **Invoice number:** 75856 **Date:** 2nd January 2014 **PO number:** 4700095685 *Company name and address:* Davids & Co, 228 West Retail Park, Ivybridge, Plymouth *Customer name and address:* CPF Building Co, Penburthy House, Falmouth, Cornwall **VAT registration number:** 663694542 For: (table: Item number / Quantity / Description / Unit Price) BS3647 — 2 — 1 tonne bag of building sand — £30 CM4324 — 12 — 25kg bags of cement — £224 Subtotal £2748.00 VAT 20% Total £3297.60 Please make cheques payable to Davids & Co Payment due in 30 days	Sent by a supplier. It lists the services or materials supplied along with the price the contractor is requested to pay. There will be a time limit within which to pay. Sometimes there will be a discount for quick payment or penalties for late payment.
Site diary	This will be filled out daily. It records anything of note that happens on site such as deliveries, absences or occurrences, eg delay due to the weather.

VERBAL COMMUNICATION

Often, managers, supervisors, work colleagues and trades communicate verbally. This can be face to face or over a telephone. Although this is the most common form of communication, it is also the most unreliable.

Mistakes are often made while communicating verbally. The person giving the information might make an error. The person receiving the information might misunderstand something because the information is unclear or it is noisy in the background, or because they later forget the details of the conversation.

Confusion can be minimised by recording conversations or by using a form of written communication. If there is a record it can be used for future reference and help to clear up any misunderstandings.

TAKING A TELEPHONE MESSAGE

It is a good idea to take down details of telephone calls and many companies provide documentation for this purpose. When taking a message it is important to record the following details:

- *Content*: This is the most important part of the message – the actual information being relayed. Take and write down as many details as possible.

- *Date and time*: Messages are often **time sensitive**, and may require an urgent response.

- *Who the message is for*: Ensure the person gets the message by giving it to them or leaving it in a place where they will find it.

- *Contact name and details*: Write down the name of the person leaving the message, and how to get back to them with a response.

UNACCEPTABLE COMMUNICATION

When communicating, it is very important to stay calm. Think about what you are going to say. An angry word will often encourage an angry response. However, keeping calm and composed will often diffuse a stressful situation. A shouting match rarely ends with a good or productive result.

There are several types of communication that are unacceptable and could result in unemployment. Unacceptable communication includes:

- aggressive communication such as swearing or using inappropriate hand gestures

An operative taking notes during a phone call

Time sensitive

When something must be dealt with quickly

- racist or sexist comments or gestures

- showing prejudice against people with disabilities.

This type of behaviour shows a lack of respect for others and does not create a safe or pleasant working environment. It will also give your company a poor image if customers see or hear this behaviour. Acting in this way is likely to result in trouble for you and your employer and could even result in a **tribunal** and loss of employment.

Tribunal

A judgement made in court

KNOWLEDGE OF THE CONSTRUCTION INDUSTRY AND BUILT ENVIRONMENT

Buildings come in a wide variety of types in relation to appearance and methods of construction. Despite the variety of buildings, they all have design features in common. In this section we will discuss various parts of buildings and their purpose.

We will also discuss sustainable construction – how buildings can be designed to sit better within the environment, with lower pollution levels and energy requirements both during the building process and when in use.

A house with solar panels

FOUNDATIONS

Foundation

Used to spread the load of a building to the subsoil

Foundations serve as a good base on which to put the building. They need to be capable of carrying the weight of the building and any further load that may be put upon it. These are known as **dead loads** and **imposed loads**.

Foundations must be designed to resist any potential movement in the ground on which the building will sit. Ground conditions can vary widely. Soil samples are taken to help decide on the type of foundation to use. This usually takes the form of bore holes dug or drilled around the site. These samples are sent away for testing in a laboratory. The results will identify:

- the soil condition (clay or sandy)
- the depth of the soil
- the depth of the water table
- if any contaminations are present.

The soil condition is important: clay soil drains poorly and can move if it gets waterlogged or dries out completely. Sandy soils drain very well, but can become unstable. A foundation that is suitable for the ground type and load of the building will be designed.

CONCRETE

Foundations are made from concrete. Concrete is made from fine and coarse aggregate (crushed stone), sand and cement mixed with water. Water reacts with the cement causing it to harden. This process is called hydration and it locks the aggregates together. Concrete is very strong under compression (when weight is put upon it) but is weak when it is pulled (put under tension). Tension can be caused in a foundation when it has to bridge softer sections of ground or when ground conditions are unstable. To prevent failure of the foundation, the concrete may need to be reinforced with steel which is cast into the concrete before it hardens.

Dead load

The weight of all the materials used to construct the building

Imposed load

Additional loads that may be placed on the structure, eg people, furniture, wind and snow

INDUSTRY TIP

The type of foundation to be used will usually be decided by the architect and a structural engineer and will be the result of tests.

INDUSTRY TIP

Remember, cement will give chemical burns so use the correct PPE while using and mixing it.

Concrete with steel reinforcement

Sulphate-resisting cement

Sulphate-resisting cement, such as Sulphate Resisting Portland Cement, is more resistant than ordinary cement to the action of mineralised water containing sulphates. It also hardens more slowly and has a higher frost resistance. The ratio of cement to aggregate in concrete will also affect its strength. Concrete can be mixed in a number of ratios to suit the type of foundation design and the strength of foundation needed to cope with different ground conditions. The ratios are outlined below.

Concrete name	Ratio	Usage
C7.5 (low strength)	1:3:6 or 7 (cement:sand: coarse aggregate)	For general non-structural use.
C10 to C15 (medium strength)	1:4:6 to 1:4:5 (cement:sand: medium aggregate)	Used in typical house foundations.
C20 (strong)	1:2:4 (cement:sand: medium aggregate)	Used as a foundation mix in house construction in softer ground and for slabs.
C25 (stronger)	1:1.5:3 (cement:sand: medium aggregate)	Can be used for foundations to larger houses and for creating floors.
C30 (very strong)	1:2:3 (cement:sand: fine aggregate)	A general-purpose, strong concrete.
C35 (industrial strength)	1:1.5:2.5 (cement: sand:fine aggregate)	Structural concrete.

Additives are used to slow down or speed up the curing process if required (known as retardants and accelerants respectively) and for frost resistance as frost can damage concrete that has not had a chance to harden sufficiently.

TYPES OF FOUNDATION

Different types of structures, such as detached houses, high-rise and low-rise buildings, all require different types of foundation.

High-rise building

Low-rise building

Detached house

Strip foundations

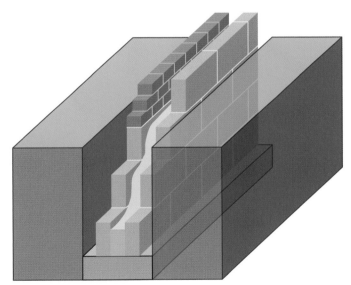

Traditional strip foundation

A strip foundation is the traditional type of foundation used for residential developments (ordinary houses). It is formed by digging a trench to the required width and depth as determined by the soil conditions and the weight of the structure. It is either filled with concrete or a layer of concrete is poured into the bottom. This layer must be a minimum of 150mm thick and is commonly 225mm thick.

Footings

The substructure below ground level. These are projecting courses at the base of a wall

Damp proof course (DPC)

A layer of plastic that prevents damp rising up through a wall needs to be positioned at least 150mm above ground level

Footings are brought up to the level of the **damp proof course** (DPC) using concrete blocks or bricks. These are set out from the centre of the strip of concrete in order to spread the weight evenly. A variety of specialist bricks and blocks are used for this purpose. They need to be able to resist water penetration and therefore frost damage.

Engineering brick

Trench block

It can be economical to fill the trench up to the top with concrete rather than build a substructure – this is known as trench fill. Sometimes it is necessary to build on the edge of the concrete – this is known as an eccentric foundation.

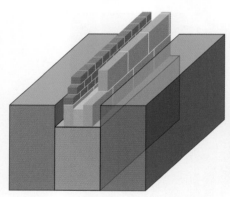

Trench fill foundation

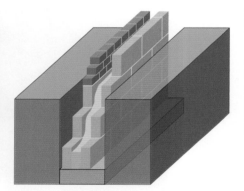

Eccentric foundation

Wide strip foundations

A wide strip foundation is very similar to a strip foundation in most of its aspects. The main difference between the two is that a wide strip foundation has steel reinforcements placed within the concrete. The steel gives considerably more strength to the foundation and enables greater loads to be placed on it. Without the steel reinforcements the foundation would need to be much deeper and would need vast amounts of concrete.

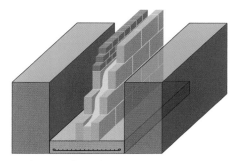

Wide strip foundation

Pad foundations

A pad foundation is used to support a point load such as a column in a steel-framed building. This type of foundation often has bolts set into the top ready for fixing the steel.

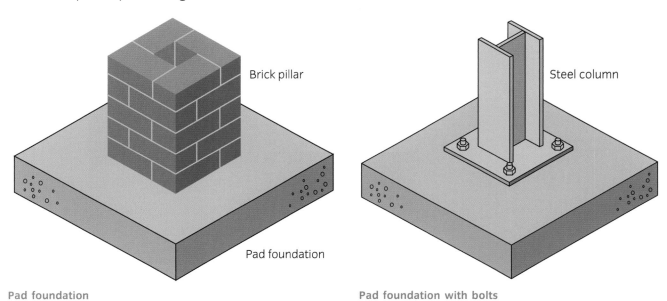

Brick pillar

Steel column

Pad foundation

Pad foundation

Pad foundation with bolts

Pile foundations

Deep **piles** are used to transfer the load through unsuitable soil layers into the harder layers of ground below, even down to rock if required (known as end bearing). Some piles use **friction** to provide support. This is known as skin friction. Tall buildings (and especially narrow buildings such as chimneys or towers) have large lateral forces due to side winds and pile foundations resist these forces well.

Pile

A cylindrical foundation used on large, heavy buildings, or where the ground has poor load-bearing capabilities

Friction

Resistance between the surface of the concrete foundation and the soil around it

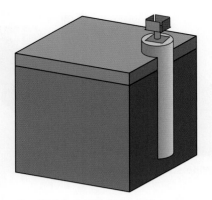

A cylindrical pile foundation

Raft foundations

A raft foundation is often laid over an area of softer soil that would be unsuitable for a strip foundation. A raft foundation is a slab of concrete covering the entire base of the building; it spreads the weight of the building over a wider area but still maintains a deeper base around the load-bearing walls.

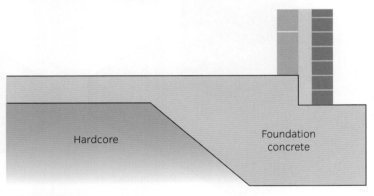

Hardcore

Foundation concrete

Raft foundation

FLOORS

Floors can be divided into two main categories:

- ground floors

- upper floors.

Floors are required to be load bearing, and there is a wide variety of construction methods depending on the type of building and potential load that will be imposed upon the floor. Floors also may need to prevent:

- heat loss

- transfer of sound

- moisture penetration.

GROUND FLOORS

These may be either solid ground floors or suspended floors.

Solid floors

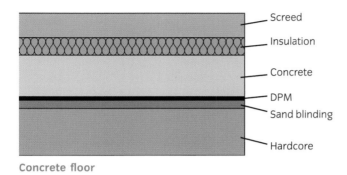

- Screed
- Insulation
- Concrete
- DPM
- Sand blinding
- Hardcore

Concrete floor

Solid concrete floors are laid upon **hardcore** and have a **damp proof membrane** (DPM) built into them to prevent damp coming up through the floor. **Insulation** is also laid into the floor to reduce heat loss. It is important that the insulation is not affected by the high water content of the wet concrete when being poured.

A finish to a concrete floor is called a screed. It can be laid 'lean' which consists of a mix of sand and cement that has only a little water added to it. Another type is known as 'self-levelling' which is mixed up very wet and finds its own level. It can be bought in bags as a powder that needs to be mixed, or delivered in a lorry and poured in.

As mentioned earlier, steel reinforcement can also be used within the concrete to increase strength and reduce cracks.

Hollow and suspended floors

Upper floors and some ground floors are suspended or hollow, meaning that instead of resting on the ground beneath, the load is transferred via beams to the walls.

Two types of beam used are Posi-Joist and I-beam. Posi-Joists are strong yet lightweight as they are made from two smaller beams connected with metal struts. It is easier to accommodate large services such as soil pipes when using this type of floor. Timber I-beams are similar to Posi-Joists, but the middle of the beam is made from a timber sheet material. Timber joists are usually covered with either chipboard or solid timber floorboards. A sleeper wall is built beneath the floor to carry the joists, making the floor stronger and reducing movement.

Hardcore

A mixture of crushed stone and sand laid and compacted to give a good base for the concrete

Damp proof membrane (DPM)

An impermeable layer that prevents damp coming up through the floor. A layer of sand known as blinding is placed below the DPM to prevent any sharp stones below piercing the membrane when the concrete is poured

Insulation

Materials used to retain heat and improve the thermal value of a building; may also be used for managing sound transfer

Modern timber frame

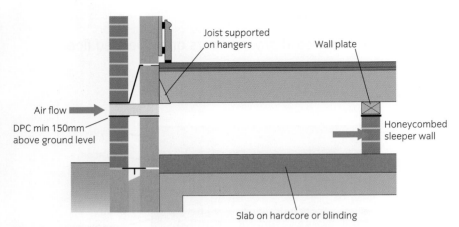

Joist supported on hangers

Wall plate

Air flow

DPC min 150mm above ground level

Honeycombed sleeper wall

Slab on hardcore or blinding

Suspended wood floor

Posi-Joist

I-beam

Suspended concrete floors can be made using two methods. They can either be cast 'in situ', which means that formwork (a mould) is set up and concrete is poured into it. Alternately, precast floors involve using concrete beams or rafts that have been made off site in a factory and are set onto walls. Concrete is then poured on top to finish the floor.

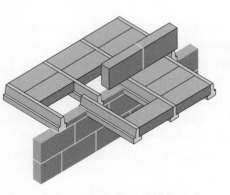

Suspended concrete floor (block and beam)

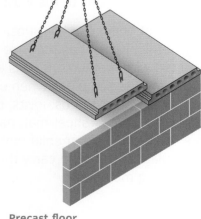

Precast floor

UPPER FLOORS

In most domestic dwellings timber floor joists are used and laid in the same way as hollow timber ground floors, while in large commercial and industrial buildings solid concrete floors are used.

WALLS

Walling for a building can usually be divided in two categories:

- external
- internal.

Walling can be load or non-load-bearing. Load-bearing walls carry the weight of the floors and roof and transfer this weight down to the foundations. A non-load bearing wall carries no weight.

Walls often have openings in them, eg doors and windows, which will weaken them if they are not constructed correctly. Openings require support (via a **lintel** or arch) across the top to give the wall support and **bond** it together.

EXTERNAL WALLING

External walls need to:

- keep the elements (wind and rain) out of the building
- look good
- fit into the surrounding landscape.

Several methods of construction are used for external walling. Common construction methods are:

- **solid wall**
- **cavity wall**
- timber framing.

Solid walls

Many older traditional buildings have solid walls made from brick, block or stone – see the table on the next page. Solid walls have the disadvantage of being more easily penetrated by damp. Older solid walls are often upgraded by having insulating and waterproofing layers applied to the outside of the wall.

Lintel

A horizontal member for spanning an opening to support the structure above

Bond

The arrangement or pattern of laying bricks and blocks to spread the load through the wall, also for strength and appearance

Solid wall

Walls of a thickness of one brick and greater

Cavity wall

Walling built in two separate skins (usually of different materials) with a void held together by wall ties

Solid wall

Material used	Description
Bricks 	A very traditional building material made from fired clay, calcium-silicate or concrete. A standard sized brick is 215mm × 102.5mm × 65mm.
Blocks 	These are made of either concrete (crushed stone and cement) or a lightweight cement mixture. They are much bigger than a brick, and are available in various sizes. The most commonly used size is 440mm × 215mm × 100mm. Wider blocks are used for walls where more strength or improved sound insulation is required. Lightweight blocks made from aerated concrete are easier to lay and cut and have greater thermal resistance. However, they are more costly and do not have the same structural properties as standard dense concrete blocks.
Stone 	A natural building material which varies widely in use and appearance from area to area. Stone may be cut to a uniform size before use or used in its quarried state.
Mortar 	This is used between bricks, blocks and stones to bind them together and increase the strength of the wall. It is a mixture of soft sand and cement mixed with water and other additives if required, eg **plasticiser**, colouring or **lime**. It is important that the strength of the mortar is correct for the type of material that is being used to construct the wall. If the mortar has too much cement in the mix it will be so strong that it will not allow movement in the walling due to settlement, and the bricks could crack resulting in the wall needing to be rebuilt. Other additives (retardant and accelerant) can slow down or accelerate this curing process and help protect from frost. Mortars are mixed to a ratio of materials, eg 1:6. The first number is always the proportion of cement with the second being the proportion of sand. A typical mix ratio for masonry walling is 1:5.

Plasticiser

An additive that is used to make the mortar more pliable and easier to work with

Lime

A fine powdered material traditionally used in mortar

Bonding is the interlocking pattern that the brick and block **leaves** are laid in, which increases the strength of the wall. There are many bond types. Here are three common examples.

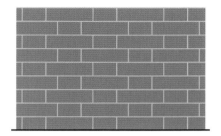

Flemish bond

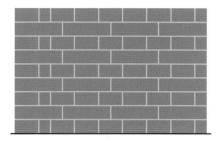

English bond

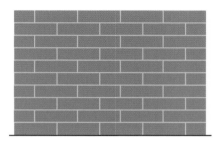

Stretcher bond

Cavity walls

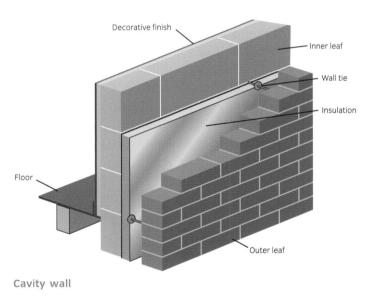

Cavity wall

The most common type of external walling used today is cavity wall construction.

Cavity walls are two masonry walls built side by side to form an inner and outer leaf (sometimes called skins). The leaves are held together with wall ties. These ties are made from rust and rot proof material and are built in as the walls are being constructed. The cavity is partially filled with insulation (typically fibreglass batts or polystyrene boards) as required by the **building regulations**. This reduces heat loss and saves energy.

The inner leaf usually carries any loads from the roof and floors down to the foundations and has a decorative finish on the inside, typically plaster which is either painted or papered. The outer leaf resists the elements and protects the inside of the building.

Building regulations

A series of documents that set out legal requirements for the standards of building work

ACTIVITY

State the minimum performance standards required for a cavity wall to meet current building regulations.

ACTIVITY

Find out the current minimum width of cavity allowed.

Timber framing

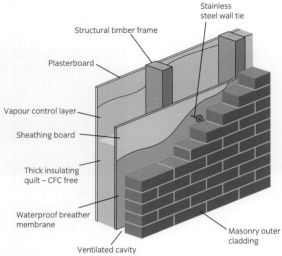

Stainless steel wall tie

Structural timber frame

Plasterboard

Vapour control layer

Sheathing board

Thick insulating quilt – CFC free

Waterproof breather membrane

Ventilated cavity

Masonry outer cladding

Timber frame wall

Elizabethan oak frame

Timber framing is both a traditional and modern method of building. Traditional buildings using timber framing were made mostly from oak with various in-fills such as brick or plaster to form the walls. Modern timber frame homes are generally built from softwood and have an outer skin of masonry or are clad with timber or plaster to waterproof the structure. Oak framing, as a traditional building method, is becoming increasingly popular again.

Prefabricated walls

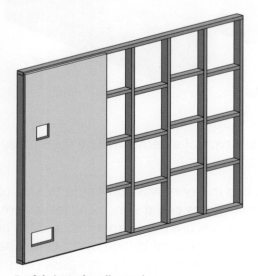

Prefabricated wall panel

There are a variety of prefabricated products available, generally made in a factory and then transported to site to be erected. These products enable quick and easy building. Often the **services** are pre-installed.

INTERNAL WALLING

Internal walling can be load or non-load bearing. Internal partitions divide large internal spaces into smaller rooms.

Internal partitions can be made from studwork or masonry. Studwork partitions consist of studs (which can be made from timber or metal) covered with a sheet material (usually plasterboard).

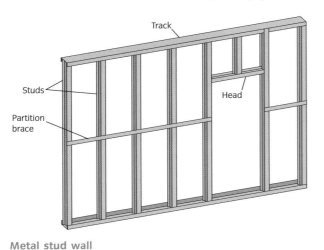

Metal stud wall

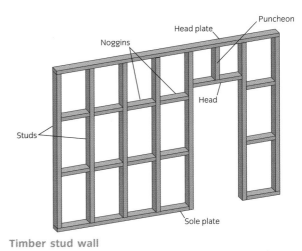

Timber stud wall

WALL FINISHES

External walls made from brick usually have no further finishes added while ones made from blocks are rendered. This is a covering of sand and cement mortar which is then finished with masonry paint.

Internal walls are most often plastered with a thin layer of gypsum plaster over plasterboard; this gives a very smooth hardwearing finish which is then usually finished with emulsion paint or papered coverings.

It is important to **size** new plaster to give a good base before applying further coverings of paint or paper coverings. This first coat of paint or paste is usually thinned down by 10% with clean water.

INDUSTRY TIP

At least two coats of emulsion are usually required for new plaster.

Size

To apply a watered-down or mist-coat of paint or paste to new plaster

ROOFS

Roofs are designed to protect the structure below by keeping the weather out. As heat rises, the roof must be well insulated to prevent heat loss and improve the energy efficiency of the building.

TYPES OF ROOFS

Roofs come in a wide variety of designs, but they come under two main categories of 'flat' and 'pitched'.

Flat roofs

Flat roofs are similar in design to floors, in that they are made from joists decked with timber sheet material. A waterproof layer such as bituminous felt (made from tar), plastic or fibreglass is also used. Although flat roofs tend to be cheaper to install than pitched roofs, they do not last as long and they can suffer from leaks.

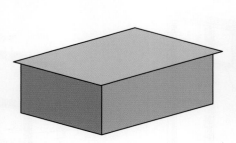

Flat roof

House with a flat roof

Pitched roofs

Pitched roofs are constructed using rafters, and come in a variety of designs. The simplest design of pitched roof is the 'lean-to', where a roof leans up against a wall. 'Gable-ended roofs' are a very common design, with walls covering the ends of the roof. These walls are known as gables or gable ends, which gives the roof its name. The weather can drive into these gables, and very often lengths of timber known as bargeboards are used to keep the elements out. 'Hipped roofs' are more complex (and rather more expensive). The roof ends are covered, making the roof more resistant to the elements. It is common to find a combination of the above roofs in the same building.

House with a pitched roof

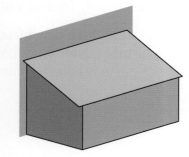

Lean-to roof

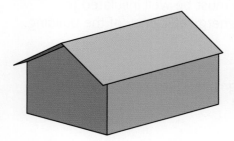

Gable-ended roof

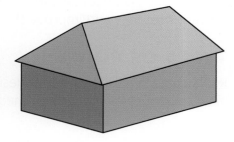

Hipped roof

ROOF COMPONENTS

You will need to know the different components of roofs. Study the illustrations below to learn what these are and how they are used to assemble a roof.

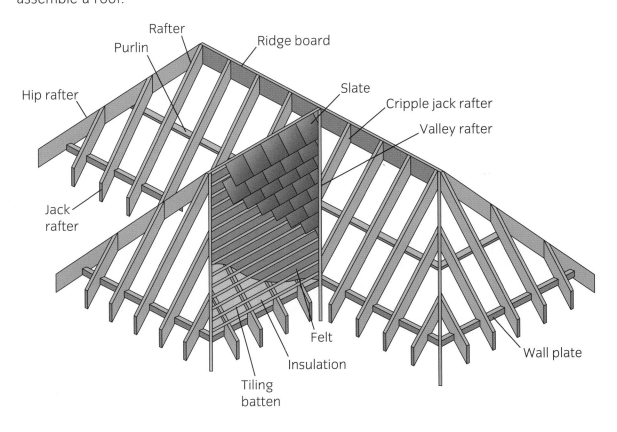

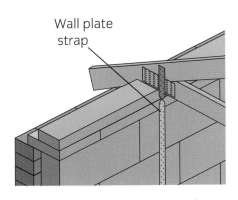

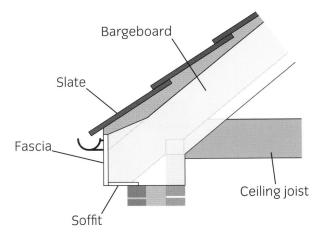

Roofs are usually constructed using **truss rafters**. This method of building a roof is quicker to install than a cut roof (where all of the components are cut and assembled on site). Roofs can be constructed using a combination of trusses and cut rafters. One type of commonly used truss is called a Fink truss (see next page).

Truss rafters

Rafters that are already cut and fixed together before being delivered on site

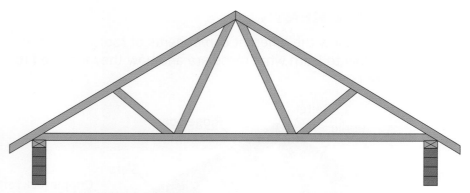

Commonly used standard Fink truss

Roofs are commonly covered with slates or tiles. Slates are a natural product. Slate is a type of mineral that can be split into thin sheets. Artificial cement fibre slates are also available; these are thin and uniform. Tiles can be made from clay or concrete.

Slate

Cement fibre slate

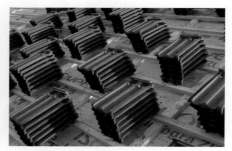

Roof tiles

A felt is laid below the roofing material to provide additional protection in case some water gets through the tiles.

Flashings are commonly made from lead and are used to provide waterproofing at joints where roofing materials meet walls and around chimneys.

Flashing providing waterproofing

Flashing around a chimney

Timber requires protection from the elements (rain, wind and sun) and this is done using timber coatings. Knotting is applied to prevent heat from the sun drawing resin out of knots in the timber. Primer is applied to give a good key to the paint or stain that is used to provide a finish. Paint also requires undercoat to be applied to give a good finish. Paint and stain can be water or solvent borne (water or oil based).

SERVICES

Buildings contain services such as:

- water

- electricity

- gas supplies.

Additionally, waste such as sewage and water run-off have to be considered.

WATER

Water is brought into a building using pipes. Supply pipes used are usually made of plastic, with internal domestic plumbing being made from plastic or copper. Plumbing is installed using a variety of fittings including tees, elbows and reducers. Bathrooms, kitchens and most heating systems require plumbing.

Copper pipe

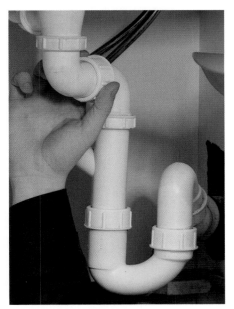

Plastic waste water pipe

Pipe fittings: Tee   Elbow   Reducer

ACTIVITY

What services are being used in the building you are sitting in? How are they brought into the building?

Not only is water carried into a building, it is also taken away. Rainwater run-off is collected into gutters and taken away via downpipes and drains and returned to the ground. It may also be stored for later use in raintanks; this is known as rainwater harvesting.

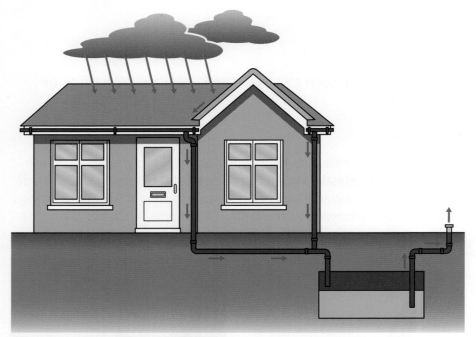

Rainwater flowing down pipes and into an underground raintank

SEWAGE

Sewage is taken away from the building via drains and is disposed of either into a sewer or into a septic tank/sewage treatment plant.

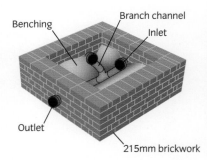

Benched drain

Septic tank

Sewage treatment plant

ELECTRICITY

Electricity is an important service provided to buildings. It powers lighting and heating. It is brought into a building through cables.

GAS

Gas is brought into a building using pipes. Gas powers heating systems and provides fuel for cooking.

OTHER SERVICES

Other services that are installed include telephone systems and other data cables for broadband and entertainment systems.

Electricity cables, switches and socket

SUSTAINABILITY

Our planet is a fixed size. Fossil fuels, eg oil and coal, that we take from the ground are not infinite, ie they will run out one day. However, the wind, the sun and the tides will always be there. These are sustainable sources of energy.

Pipework to boiler

Building materials can be sustainable if they are chosen carefully. For example, the process of manufacturing concrete uses a lot of fuel and produces a lot of carbon dioxide (a gas that some say is damaging the climate).

On the other hand, trees absorb carbon dioxide as they grow, look nice and the timber they produce is an excellent building material. However, some timber is harvested from rainforests without thought for the surrounding environment, or is harvested to such an extent that certain species are close to extinction. Managed forests where trees are replanted after harvesting provide a sustainable source of timber.

Here are some questions to consider regarding sustainability in construction.

MATERIALS

- How far have the materials been brought? Locally sourced materials do not have to be transported far, thus reducing fuel use.

- Are the materials sustainably sourced? Has the timber come from a managed forest or has it come from a rainforest with no regard to the environment?

- Have the materials been manufactured with the minimum of energy and waste?

DESIGN

Is there an alternative design that can be used that uses more sustainable materials? For example, a timber frame could be used instead of concrete block or brick.

The table below shows some sustainable materials:

Material	Image
Straw bales	
Cob (soil)	
Timber	Redwood Spruce Oak
Bamboo	

Material	Image
Lime	
Sheep wool	

ENERGY EFFICIENCY

Energy is expensive and is only going to get more expensive. As the population increases, more and more energy will be required. This needs to come from somewhere and its production can be damaging to the environment. The less power a building uses the better and if it can produce its own that is a bonus. Energy-saving measures can save a lot of power consumption.

Insulation

Light, air-filled materials tend to have better thermal insulation properties than heavy, dense materials. This means that heat cannot easily pass from one side to another, and so if these materials are used in a building it will require less heating during the winter and will remain cooler during the summer.

The following drawing shows how much heat a typical home loses through different parts of the property. Better insulation will reduce the amount of heat lost.

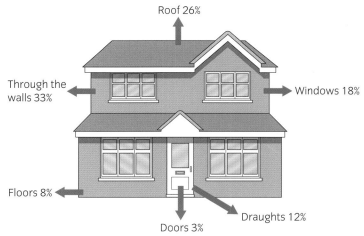

Sources of heat loss from a house

INDUSTRY TIP

There are many ways of reducing the energy consumption of buildings, such as the use of low-energy light bulbs or lights that come on only when a sensor detects movement and turn off when there is no one about.

The table below shows some examples of insulation:

Type of insulation	Description
Blue jean and lambswool	Lambswool is a natural insulator. Blue jean insulation comes from recycled denim.
Fibreglass/mineral wool	This is made from glass, often from old recycled bottles or mineral wool. It holds a lot of air within it and therefore is an excellent insulator. It is also cheap to produce. It does however use up a fair bit of room as it takes a good thickness to comply with building regulations. Similar products include plastic fibre insulation made from plastic bottles and lambswool.
PIR (polyisocyanurate)	This is a solid insulation with foil layers on the faces. It is lightweight, rigid and easy to cut and fit. It has excellent insulation properties. Polystyrene is similar to PIR. Although polystyrene is cheaper, its thermal properties are not as good.
Multifoil	A modern type of insulation made up of many layers of foil and thin insulation layers. These work by reflecting heat back into the building. Usually used in conjunction with other types of insulation.

MAKING BETTER USE OF EXISTING AND FREE ENERGY

Solar power

The sun always shines and during the day its light reaches the ground (even on cloudy days). This energy can be used. A simple use of this is to allow sunlight to enter a building. With a little thought in design, light can reach deep into a building via roof lights and light tunnels. This means that internal artificial lighting requirements are reduced, therefore saving energy.

Solar panels can generate hot water or electricity, and once the cost of installation has been covered the energy they produce is totally free.

Solar panel

A panel that absorbs sun rays to generate electricity or hot water

Solar panels

Heat source and recovery

Humans give off a fair bit of energy as they go through a normal day (eg body heat, heat given off by hairdryers, cookers, refrigerators and other activities) and this can be conserved. Modern air-conditioning systems take the heat from stale air and put it into the fresh air coming in.

Heat can be taken from the ground and even the air outside.

Air-conditioning unit

Turbines

A machine designed to allow continuous movement to create electrical energy

Wind power

Wind power is becoming more widespread. However, some people feel that wind **turbines** are damaging the visual environment as they spoil the appearance of the countryside. Individuals will have their own opinion on whether wind power is a good thing or not as there are many considerations to be taken into account.

Wind turbines

Water power

Water is another source of power, whether that be hydro-electric (water from dams turning turbines) or wave power (which is currently under development).

Another method is through extracting heat energy contained in the air and ground. This can be extracted by the use of a heat exchanger. Water in pipes buried in the ground circulates, picking up heat, which is then taken out and used in the building. This can also be achieved with air from outside.

A hydro-electric dam

Biomass heating

Biomass heating (using wood and other non-fossil fuels) is also becoming more popular as these systems can heat water efficiently as well as heat rooms, and of course a well-insulated building does not require a lot of heating.

Energy-efficient goods and appliances

Energy-efficient electrical goods (eg low-energy light bulbs) and appliances (eg dishwashers, fridges and washing machines) which use a reduced amount of power and less water are available.

Biomass fuel

PROTECTING THE ENVIRONMENT

Building work can create a lot of waste, and can pollute the environment. To avoid this, careful consideration needs to be given to how waste is disposed of. There are many regulations that control the management of waste (ie COSHH, see Chapter 1 page 9) that also need to be followed.

An energy-efficient light bulb

Proper stock control and efficient use of materials reduces waste. Dust and fumes can be reduced by using water or LEV (local exhaust ventilation), which sucks dust from the air. Materials such as glass or plastics can be recycled, very often into other building materials. Timber can be reused instead of being thrown away or taken to a salvage yard. The waste that is left (the waste that cannot be recycled or reused) then needs to be disposed of carefully in a skip. Hazardous waste such as asbestos is usually removed by specialists.

Case Study: Tristan

Tristan has been asked to help design and produce specifications for a house. He has been asked to research how to make the house energy efficient. The house will have four bedrooms and has a gable-ended roof that faces south.

Tristan consulted manufacturers' catalogues and websites to determine the most efficient system for generating energy. As the roof faces south, Tristan decides that panels on the roof are a good option. Tristan decides that five solar thermal collectors will be enough to provide hot water for the occupants of the house. Ground source heat pumps will provide additional heating for the house.

The walls, roof, windows and floor are to be insulated. The building regulations provide minimum requirements that Tristan refers to. Again, using manufacturers' information he decides which is the best insulation systems to use, balancing effectiveness with cost.

- Do you agree with Tristan's design?

- Could it be improved?

- Are there any drawbacks to his design?

Work through the following questions to check your learning.

1   Which one of the following identifies the details of materials needed for a project?

   a   Specification.

   b   Programme of work.

   c   Delivery note.

   d   Site diary.

2   Which scale should be used for a detail drawing?

   a   1:5.

   b   1:75.

   c   1:500.

   d   1:7500.

3   What is the hatching symbol shown below?

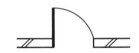

   a   Door.

   b   Roof light.

   c   Window.

   d   Hallway.

4   What is the hatching symbol shown below?

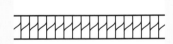

   a   Plastic.

   b   Insulation.

   c   Timber.

   d   Blockwork.

5   What is the point shown below?

   a   A point of a known height used for setting out.

   b   A point of unknown height used for setting out.

   c   A point of known position used to determine the building line.

   d   A point of unknown position used to determine the building line.

6   What type of brick is shown below?

   a   Flemish.

   b   Concrete.

   c   Trench.

   d   Air.

7   What foundation type covers the footprint of the building?

   a   Strip.

   b   Raft.

   c   Pile.

   d   Pad.

8   In a concrete mix ratio of 1:2:3, what does the 3 represents

    a   Retardant.

    b   Fine aggregate.

    c   Coarse aggregate.

    d   Cement.

9   What part of a roof retains heat within the building?

    a   Insulation.

    b   Restraint strap.

    c   DPC.

    d   Concrete tiles.

10   What brick bond is shown below?

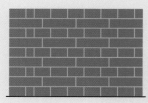

    a   German.

    b   English.

    c   French.

    d   Flemish.

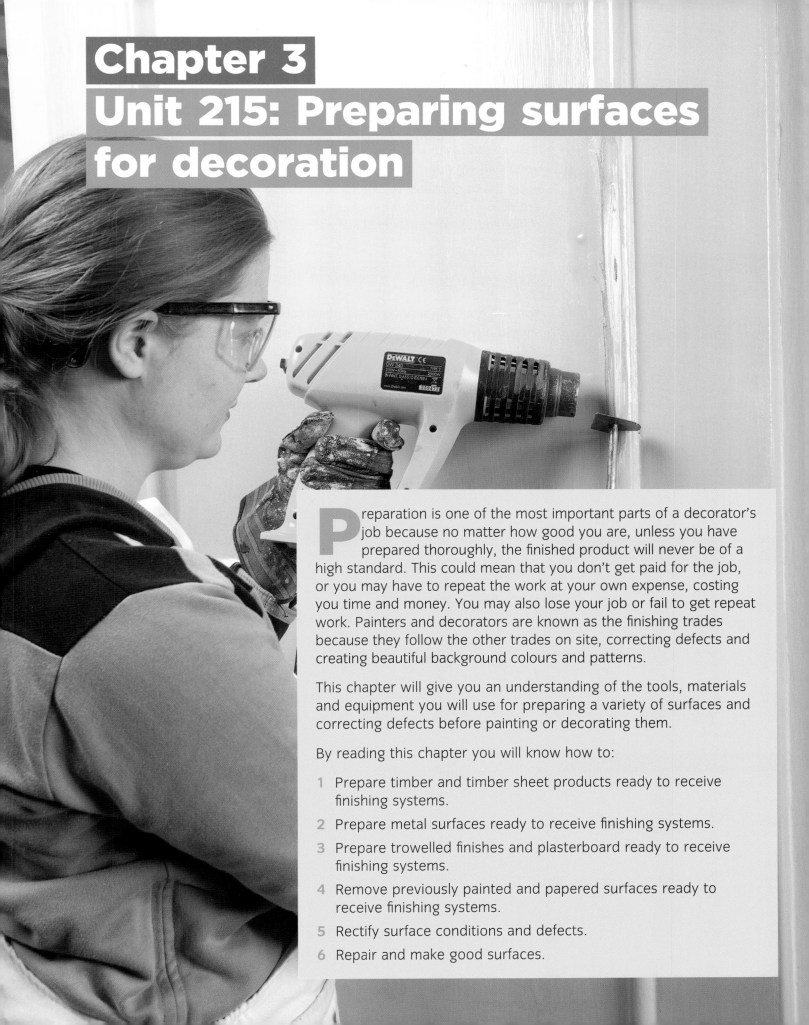

Chapter 3
Unit 215: Preparing surfaces for decoration

Preparation is one of the most important parts of a decorator's job because no matter how good you are, unless you have prepared thoroughly, the finished product will never be of a high standard. This could mean that you don't get paid for the job, or you may have to repeat the work at your own expense, costing you time and money. You may also lose your job or fail to get repeat work. Painters and decorators are known as the finishing trades because they follow the other trades on site, correcting defects and creating beautiful background colours and patterns.

This chapter will give you an understanding of the tools, materials and equipment you will use for preparing a variety of surfaces and correcting defects before painting or decorating them.

By reading this chapter you will know how to:

1 Prepare timber and timber sheet products ready to receive finishing systems.

2 Prepare metal surfaces ready to receive finishing systems.

3 Prepare trowelled finishes and plasterboard ready to receive finishing systems.

4 Remove previously painted and papered surfaces ready to receive finishing systems.

5 Rectify surface conditions and defects.

6 Repair and make good surfaces.

PREPARING TIMBER AND TIMBER SHEET PRODUCTS READY TO RECEIVE FINISHING SYSTEMS

Whatever task you are undertaking in the construction industry it is essential to consider the health and safety implications of what you are doing. This section looks at aspects of health and safety that relate to the preparation of surfaces.

Take measures to ensure the safety of your work area

HEALTH AND SAFETY

You will have already covered health and safety in Chapter 1, and should have a good understanding of what you need to do to ensure that you, your colleagues and others around you are safe. Many health and safety rules are common sense and apply to all trades, but there are situations in which decorators face specific dangers. Before starting work, whether on a building site, a domestic site or at college, it is important to consider:

- what causes accidents

- how to stop accidents happening

- reporting accidents

- risk assessments.

RISK ASSESSMENT

Before starting preparation, you will need to carry out a risk assessment. Much of the work carried out on site can be hazardous, not only to yourself but to others. You will face different hazards at every new site and in every new situation. Remember, a risk assessment is not only the responsibility of the employer but of everyone working on site.

Here are some things to consider when you are carrying out a risk assessment:

- Is the work across an exit or on steps?

- Does the work involve using a stepladder? If so, is it secure?

- If the work involves rubbing down, what is the correct PPE?

- Are tools and equipment being used safely?

- Are hazardous substances being used correctly?

Although health and safety instructions are common to all trades, there are some things that are particularly important to a painter and decorator. For example:

■ As a decorator you will come into contact with many chemicals and irritants, so you will need to apply barrier cream to protect your skin from contaminants that may cause infections or irritations such as dermatitis. You should do this at the start of every day.

■ It is important to wear goggles, a dust mask and overalls when rubbing down, as the dust this creates can get into your eyes, be breathed into your lungs and irritate your skin. Make sure that the work area is well ventilated and damp down the floor when sweeping up. When working in a room that cannot be ventilated, it may be necessary to wear a ventilator.

■ Light cotton or latex gloves will protect your hands from cuts and abrasions when you are rubbing down, and are comfortable to use. Gauntlet gloves should be worn for heavy-duty work such as washing down walls or using liquid paint remover.

Latex glove   Gauntlet gloves

■ When using liquid paint remover to remove old paint films, be aware that the paint remover may be toxic and highly flammable. Check the manufacturer's instructions (COSHH Regulations, see Chapter 1), make sure that the work area is well ventilated, wear a mask and goggles (Personal Protective Equipment at Work Regulations 1992, see Chapter 1) and wear rubber gloves, as paint stripper can burn.

■ Be aware of how to lift heavy weights safely (stepladders, paint tins, wallpaper, etc) and don't be afraid to ask for help, as they may need more than one person to lift them (Manual Handling Operations Regulations 1992, see Chapter 1).

ACTIVITY

Go online or to a local DIY store/builders' merchant and research hazardous products such as two-pack fillers and paint removers. Can you find the manufacturers' data sheets? What should you be aware of when using these products?

You'll need to wear a hi-viz and hard hat when working on building sites

■ For some jobs a secured stepladder will not be sufficient – you may need to use a scaffold tower. Make sure you don't overstretch yourself.

■ Although you will always need to wear toe-cap boots wherever you are working, it is unlikely that you will need a hi-viz jacket or a hard hat on a domestic job. However, if you are working on a building site these items will be required.

■ Tools and equipment need to be regularly tested, and toxic and flammable materials must be stored correctly.

TIMBER AND TIMBER SHEET PRODUCTS

Timber is the wood prepared for building, and whether it is hardwood, softwood or timber sheet products (manufactured boards), it will have to be prepared before paint, stains or varnish can be applied. You may be following a carpenter who has just fitted bare timber or preparing previously painted wood surfaces.

FIRST FIX AND SECOND FIX

Wall studwork is part of the first fix

To a carpenter the first fix usually refers to structural work, which is done before a property is plastered. This includes fitting the wall studwork, rafters, floor joists and floorboards. The second fix carpentry is the finishing work, usually done after the plastering, and includes fixing **architraves**, windows and skirtings, and hanging doors.

Architraves

The moulded frames around doors or windows

SOFTWOOD

Coniferous or evergreen timbers such as pine, cedar and spruce are used for construction because, generally speaking, they grow very quickly. This abundance of raw material makes the wood cheaper to produce. Although they are called softwoods they can still be quite hard and capable of bearing weight. The table below describes some common types of softwood.

Coniferous or evergreen

Cone-bearing evergreen trees which keep their leaves in winter

Softwood	Description
Pine 	Pine trees are valued worldwide for their pulp and timber, and are used to make furniture, panelling, window frames, floors and roofing. This timber is mainly for internal use, but is sometimes treated for external use.
Cedar 	There are many species of cedar trees grown around the world, and the wood is used to make anything from pencils and guitars to log cabins and fences. Some varieties are highly scented and act as an insect repellent.
Spruce 	Spruce is used in general construction and for making crates and musical instruments. Its pulp is widely used to make paper. In construction it is used for first- and second-fix joinery work, particularly skirting boards, **dado rails**, architraves, doors and window frames. Spruce is used because it is relatively cheap and easy to work with, and is nearly always painted because of the knotty and resinous nature of the timber.

Dado

An area of wall immediately above the skirting in a room, and separated from the wall filling by a timber, plaster or plastic strip secured to the wall

Dado rail

The wooden decorative rail that separates the dado from the rest of the wall

HARDWOOD

Hardwoods are slower growing than softwoods, making them more expensive. They are used for interior and exterior work, especially for doors and windows and where a more decorative finish is required. They can be finished with lacquer, varnish or French polish to protect and enhance the grain, as painting masks the appearance of the wood. Hardwood can also be painted to protect the surface from poor weather. The table below describes some common types of hardwood.

Hardwood	Description
Oak 	Oak is a fairly hard, heavy and dense timber with a high crushing and bending strength. It is used for high-quality cabinet making and joinery for decorative effect. The colour of natural oak varies from a rich honey colour to a yellowish brown, but it can be stained to make it darker. It can also be used for exposed roof beams, skirting and panelling.
Beech 	Natural beech wood is pinkish brown in colour and is not as decorative as some other hardwoods so is usually painted, lacquered or oiled. It is used in construction for doors, cabinets and log cabins, but it also makes good firewood and is used for smoking sausages and beers.
Mahogany 	Mahogany is a reddish-brown wood sought for its beauty and durability. It is used to make furniture, boats and musical instruments, and has a fine, even grain.

TIMBER SHEET PRODUCTS

These are made from timber in sheet form that can be cut to size for both interior and exterior construction work. You will come into contact with a number of different timber sheet products. Each will require specific preparation to ensure that it is not damaged. Things to consider include:

- composition of the board

- whether there are any health risks when preparing the surfaces

- the type of abrasive to use

- the type of primer or sealer to be selected for use

- the paint system to be applied.

The table below describes some common types of timber sheet product.

ACTIVITY

Research MDF, plywood and hardboard. Find out what they look like, what are they used for (and not used for) and list what a decorator has to be aware of when preparing and painting these products. Discuss your findings with your tutor or colleagues.

Hygroscopic

Tending to absorb moisture from the air

Timber sheet product	Description
Plywood 	Plywood is made from thin layers of wood, with the grain running in different directions, glued together under pressure. The laminates can be glued together with an internal or external grade of adhesive depending on the end use requirement.
Hardboard 	Hardboard is composed of wood pulp and wood fibre or another vegetable fibre together with suitable fillers and bonding agents, and is densely compacted under high pressure. Hardboard is a thin board, and is usually flexible with a smooth, polished surface. Hardboards are **hygroscopic** and therefore it is advisable to paint the back and edges before fixing in order to prevent any moisture penetrating though the hardboard.
Blockboard 	Blockboard is a wood-based panel made up of a core of softwood strips that are glued together. The strips may be up to 28mm wide and are placed edge to edge and sandwiched between veneers of softwood and glued under high pressure. The inner strips are generally made of lightweight poplar wood or spruce. Blockboard is used to make doors, tables, shelves, panelling and partition walls. It is normally used for interior work because of the type of glues used. To achieve maximum strength, it is important to ensure that the core runs lengthways. Blockboard panels are produced in three layers (with one veneer sheet covering each side), or five layers (with two veneer sheets per side for better stability). It is seldom used now as it has been superseded by MDF.

Timber sheet product	Description
Medium-density fibreboard (MDF) 	MDF is a type of hardboard, which is made from wood fibres glued under heat and pressure. There are a number of reasons why MDF may be used instead of plywood: it is dense, flat and stiff, it has no knots in it, and it is easily cut on a machine. It is made up of fine particles and does not have an easily recognisable surface grain, so MDF can be painted to produce a smooth, quality surface. It can be cut, drilled, machined and filed without damage to the surface. It may be used to make display cabinets, wall panels and storage units, and is almost always painted.

Safety note

A disadvantage of using MDF is that it can be dangerous if the correct safety precautions are not taken. MDF contains a substance called urea formaldehyde, which may be released from the material by cutting and sanding. Urea formaldehyde may cause irritation to the eyes and lungs. Proper ventilation is required when using it, and facemasks should be worn when sanding or cutting MDF with machinery.

TOOLS, MATERIALS AND EQUIPMENT

Your tool kit will contain some general equipment used by various trades, but it will also include some special tools used solely by painters and decorators. Make sure that you buy good-quality tools, and clean, store and maintain them correctly to get the best out of them.

TOOLS AND EQUIPMENT

This table includes the tools and equipment you will need for preparing timber and timber sheet materials.

Tempered

Metal that has been hardened by heating

Nibs

Small particles of foreign matter, such as paint skin or grit, that have dried in the film of a coating and which cause it to feel rough

Tool	Description
Stripping knife	Also known as a scraper. A good-quality knife will have a hardwood handle, and the steel blade will be **tempered**. Knives are available in blade widths of 25mm, 50mm, 75mm and 100mm. They are used to remove wallpaper, loose or flaking paint and other debris or **nibs** from woodwork to ensure that the surface is ready for painting or decorating.

Tool	Description
Putty knife 	Also known as a stopping knife. It is used for applying facing and bedding putty to traditional wood and metal windows when glazing or replacing broken or cracked panes of glass. It is also used to fill small nail holes, open timber joints and cracks in woodwork.
Chisel knife 	Chisel knives are available in widths of 25–50mm. They are constructed in the same way as stripping knives, and are used to strip and remove paint, wallpaper, bits and nibs from windows and door mouldings where a broader knife would not fit.
Nail punch 	This is a metal tool used with a hammer to punch or drive protruding nails below the surface of the timber.
Hammers 	The two main types of hammer used by a decorator are the claw hammer, used for pulling out nails and driving nails in, and the lighter pin hammer, used on more delicate surfaces, for example to drive pins in when replacing broken glass.
Knotting brush 	A knotting brush is used to apply shellac knotting to knots on a timber surface before priming.

Tool	Description
Rubbing block 	Rubbing blocks, also known as sanding blocks, are used to make handling dry, or wet and dry, abrasive paper easier. They come in wood, cork and rubber. Wood and cork are used with dry abrasive paper and rubber is used with wet and dry.
Synthetic and natural paint brushes 	Although there will be more information on brushes in Chapter 4, you may also need them for preparation work such as spot priming. Natural pure-bristle brushes are made out of animal hair and are used mainly for applying oil based paint (gloss). Synthetic brushes are composed of man-made fibres and are mainly used for water-borne paints (emulsion).
Roller trays 	A flat-bottomed container with a 'reservoir' which holds only small quantities of paint. It is used to charge the roller with paint or primer before application.
Short-pile and foam rollers 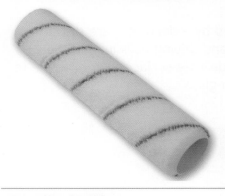	Rollers can be used to apply primer to a smooth surface such as a timber door. A disadvantage when using either a short-pile or a foam roller is that it can give an orange-peel effect to the paintwork, which will show through the final coat.
Dusting brush 	A dusting brush is used to remove dust, debris and other particles from a surface before painting.

Tool	Description
Paint kettles	Also known as paint pots. These are made from either plastic or metal and are used to decant paint for use. Plastic is generally used for water-borne paint and metal for solvent-borne paint.

MATERIALS

You will need to use a variety of materials in order to prepare surfaces without damaging them.

Solvents

'Solvents' is a generic term for liquids used to dissolve or disperse the paint film and make a paint mixture thin and fluid enough for easy application. The solvents most widely used by decorators are white spirit, turpentine and methylated spirits. They are all volatile spirits, so make sure you keep them away from naked flames.

■ Turpentine is used in the making of paint and can also be used to thin paint and varnishes to the correct consistency.

■ White spirit is used for thinning oil paint and varnish to the correct **consistency**, and for washing paint from brushes and equipment and wiping paint splashes from surrounding surfaces. Methylated spirit is used in the making of cellulose materials such as shellac knotting and cellulose paint, and can also be used to thin them. It can also be used to clean equipment and tools.

Cleaning agents

It is essential that all surfaces are clean and grease free to ensure a good finish. On previously painted surfaces you will use hand-hot water and either sugar soap, washing soda or detergent (a small squeeze of washing-up liquid is good, because it is readily available). Stubborn marks may require a dilution of household bleach in cold water. After washing down with the cleaning agent the surface will need to be decontaminated with clean water before decorating. Solvent wiping is the process of using white spirit, methylated spirit or acetone on a cloth to de-grease and clean an area, and is convenient because the surface does not need to be decontaminated after use.

Consistency

Related directly to the viscosity of a coating, which can be altered by the addition of thinners or solvents

Patent knotting solution

Knotting bottle and brush

Shellac/patent/white knotting

These are sealers used to prevent resin, marks and stains bleeding through the final paint surface. Knotting solution is most often used to seal knots, but it can also be used on other stains such as felt-tip pen marks and tar splashes.

Don't forget to use the appropriate PPE when using knotting solution, as it is highly flammable.

Knotting solution is best kept in a knotting bottle or a glass container, which will prevent the knotting solution evaporating and drying out. Always make sure that the surface is clean and dry before applying the knotting solution with a brush, taking care to cover the knot or stain entirely. The knotting solution should dry quickly and when it is completely dry the surface coating can be applied. The brush should be cleaned with a cleaning solvent (see the manufacturer's instructions on the bottle).

Stoppers/stopping

Stopping is a stiff paste used to fill small cracks. It should be used for exterior work, as it is more stable in damp conditions. The stopper is pressed into holes and cracks with a small filling knife and then levelled off.

Wood stopping

Single-pack fillers

Powder fillers are probably the most common types of filler, consisting of powder that you mix with clean cold water. Once mixed the filler is usually workable for 30–40 minutes, and sets hard within a couple of hours. When dry it can be sanded back to a smooth finish ready for decorating. Single-pack fillers are ideal for small to medium holes, scratches, cracks and imperfections, and they can even be drilled and screwed into once hardened. They can be used on wood, masonry, ceilings and plasterboard and are normally sold as general-purpose fillers.

Powder fillers are good all-round fillers, but despite what it says on the box they will shrink, so be prepared to fill larger holes and cracks more than once to get them level. For larger holes it is often best to mix the filler on the dry side (but not so dry it is not workable) and apply this to the area you are filling. Once dry you can mix up a smoother, wetter paste and apply this over the first coat. Once that is dry it can be sanded smooth and level.

Two-pack fillers

Sometimes called two-part or deep-hole fillers, these types of filler **cure** by chemical reaction. When the two parts are mixed together the filler sets within a few minutes and is ready to be rubbed down within about 30 minutes. This type of filler can be used for larger repairs, as it doesn't shrink or crack, but it is harder to rub down than powder filler. It is ideal for repairing rotten window and door frames, and is very tough – it can be drilled, screwed into and even planed. It can also be used for interior and exterior repairs, but is more expensive than single-pack filler or stopping.

Plastic wood filler

This is a fast-drying filler/stopper for small nail holes and cracks, and it can be used on exterior and interior softwoods and hardwoods. It can be sanded when dry, and sticks well to bare wood. It can also be coated with wood stain, paints and varnish.

The application process is as follows:

- Select the colour of the filler to match the colour of the timber or stained timber that is to be filled.

- Use a filling knife or putty knife, and fill slightly proud.

- Allow to dry, and then rub down with the grain until the filler is flush with the surface using a fine abrasive (silicon carbide paper).

DEFECTS IN TIMBER AND TIMBER SHEET PRODUCTS

Timber, new or old, may have defects that have occurred naturally or been caused by accidental damage or wear. These will need treatment and preparation before the finishing coatings are applied. Thorough preparation lays the foundation for a high standard of finish – a finish that not only looks good but will last. The table describes some of the defects that you may find in timber.

INDUSTRY TIP

Mix only as much filler as you think you will need, and mix it close to where you are going to use it. By the time you have walked from your van to the back of the house and up a ladder, the two-pack filler may already have set.

Cure

To harden

Two-pack filler

Defect	Description
Knots	A knot is a place in the timber where a branch was formed during the growth of the tree, and produces sap that can bleed through the paintwork and stain the paint finish. It will need to be sealed with knotting solution. (See Step 5 on page 127.)

Defect	Description
Resin exudation 	**Exudation** is where the natural oily resin in timber comes to the surface and stains the wood. Some softwoods (eg Columbian pine and pitch pine) are extremely resinous and exude resin all over the surface of the wood, not just from the knots, making it difficult for paint to adhere. An aluminium primer should be applied, as it will not penetrate the wood and will form a metallic barrier to stop the resin from seeping through.
Splits and shrinkage cracks 	Excessive heat or very dry conditions reduce the moisture content and can lead to splitting along the grain and other damage. Timber should always be stored in dry conditions. The area surrounding the crack or split will need to be lightly rubbed down using a fine abrasive, with the grain rather than against it. It will then need to be primed and then made good using stopper. These processes are explained later in the chapter.
Open joints 	Open joints form when timbers that have been butted together during construction shrink away from each other, causing a gap. The open joints will need to be treated in the same way as splits and shrinkage cracks.
Indentations 	Surfaces may be damaged by knocks, particularly in softwood, causing dents in the surface. They will require filling to make the surface level. If the surface has been previously painted it will need rubbing down with a fine abrasive before filling. Timber sheet products may have to be replaced.

Exudation

Oozing; the release of a liquid

Defect	Description
End grain 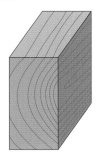	This is the pattern seen when wood is cut across the grain. It is much more absorbent than the face of the wood because the cells that used to suck up moisture into the tree have been cut across. It is essential to seal the end grain twice with primer to stop liquids being absorbed into the timber before making good.
Protruding nail heads 	**Protruding** nails occur where a carpenter has not punched nails fully below the surface when working on site. You will need to use a nail punch and hammer to drive them below the surface so that the hole can be filled.
Nail holes 	This is the opposite of protruding nails – where the nails have been punched in below the surface and the holes will need filling.
Glue residue 	When preparing timber/timber products it is likely that you will come across glue residue where timber has been constructed and glued together. The dried glue can be removed using a stripper or chisel knife or, if it is still wet, by wiping it off with a rag.

Protruding

Extending above or beyond the surrounding surface

Moisture content

Although not necessarily a defect, it is important to consider the moisture content of timber. Wood shrinks as it dries, and swells when it absorbs moisture, which may affect the paint finish.

If timber with a high level of moisture content is painted, it is likely that the coating will break down through a series of defects, such as:

- blistering
- wet rot
- fungal growth.

A moisture meter can be used to test the amount of moisture in the timber. A result of more than 20% moisture content may result in blistering and the paint film flaking.

Moisture meter

SURFACE AND PHYSICAL PROPERTIES

It is important for you as a decorator to be aware of how wood should be treated to get the best out of it.

SURFACE PROPERTIES

The surface properties of the wood will have an impact on how material should be prepared, and also on how it will look and feel as part of a building or structure.

Aesthetics

In this context, aesthetics are the way in which we respond with our senses to something that is visually pleasing or beautiful. Wood is a beautiful, natural product that can blend seamlessly with the existing style of a home, whether it is painted or varnished. Some timbers are more attractive than others, and the beauty of a particular wood may determine what it is used for. There is little point in installing aged oak beams if they are to be painted over. A decorator should enhance the grain of the wood by staining, oiling or varnishing. Wood is extremely durable and flexible and the natural gloss (the patina) that develops over years of handling only increases its desirable aesthetic qualities.

Aesthetically pleasing timber, for example oak beams, can become a main feature of a room

Tactility

Timber is not only visually attractive – it can also be very pleasant to touch, or **tactile**, even before the surface has been coated with paint or varnish. To touch bare timber can be a pleasing experience, but do not try to run your hands over rough timber or you will get splinters. Always wear gloves when handling rough timber.

Tactile

Relating to the sense of touch

Porosity

This term is often used loosely as an alternative to absorbency. To be precise, however, the porosity of building materials such as brick, stone, plaster and timber is the ratio of pore space to the total volume of the material. Pores do not usually absorb water to their full capacity, with their rate of **absorption** being governed by their **capillarity**. Some surfaces are very absorbent, like blotting paper, and some surfaces, such as plastic, are non-porous and do not soak up liquid at all.

If the surface of the timber contains small pores it will draw the paint into the surface and help the paint to **key** on to the timber.

PHYSICAL PROPERTIES

Different types of timber will deliver varying degrees of strength, hardness, flexibility and insulating properties, and it is the job of a skilled carpenter or joiner to choose the correct wood for the task. Generally speaking, softwoods are more flexible than hardwoods and are much easier to bend into shape. Hardwoods such as oak and mahogany can be curved, but this is a long process, so structures requiring curved wood are usually cut out of a larger single piece of wood. Plywood and hardboard are quite flexible, but MDF cannot bend without breaking.

ABRASIVES

There are several types of **abrasive,** and it is important to use the right type and the correct grade when preparing treated and untreated timbers to avoid causing damage.

TYPES OF ABRASIVES USED IN PREPARATION

Using an abrasive that is too coarse can damage the **substrate** and leave scratches that may show through when painted. On the other hand using an abrasive that is too fine may be ineffective at removing or levelling surface imperfections. Badly prepared substrates will require making good before repainting (see pages 161–167 for making good processes).

Abrasive paper for use with a drum sander

Absorption

The process of fluid disappearing and being incorporated into a material – highly absorbent surfaces such as softwoods suck up primers and paints, impairing the finish

Capillarity

The rate at which liquid is drawn into a material through pores or small tubes

Key

When a surface is naturally porous or has been roughened up by abrading, it is said to provide a key to help paint coatings to adhere

ACTIVITY

Take two small sheets of glass and hold them lightly together. Immerse the lower edge into a bowl of water and see how high the water is drawn up between the sheets of glass. Open the gap slightly to see whether the amount of water rises to a different level. This demonstrates capillary action. The bigger the gap, the less the water should rise.

Abrasive

Any material, which by a process of rubbing or grinding down tends to make another surface become smooth. Such materials are very important to a decorator during preparation, as inadequate rubbing down of a surface will result in a poor paint finish

Substrate

Surface to be painted or decorated

Abrade

To scratch a surface with a coarse material to provide a 'key', which will help coatings adhere

EXAMPLES OF MATERIALS USED FOR ABRADING TIMBER

The table shows some types of materials used for **abrading** timber, along with their properties, characteristic and uses.

Abrasive type	Material/backing	Glue	Characteristics	Use
Glass paper	Made from ground-up glass particles, with either a paper or a cloth backing.	Bone glue	Used on dry timber and painted surfaces. Various grades available, ranging from 40–60 (rough or coarse), to 240 and upwards (very fine).	Dry
Garnet paper	Natural semi-precious mineral on either a paper or cloth backing.	Soluble and non-soluble glues	Harder wearing than glass paper.	Paper backing for dry abrading, cloth backing for wet abrading.
Aluminium oxide	Bauxite with either a paper backing or a cloth backing.	Soluble bone glue	Comes in disc, belt or sheet form, and may be used by hand. Extremely hard wearing, long lasting and very economical. Grades available include 60, 80, 100, 120, 150, 180, 210, 240 and 270, and range from coarse/rough to fine/smooth.	Dry

PRIMERS

A primer is the first coat of paint applied to a surface and is the foundation of the entire paint system. A coat of primer provides a durable and protective coating that acts as a bridge between the substrate and the rest of the paint system. In porous materials such as softwoods some of the primer will be absorbed into the wood, but it will leave enough binding medium on the surface for the subsequent layers of paint to **adhere** to. Although it can be applied with a brush, a roller or a spray gun, you will get a better finish if you apply the primer with a brush, even if further layers of paint are to be applied with a roller or spray. There are many different types of primer, but the main ones used for priming wood are described in the table.

Adhere

To stick to a substance or surface

Primer	Description	Use
Acrylic primer/undercoat	Water-borne paint thinned with water, formulated both as a primer and an undercoat. It is usually available in white, but some manufacturers supply other pastel colours. Paint brushes and equipment are to be cleaned with water. Method of application: brush, roller or spray.	Can be applied to both exterior and interior surfaces: woodwork (softwood), old and new plaster, cement, concrete, hardboard and building boards. Not to be used on metal as acrylic primer contains water and may cause metal to rust. Can also be used as a matt finish for interior ceilings and walls.
Oil based wood primer	A general-purpose wood primer, available in white and pink. Provides good adhesion for the undercoat and is non-toxic, unlike lead-based primers (although lead-based primers are not sold any longer, they may still be found on some old paintwork). Paint brushes and equipment are to be cleaned with solvent (white spirit). Method of application: brush.	This primer is harder wearing than water-borne paint, so it can be used on exteriors. It can also be used on interior surfaces, particularly where children and pets may come into contact with the surface, for example in hospitals, nurseries and places where food is stored.
Aluminium wood primer	A dull, metallic grey oil based primer. Paint brushes and equipment are to be cleaned with solvent (white spirit). Method of application: brush.	Wood primer is used for resinous timber (softwoods), and can be used to seal surfaces that have previously been treated with wood preservative. It can also seal old bitumen-coated surfaces.
Universal wood/metal primers	A solvent-borne primer formulated for interior and exterior use. Based on an anti-corrosive zinc phosphate pigment and alkyd resin. Paint brushes and equipment are to be cleaned with solvent (white spirit). Method of application: brush.	Use on new or bare wood, metal, plaster and masonry. It is particularly suitable for multi-surface work.
Shellac knotting	See page 118 for more information. Brushes should be cleaned using methylated spirits.	Use for sealing in knots on timber surfaces before priming.

WATER-BORNE AND SOLVENT-BORNE PRIMERS

The table below describes some of the advantages and disadvantages of water-borne and solvent-borne primers.

Water-borne primers		Solvent-borne primers	
Advantages	**Disadvantages**	**Advantages**	**Disadvantages**
<ul><li>Cheap</li><li>Versatile</li><li>Non-toxic</li><li>Can be thinned with water</li><li>Equipment can be cleaned with water</li></ul>	<ul><li>Not as hard wearing</li></ul>	<ul><li>Hard wearing</li><li>Good for exterior use</li><li>Non-toxic</li><li>Stable enough for use in hospitals and children's rooms</li></ul>	<ul><li>Higher VOCs, so smell is stronger</li><li>More expensive</li><li>Equipment needs to be cleaned with white spirit</li></ul>

THE PREPARATION PROCESS

Now you have some idea of the things you will need to prepare timber and sheet timber products for decorating, it is time to look at the processes in depth. Before starting any project it is essential to protect your work area and surrounding areas to make sure that nothing is damaged. The process of preparing domestic and commercial areas is covered in detail in the next chapter.

PREPARING SOFTWOOD FOR DECORATION

Softwoods that are to be painted should be lightly sanded using fine glass paper diagonally across the grain, and then finished off by very lightly sanding along the line of the grain. This creates a scuffing of the surface and enables the paint to adhere to the painted surface. However if you are going to apply a clear or coloured stain or varnish, do not sand across the grain as the sanding marks will show through and look unsightly.

Sanding softwoods along the grain line

STEP 1 Remove any loose debris such as plaster, nibs and bits of building material using a stripping knife.

STEP 2 Protruding nails or pins should be punched below the surface using a hammer and nail punch before using the appropriate filler.

STEP 3 When the filler is dry, abrade the whole surface using a fine abrasive. Remember to rub with the grain.

STEP 4 Dust off the surface with a dusting brush.

STEP 5 Apply two coats of shellac knotting to any knots on the face of the timber, ensuring that the coats are thin and well brushed out with no edge build-up. You will need to go slightly beyond the area of the knot. Allow for drying between coats. This should take about 15–20 minutes.

The timber is now ready to receive its first coat of primer (see the table on page 125 for detailed descriptions of primers). Traditional oil based primers should be used for external work, as they are hard wearing, while acrylic water-borne products are preferred on internal timber surfaces, as they dry more quickly. It should be possible to re-coat the surface the same day, as soon as it is dry, but it is good practice to wait until the following day to make sure that the primer has formed a solid foundation. Acrylic coatings are available as primers, undercoats, eggshells and glosses.

INDUSTRY TIP

If you rub down before you punch in the protruding nails, you are likely to cut your hands. Punch in the protruding nails first.

Use a dusting brush to dust off hardwood

PREPARING HARDWOOD FOR DECORATION

The cellular structure of hardwood is a lot finer than that of softwood, so the pores are not as open or absorbent. Some hardwoods have an oily nature, while others are acidic. The finer grain on some hardwoods, such as oak and ash, makes it difficult for the paint to adhere to the surface. Because of this, a primer must have special properties to enable good adhesion. Aluminium primers that contain leaf or flake pigment are ideal, as is a type of primer called calcium plumbate.

To prepare hardwood:

- Abrade using a fine abrasive, remembering to rub with the grain.

- Dust off using a dusting brush.

- If the surface feels greasy to the touch, the surface will need de-greasing using white spirit.

- Dry off the surface or allow it to dry naturally.

- Use shellac knotting to seal any knots (apply two coats and leave to dry).

- Apply one coat of primer.

It is essential when painting timber that all end grains are properly primed to stop moisture being absorbed into the timber. Two coats of shellac knotting should be applied to the end grain before priming. You may also need to apply shellac knotting to knots in hardwood and resinous areas if the surface is to be painted.

PREPARING TIMBER FOR VARNISH, OIL OR STAINING

Use the following preparation process:

- Use white spirit on a lint-free cloth to remove any resin exudation or grease.

- Lightly rub down using fine glass paper or garnet paper.

- Use a dusting brush to remove dust and particles.

The surface is now ready to receive a coating of vanish, oil or wood stain.

DECAYED AND DENATURED TIMBER

Unless the surface to be painted is sound, the coatings will not adhere sufficiently, making it impossible to paint – or if you do manage to cover the surface, the paint will very soon peel and crack. Decayed or denatured timber will need to be prepared and treated to make the surface ready for coating.

DECAYED TIMBER

When timber has decayed due to wood rot, it should be cut out completely and replaced with sound timber, with the inserted timber joints made well beyond the edge of where the decay seems to end. Treat both the new insert and the remainder of the old wood with a fungicidal wash before repainting.

Fungicidal washes

An area that has become infected with mould, mildew or other kind of fungal growth will need treating with a **fungicidal** wash before decorating, or else the stains will show through the final finish and the fungi will continue to grow. You will need to follow the manufacturer's instructions for applying the wash, and wear PPE which will include a mask, goggles, gloves and overalls.

Fungicidal wash

Fungicide

A substance that destroys fungi

DENATURED TIMBER

When timber is exposed to the weather for long periods its cellular structure begins to break down, leaving the surface dull and furry. This is known as **denatured timber**, and paint is unlikely to adhere to the **friable** surface. It will need to be treated before you can proceed.

- Abrade the surface with a fine abrasive to remove the dead fibres.

- Remove dust with a dusting brush.

- Treat the surface with a wood preservative and allow it to dry.

- Apply a coat of raw linseed oil to the surface and leave for 15–20 minutes.

- Remove the surface oil with a cloth and leave for a week to fully dry out.

- Repaint, using the same method as for softwood.

Denatured timber

Wood that has been exposed to UV light and become grey and friable

Friable

Easily crumbled or reduced to powder

PREPARING METAL SURFACES READY TO RECEIVE FINISHING SYSTEMS

Metal is used in various construction stages, from laying the structural foundations, through first fix and second fix, to decorative finishing touches. It is used because it is strong, durable and waterproof, and it can also be very beautiful. Most metals suffer **corrosion** at varying rates and must be treated. Corrosion can be caused by contact with any kind of moisture, exposure to oxygen or hydrogen, and also pollution in the atmosphere.

Corrosion

The wasting away of metal due to chemical attack when it is exposed to water, oxygen, acid, alkali or salts. Rust is specifically the corrosion of ferrous metals

Ferrous

Containing iron

FERROUS METALS

Ferrous metals contain iron and will need to be cleared of all rust before painting.

The following table describes common ferrous metals used in construction.

Ferrous metal	Surface properties	Uses
Cast iron 	Non-toxic corroding metal.	■ Handrails ■ Bridges ■ Railings ■ Building frames ■ Stairs ■ Columns ■ Radiators
Wrought iron 	Corroding metal available in bar form, or sheets and hoops. Can crack if heated and may be brittle when cold. Rough texture.	■ Ornamental ironwork ■ Pipework ■ Handrails ■ Roof trusses
Mild/sheet steel 	High carbon content, and likely to rust. It is strong but bends easily.	■ Girders ■ Tubes ■ Screws ■ Nuts and bolts ■ Garage doors

NON-FERROUS METALS

Non-ferrous metals do not contain iron and are less likely to corrode than ferrous metals. Some examples include zinc, copper and aluminium.

The following table describes common non-ferrous metals used in construction.

Non-ferrous metal	Surface properties	Uses
Galvanised steel	Available in tubes, sheets and flat bars. Highly resistant to corrosion, and can withstand salt water, moisture, rain and snow. It is comparatively lightweight, fire resistant and maintenance free.	■ Girders ■ Frames ■ Roofing ■ Support beams ■ Piping
Copper	Available in tubes, sheets, wires, rods and flat bars. It is easy to bend but also easily damaged so must be stored carefully. Tarnishes quickly.	■ Water pipes ■ Electrical wiring ■ Roofing
Aluminium	Lightweight and extremely resistant to corrosion.	■ Window frames
Lead	Very soft and heavy. Highly resistant to corrosion. Discolours to grey when exposed to the air. Poisonous, so care must be taken when using.	■ Roofing

Structural steel must be protected from rust before painting

Ferrous metals that contain iron corrode more readily than non-ferrous metals. When iron and steel corrode, rust (or hydrated ferric oxide) is formed. This can only happen when moisture is present. Structural steel needs to be coated with a rust-inhibitive primer and then covered with several coats of paint to prevent moisture getting to the metal. Rust itself contains moisture and takes up more space than the metal it replaces, so as it swells it will not only push off the paint but also result in more corrosion. It is therefore extremely important that bare metal is totally covered with primer and paint film to keep moisture out and prevent corrosion.

TOOLS, MATERIALS AND EQUIPMENT

This section contains information on the tools, materials and equipment you will need to prepare metalwork, in addition to those you have already learnt about.

TOOLS

You may need to use a range of power tools as well as some manual tools for preparing metalwork.

Power tools

Preparing metal can be time consuming, so power tools make life a little easier. It is essential to wear the correct PPE, which will include hand protection, eye protection and a mask. Some commonly used power tools are described in the table.

Tool	Use
Rotary disc sander 	A disc sander has a flexible rubber sanding head that can be fitted with a range of abrasive papers. It is suitable for removing rust from curved surfaces. Note: A rotary disc sander takes practice to control and is liable to damage the surface or leave it uneven in unskilled hands.
Orbital sander 	An orbital sander consists of a flexible platform pad, onto which various types of abrasive paper are fixed. The sander moves in a small circular or orbital motion to abrade the surface. An orbital sander is comparatively light in weight and can be used for long periods without fatigue. It produces a finer surface than a rotary disc sander.

Tool	Use
Belt sander 	This is a sanding machine with a continuous belt of abrasive paper that has a flat sanding action. It abrades faster than an orbital sander (or sanding by hand) and comes in two sizes – 75mm or 100mm wide and 610mm long. Larger heavy-duty sanders are available for sanding floors. They are used to sand metal surfaces to remove light rust.
Rotary wire brush 	A fitting that can be attached to an electric drill, used for the preparation of ferrous metal surfaces. It is ideal for removing heavy rust.
Needle de-scaling gun 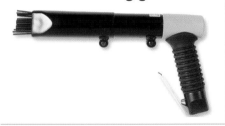	This consists of an outer body containing a number of hardened steel needles which are propelled forward by a spring-loaded piston. On hitting the surface, the needles rebound and are forced forward by the piston in a continuous action. The individual needles are self-adjusting, making it ideal for uneven surfaces and working around awkward areas such as nuts and bolts.

Manual tools

In addition to the power tools shown in the table above, you may also need to use a wire brush or steel wool to remove loose rust and corrosion from metalwork.

Wire brush

MATERIALS

There are some specific materials that you will need to prepare metalwork to ensure that it is ready to receive finishing coatings.

Primers for metal surfaces

The following table contains information about the types of primer you will need for preparing metal surfaces.

Metal primer	Description	Uses	Method of application
Etch primer	Designed for retreatment of clean ferrous metals to ensure adhesion of the paint system to the surface. Paint brushes and equipment are to be cleaned using the manufacturer's recommended cleaning solvent.	For pre-treatment of untreated surfaces such as aluminium, galvanised iron, zinc, copper, brass, lead, tin, clean iron and steel.	Brush or spray
Zinc phosphate metal primer	A special rust-inhibitive (stopping) primer. Paint brushes and equipment are to be cleaned with white spirit.	Suitable for all ferrous metal surfaces.	Brush or roller
Water-borne primer	A quick-drying water-borne primer that can be used on all metals, including galvanised steel.	Suitable for internal and external surfaces, it can be used under oil based and water-borne paints.	Brush or roller

Aluminium oxide paper

Aluminium oxide paper is used for dry abrading.

De-greasing agents

De-greasing agents include white spirit, methylated spirits and acetone.

Mordant solution

This is used to chemically etch and prepare the surface of new, bright, galvanised metal to provide adhesion for subsequent paint systems. Surfaces will need to be perfectly clean and de-greased, and then rinsed with clean water before the mordant solution is used. Apply the mordant solution with a brush and leave to dry. Rinse again and abrade before applying a second coat. Rinse once more and then allow the solution to dry before applying primer.

A proprietary de-greaser

Rust remover

There are a number of rust removal products on the market that will strip corrosion down to the bare metal. Read the manufacturer's instructions carefully before use.

Remember to always wear the correct PPE when using any of the tools described, and make sure that your work area is well ventilated. Put up safety signs and barriers to warn others of what you are doing.

Rust removing gel

Steel wool

Steel wool, also known as wire wool or wire sponge, is a bundle of strands of very fine soft steel filaments. It is used as an abrasive in finishing and repair work, for polishing wood or metal objects and for cleaning household cookware. It is available in seven grades, ranging from ultra-fine (0000) through to fine-to-medium (00, 0, 1) and medium-to-coarse (2, 3, 4). The coarse grades can be used to remove rust.

Emery paper and cloth

Emery paper is a type of abrasive paper used to abrade and polish metal. It has a rough-textured surface with a smooth paper backing. It is made by gluing naturally occurring abrasive mineral particles to sheets of paper with special adhesive. It can be glued to cloth to make emery cloth, or cardboard to make emery boards, and is also sold in discs to be used with sanding tools.

Steel wool

Personal protective equipment (PPE)

The following PPE should be worn when you are preparing metalwork:

- a boiler suit to protect you from flying debris

- goggles

- a face mask to prevent dust and rust particles entering your lungs via the nose and mouth

- rubber gloves – not light cotton gloves, as they may get caught in the equipment.

Emery cloth on a roll

DEFECTS IN METAL SURFACES

If defects in metal are not identified and treated before you apply paint, the surface may continue to corrode. The results of this happening can range from being unsightly to being dangerous.

Surface corrosion on metal pipes

The surface around this bolt has become pitted

Rotary wire brush

TYPES OF DEFECT

Some of the defects you will need to be aware of are described below.

Surface corrosion

Surface corrosion is an orange-red coating that forms on metal surfaces which will need to be removed to stop further corrosion. Priming and painting will further protect the surface from moisture.

Pitting

Pitting is the formation of holes, pits and craters in a metal surface due to severe corrosion. It may also be caused by the heavy-handed use of tools for de-scaling. If a smooth finish is required, the holes will have to be filled.

Mill scale

Mill scale is a blue/black film that forms on sheets of steel and wrought iron in the manufacturing process. After a while it becomes loose and flaky and provides an unstable foundation for painting. If mill scale is present it should be completely removed either with a wire brush or by the use of a rotary disc sander, rotary brush or needle de-scaling gun.

Galvanic action and cathodic protection

If different types of metal are used together, galvanic action can make the different metals corrode at different rates. Sometimes metals are combined so the one that corrodes faster is sacrificed to protect the slower-corroding metal. This is called cathodic protection. An example of this is the rusting of corrugated iron sheeting which happens when the zinc coating is broken, allowing the underlying steel to be attacked.

PREPARATION PROCESSES

De-scaling

Ferrous metal surfaces that are contaminated by rust will need to be de-scaled before priming or making good, or else the underlying surface will continue to flake and push the new paint off. The most effective tools for this are a needle de-scaling gun, rotary wire brush or wire brush.

De-greasing

This is the process of removing grease, particularly from metal surfaces, as paint coatings will not stick to greasy surfaces. De-greasing is usually accomplished by wiping the area over with a solvent such as white spirit, methylated spirit or acetone.

Priming

A primer is the first coat of paint applied to a surface. The main purpose of priming is to give a surface some protection and to make a surface suitable to receive further coatings. See the table on page 125 for primers used on metal surfaces.

PREPARING TROWELLED FINISHES AND PLASTERBOARD FOR FINISHING SYSTEMS

Much of your work as a decorator will be applying paint systems and other wall coverings to trowelled finishes and plasterboard. Although bricks and blocks are not usually painted, this is not unheard of. The trend for having exposed brickwork on internal walls requires the surface to be sealed with stabilising solution, and bricks and blocks are sometimes painted. However, the majority of your work will be on plasterboard and gypsum plaster. This section looks at how to prepare these substrates for decorating.

Plasterboard

SURFACE TYPES AND THEIR PROPERTIES

As a decorator you will come across various finishes in different contexts. The most common are described below.

BRICKWORK

A brick is a block, or a single unit of baked clay, used in masonry construction. Typically bricks are stacked together or laid as brickwork using various kinds of mortar to hold the bricks together and make a permanent structure. Bricks are typically produced in common or standard sizes in bulk quantities. With their attractive appearances and superior properties such as high compressive strength and durability, excellent fire and weather resistance, and good thermal and sound insulation, bricks are widely used for building, civil engineering work and landscape design. They are usually rough to the touch so are not used where a smooth, tactile finish is required. Different styles of bricks have pores of varying sizes and will absorb water by capillarity. Paint adheres well to brick, as it keys into the pores, but if the bricks have absorbed a large amount of moisture the surface may crack and blister as the moisture dries out. They have an **alkaline** nature and a high soluble salt content.

Brickwork

Alkaline

A substance that has a pH greater than 7. Alkalis form a caustic or corrosive solution when mixed with water. Examples include lime and caustic soda

BLOCKWORK

Blocks are made of concrete and are heavy but produce strong finished work. They are used to support heavy structures such as floors and walls. The advantage of using blocks is that they are bigger than standard bricks and therefore it is quicker to erect structures. They are often used where the face of the blocks will not be visible, as they are not usually as aesthetically pleasing as bricks. The physical properties of blockwork are similar to brickwork.

GYPSUM PLASTER

This is a material applied to internal surfaces such as ceilings and walls. It is usually smooth and tactile, although a rough surface can be achieved if required. It is usually applied over plasterboard to give

Blockwork

Niche

A shallow recess in a wall to hold a statue, vase, etc

Inert

Without power, motion or resistance

Saponification

A defect which is a soft sticky paint film caused by alkali contamination. It sometimes exudes a brown soapy liquid

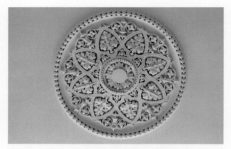

A ceiling rose made of gypsum plaster

ACTIVITY

Can you find an area covered in plaster that you can work on? If so, try rubbing down a small area with glass paper and another small area with the blade of a stripping knife. Can you see the difference in the surfaces? Apply a coat of emulsion – can you see the abrasion marks?

Gypsum plasterboard

a better, longer-lasting finish for both paint and wallpaper. It comes as a powder and has to be mixed with water for use. Unlike mortar and cement it remains fairly soft when it dries, so it can be sanded down and cut with metal tools. It is often moulded into decorative shapes for ceiling roses, coving and **niches**. It is an **inert** material, which means it does not have a chemical reaction with the paint applied and receives paint systems well. As the plaster surface is porous, a thin layer of paint should be applied to key into the surface – a thick layer would lie on top of the surface and quickly break down and flake. Although plaster is an inert material, if it comes into contact with lime it forms a caustic alkali which may cause **saponification** when painted (see page 158).

Like timber, plastered surfaces can be affected by cracks, nail heads and open joints, and should therefore be treated in a similar way. New plaster should never be rubbed down using abrasives, as this will scratch the surface and show though once painted. You should use a stripping knife to remove any nibs, then dust the surface using a dusting brush before painting or making good (filling).

Some surface finishes such as artex are textured and are worked in a number of different patterns, so you will not be able to achieve a smooth surface. If a small area is damaged it may be possible to fill the area and roughen up the surface to match the pattern, but usually the whole area will have to be re-artexed or plastered to a smooth finish by a skilled plasterer.

PLASTERBOARD (SQUARE- AND FEATHER-EDGED)

Plasterboard is a type of smooth building board composed of a layer of gypsum, on either side of which is a layer of very stout paper or fibre. The paper adheres tightly because the gypsum contains a small quantity of glue. The light grey or ivory side should face out, as it is pre-primed ready for decorating. It comes in square- (sometimes called un-tapered) or feather-edged (tapered) form. Tapered edge plasterboard allows space for taping and filling, to achieve a perfectly flush surface.

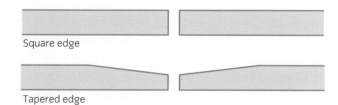

Square edge

Tapered edge

Plasterboards with square and tapered edges

Plasterboard is widely used in construction as it is cheaper and quicker than wet plaster, and this is known as dry lining. It will usually be installed by a plasterer, but as a decorator it is important to be able to patch up small holes and cracks to make good the surface before applying finishing systems. Care should be taken when storing and handling plasterboard, because it is very easy to damage the edges and corners. As it is very porous it should be kept dry to prevent it from warping and the paper facing separating from the plaster. Do not store it directly on the floor, but raise it up on timber battens to prevent damp seeping through the layers.

The boards are attached by either sticking them with adhesive to walls or by fixing them to timber studwork with clout nails or plasterboard screws. The nails and the joints will have to be filled and taped to ensure that the surface is smooth.

Plasterboarded wall

DEFECTS

There are various things to look out for which will influence your preparation when working with trowelled finishes and plasterboard. The age and state of repair of the structure will be significant.

Efflorescence

This is the appearance of a fine white powder that forms on the surface of brickwork and plaster. Both of these materials contain soluble salts, which may originate from the raw material of bricks. However, in most cases efflorescence is caused by salts from external sources such as ground water, contaminated atmosphere, mortar ingredients and other materials in contact with the bricks. As the materials dry the moisture evaporates and the salt is drawn to the surface, leaving a white powder on the bricks. The powder should be removed by using a stiff brush on the dry bricks. Do not wet the surface, as the efflorescence will return when the bricks dry.

Efflorescence on plaster

Settlement and shrinkage cracks

Cracks are usually found in new constructions where the moisture has dried out and materials have shrunk and cracked. The crack will need to be cut or raked out with the edge of a stripping knife to give the new filling something to adhere to. The surface can then be wet in (see page 164) with water or coated with PVA adhesive. Once dried the crack will need to be filled with the appropriate material (plaster, render, etc) and then rubbed down with a fine abrasive.

Settlement cracks

Open joints

Open joints are where mortar (or pointing) between stones or brick is defective, and this is a very common cause of water penetration. The making good process is the same as for settlement and cracks.

Mould growth

Mould is a furry growth of micro-organisms or fungi which grow in damp, warm conditions and must be removed before painting. This is because they can continue to grow under the paint, spoiling the appearance and damaging the substrate below. There are a number of different solutions on the market but you may have to call for specialist help.

Mould growth on an interior wall

Moss growth on an exterior wall

Mould can also be a threat to your health, so you must take extra care to wear the correct PPE: mask, rubber gloves, goggles and a boiler suit.

Moss and lichen

These are naturally occurring plant growths that thrive in damp conditions. They are usually found on exterior walls and pathways where there is excessive moisture. They can be removed by brushing or scraping, or by applying proprietary moss and lichen removers that will also inhibit their re-growth.

Dry-out

This is a fault found in gypsum plaster, usually caused by the plaster drying too quickly in hot weather or by heat being applied to aid the drying process. It is also called delayed expansion, and is often not visible until water-borne paint is applied. When moisture is introduced to the surface it starts off the setting action again and can cause buckling and rippling of the plaster.

Nail heads

Masonry nails in brick or blockwork will usually be removed using a claw hammer or pinchers. If this is difficult they will need to be hammered below the surface, and then the hole should be filled. Plasterboard is attached by clout nails or plasterboard screws, so these should be covered with plaster or filler to ensure that they do not show through when the finishing coats are applied.

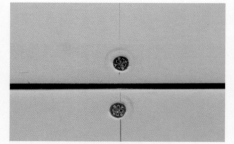

Correctly fixed plasterboard screws

TOOLS, MATERIALS AND EQUIPMENT

In addition to what you have already seen in this chapter, you may need some specific tools, materials and equipment for working with trowelled finishes and plasterboard.

TOOLS

The table describes some tools commonly used for trowelled finishes and plasterboard.

Tool	Description
Filling board/hawk 	Typically, a piece of plastic 100mm square for mixing small quantities of plaster or filler when making good cracks and holes in plasterwork. The handle is fastened centrally on the back at right angles to the board. For applying plaster, a larger hawk is needed (about 300mm square) and the mixing of the plaster is done in a bucket or on a large clean spot board. Hawks come in metal as well as plastic.

Tool	Description
Trowel	Used for making good defective plasterwork.
Caulking blades/boards/tools	Caulking is the process of covering joints in dry lining. After the joints between the boards or at the angles have been filled, paper tape is sandwiched between thin layers of filler. This work is carried out with the use of a caulking tool.

MATERIALS

There are various specialist materials you will need for preparing trowelled finishes and plasterboard.

Primers

The table below shows the additional priming materials you will need for these types of finishes.

Name	Description	Uses	Method of application
Alkali-resisting primer	Primer designed for surfaces that are alkaline in nature. Paint brushes and equipment are to be cleaned with solvent (white spirit).	To prime new and old building materials which are of an alkaline nature, eg plaster, brickwork, concrete blockwork.	Brush, roller or spray
Stabilising solution	Comes in clear or coloured form. The clear solution has better penetrating properties and is easier to apply. Paint brushes and equipment are to be cleaned with solvent (white spirit).	To stabilise old powdery surfaces before painting. Can also be used to seal plasterboard before paperhanging.	Brush or roller

Name	Description	Uses	Method of application
Emulsion (water-borne paint)	Emulsion may be thinned out with water to form what is often called a mist-coat.	Used on newly plastered surfaces, the mist-coat soaks into the porous surface to provide a key for further paint coatings.	Best mixed up in a bucket and applied with a large brush. It can be applied by roller or spray gun (which is messier).

Ready-mixed plaster

Plaster-based fillers

These come ready mixed and are a convenient way of filling small holes and cracks in plaster.

Joint fillers

These consist of powder that, when mixed with water, is used to fill plasterboard joints. They are fast setting, so should only be mixed in small amounts to prevent them hardening before application.

Joint tapes and reinforced corner tapes

Joints in plasterboard need covering with a fine mesh tape to prevent the joint showing through the finished paint system. Reinforced corners are available to offer added protection.

Glue size

Apply tape to plasterboard joints for a smooth finish

Reinforced corner tape for plasterboard joints

Size or glue size

This product is applied with a large brush to new plaster to prepare it for paperhanging. It contains an adhesive which helps the paper slide over the surface for pattern matching.

THE PREPARATION PROCESS

As with timber and metal preparation, the aim of the decorator is to achieve a firm foundation on trowelled finishes or plasterboard, ready to receive finishing systems. Defective pointing or dry friable surfaces need to be made sound or the paint will not adhere. Detailed instructions are provided in the sections on rectifying surface conditions and making good, but following are the general principles.

BRICK AND BLOCKWORK

1 Check the surface for irregularities, holes, loose pointing and other surface defects.

2 Fill, using a filling knife and hawk, with sand and cement mixed to a stiff paste with water.

3 Check for efflorescence (see page 139) and moisture content with a moisture meter (see page 122).

4 Allow filling to dry thoroughly before coating with alkali-resistant primer, using a large brush (100mm).

Repair defects in brickwork before decoration

NEW PLASTER

1 When the plaster is thoroughly dry, de-nib the surface using the blade of a stripping knife. Work in a chequerboard pattern, taking care not to dig the blade in and score the surface.

2 Mix up a light-coloured emulsion with water in a bucket to make a thin coating. Apply a mist-coat to the plaster surface with a large brush.

3 When dry, check for cracks, holes and other defects, and fill as necessary.

4 When the filler has dried, lightly rub down with a fine aluminium oxide paper and dust off.

5 Coat with a mist-coat of thinned emulsion or a thin coating of alkali-resistant primer.

OLD PLASTER

1 Strip wall coverings if necessary, and wash walls down to remove paste residue.

2 When the surface is dry, rub down with fine aluminium oxide paper.

3 Make good surface defects and allow filler to dry.

4 Rub down with fine aluminium oxide paper and dust off.

5 If the surface is to be papered, coat the wall with glue size.

Remove existing wallpaper before making good old plaster

PLASTERBOARD

1 Fill joints, nail and screw holes, and other defects, and ensure that the joints are sufficiently taped.

2 When the filler is dry, rub down lightly with fine aluminium oxide paper.

3 Coat with alkali-resistant primer.

Filling holes in plasterboard

REMOVING PAINTED AND PAPERED SURFACES TO RECEIVE FINISHING SYSTEMS

All contaminants should be removed before decoration

On new building projects you will probably be faced with bare substrates, but the majority of a decorator's work is on surfaces that have already been painted or wallpapered. These have to be prepared to receive a new coating so that the finished coating will adhere with a smooth, flawless finish.

Previously painted woodwork should be washed down using sugar soap and warm water and then rinsed off using clean water. This will remove grease and dirt and it may then be ready for painting. Make sure that the surrounding areas are protected with waterproof coverings to keep the area dry and free from any contaminants that may be present in the solutions you are using. The removal of contamination using cleaning agents is covered on page 158. Some surfaces will require abrading and should be rubbed down using wet and dry and then rinsed off before paint is applied.

REMOVING EXISTING OR DEFECTIVE PAINT SYSTEMS FROM SUBSTRATES

Some previously painted surfaces may require burning off with heat using a hot air gun/stripper. This is the quickest method of removing coatings from timber surfaces. As always it is important to wear appropriate PPE, which will include protective gloves, overalls, goggles and a mask, but if you are removing old paintwork containing lead you will need to take extra care. Burning off lead can give off fumes that may be **carcinogenic**, so a respirator must be worn. The use of lead paint started to be phased out in the 1950s but the law banning its use did not come into effect until 1978. If you suspect that old paintwork contains lead you can test it with a kit before proceeding.

Carcinogenic

Cancer causing

Lead testing kit

ENVIRONMENTAL HEALTH AND SAFETY REGULATIONS

As you read in Chapter 1, the way you work is governed by certain regulations, and it is important to keep them in mind while you work. Many of the materials that you are working with are considered hazardous to health and need to be treated with caution (see COSSH Regulations, pages 9–11). All paints give off vapours that are known as volatile organic compounds (VOCs).

VOCs

These are vapours that evaporate into the air from everyday products at room temperature – from chemical substances such as cleaning products, cosmetics and paint. VOC emissions contribute to air pollution and affect the air we breathe. The paint industry is trying to reduce emissions, and many low-odour paints are now being produced. The European Parliament has set maximum VOC levels for different paints and varnishes (EU Directive 2004/42/EC) and has ruled that containers should have a VOC content label so that the consumer can compare products and choose an alternative if they want. You can also ask your supplier for a copy of the data sheet (COSHH).

If you are using a product that gives off vapours, you may have to put up a notice to warn people. You should also make sure that you are using appropriate PPE (see Chapter 1 for more information).

REMOVING PAINT USING LIQUID PETROLEUM GAS (LPG)

LPG is generally only used to remove paint from timber surfaces. It can be used on metal, but it is less effective as it is slow and it can burn the paint surface. It should not be used on trowelled surfaces, plaster or plasterboard.

Before starting work you must check your tools and equipment – check the hose and fittings for any signs of damage. To check for gas leaks you can use a solution of detergent (washing-up liquid). By applying the liquid around all the fittings you can see if gas is leaking – bubbles will show where there is a leak. If any leaks are found, replace the equipment and do not use it.

- The hose is made from rubber and deteriorates over time, so check it and replace it if in doubt.

- Before you start to burn off, ensure that a fire extinguisher is nearby.

- Check whether a hot works permit is required before commencing work.

- If you are burning off inside, remove all combustible materials such as curtains and furnishings.

- When burning off doors, for example, start from the bottom. Heat rises and will start to soften the paintwork as you work upwards.

- Avoid burning off timber that may cause a fire, such as timber adjacent to the roof structure of a building. There are often birds' nests present or denatured timber which can easily catch fire from the flame of the torch.

- Stop burning off at least one hour before you leave the site, and always carry out a final check for smouldering timber before you go home.

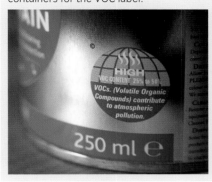

Fire extinguisher for gases

The table shows the advantages and disadvantages of using LPG.

Advantages	Disadvantages
■ Low running cost. ■ Can be used when there is no electricity on site. ■ Is a very fast and efficient way of removing thick layers of paint.	■ Some local authorities have already banned (and many more are considering whether or not to do the same) the use of using LPG burning-off torches because of the risks involved. ■ Scorches the timber easily and should not be used on surfaces to be varnished. ■ There is a danger that heat may crack the glass in windows. ■ You will need to take extra care when using a LPG burning-off torch, as there is a risk of causing a fire or burning yourself.

REMOVING PAINT USING A HOT AIR GUN/ STRIPPER

Hot air gun

Hot air guns or strippers are used on timber, particularly if a transparent coating is to be applied, and metal. They are not suitable for use on plastered and trowelled substrates.

Before using a hot air stripper, check that the equipment has got a PAT (portable appliance test) certificate showing that it has been inspected and passed as safe by a competent electrician.

Although they are similar in appearance to a hairdryer, hot air strippers produce a much higher heat output, and can burn, so use them with extreme caution. The hot air is produced by an electric filament which can easily reach temperatures between 200°C and 600°C, depending on the gun.

There is less risk of fire when using a hot air stripper than there is with an LPG blowtorch. There is also less chance of cracking glass or scorching timber.

The table shows the advantages and disadvantages of using a hot air gun/stripper.

Advantages	Disadvantages
■ Does not scorch timber when burning off. ■ When used on window frames there is less chance of glass cracking. ■ Ideal for use on old or delicate surfaces and in areas of high fire risk such as the eaves of old buildings.	■ Slower than LPG. ■ Needs power to run. ■ Effectiveness can vary, eg when using in high winds.

How to use a hot air stripper:

1 Hold the nozzle about 3–5cm from the surface.

2 When the paint has softened and starts to blister, use a stripping knife or shavehook to remove the paint.

3 Do not hold the gun in one position for too long, or you may damage the underlying substrate.

4 If possible, work from the bottom up to take advantage of the rising heat.

5 Burn off in the direction of the grain.

6 Direct the flame or hot air away from the glass so as not to crack it.

7 In some cases two applications of heat may be necessary to remove all paint from the surface.

8 Water-borne paint can be difficult to remove by heat, and it is advisable to use a chemical stripper.

Use a shavehook to remove paint

Burning off paint from a panelled door:

1 As with all paint stripping, make sure that the surrounding surfaces are protected.

2 Apply the heat to the mouldings on one side of the bottom panels of the door.

3 Work from the bottom to the top of the moulding to remove the paint.

4 Repeat the process on the next panel.

5 Repeat the process on all of the mouldings and panels up the door.

6 Apply heat to the bottom rail, then the middle rail and finally the top rail.

7 Apply the heat to the hinge stile from the bottom to the top.

8 Apply heat to the latch stiles and edges to remove the paint.

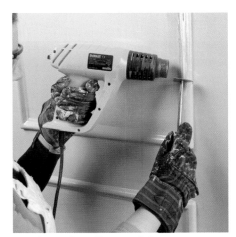

Burning paint off a panel door

REMOVING PAINT WITH CHEMICALS (LIQUID PAINT REMOVER)

Liquid paint remover (LPR), also known as solvent-borne paint remover, is very efficient at removing thick layers of paint, leaving behind a smooth, glossy surface, it is increasingly being replaced by water-borne paint remover because of its high VOC emissions. The strong smell, slow drying time and the fact that brushes have to be cleaned using white spirit outweigh the advantages of using it.

LPR is used on timber, particularly if a clear coating is to be applied, and metals. It is not suitable for use on plastered or trowelled finishes.

Before using paint strippers, there are rules to follow:

- Read and follow the manufacturer's instructions.

- Remove ironmongery from the surface to be stripped, eg door handles.

- Protect surrounding areas from any splashing or contamination.

- Protect yourself with the appropriate PPE.

- Always make sure that the work area is well ventilated, or protect yourself by wearing breathing apparatus.

Opening the container

Sometimes pressure builds up in the metal container holding the paint remover. This can cause gas and liquid to spurt out when the cap is removed. This could result in damage to the eyes and skin, so when opening the can, slowly unscrew the cap, letting the pressure escape before you fully remove it.

Avoid getting paint stripper on your skin or in your eyes, as this will cause burning and eye damage. If you do get the stripping solution on you, you should rinse it off using cold water and seek medical advice.

Water-borne paint remover needs to be poured into a metal paint kettle before use (make sure it *is* metal, as stripper can eat right through a plastic one). Apply to the surface using an old paint brush. After a while the paint will start to blister, showing that it is ready to remove with a stripping or scraping knife. The amount of time that this takes will vary depending on the thickness of the paint.

Decontamination

It is very important that, after using liquid paint remover, the surface is washed down with clean water to decontaminate the area. Leaving chemicals on the surface can cause the breakdown of subsequent paint systems, leading to defects such as flaking or blistering.

Respirator

Liquid paint remover

ACTIVITY

Look for a container of paint stripper in your college or workplace, and read the label. What does it tell you? Make a list of the PPE required, how to use it and how to store it.

REMOVING EXISTING OR DEFECTIVE WALLPAPER FROM PLASTERBOARD AND PLASTERED SURFACES

Before a new wall covering can be applied, the existing covering will need to be removed. There are many types of wallpapers on the market, but most can be removed using water and a stripping knife. Vinyl wallpaper is mostly used in kitchens and bathrooms, as it is protected from steam and moisture, and must be treated differently. The top layer needs to be peeled off dry before proceeding as below. The type of paper, the adhesive used to stick it and the length of time the covering has been on the walls for will determine how easy it is to remove. You will have to persevere with wetting in (see page 164) until all traces of wall covering are removed. The water needs to penetrate the paper to cause the adhesive to revert to its liquid state and release its hold on the paper.

HAND SOAKING

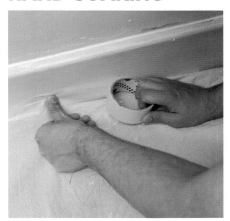

STEP 1 Cover the floor using dust sheets to protect it from any water damage, making sure that you secure the sheets using masking tape. The sheets may become very wet, so use a sign to let people know that the floor is wet.

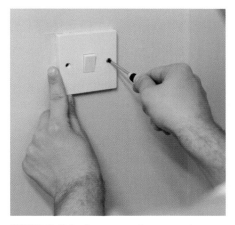

STEP 2 It is dangerous to use water where there is electricity, so turn electricity off at the mains and then loosen light switches and plug sockets so that you can strip off the paper behind them. Never switch the electricity back on until you are sure that the surfaces are dry.

STEP 3 Fill a bucket with warm water and a small amount of washing-up liquid. Now you are ready to wet the walls in, working from the bottom to the top. Apply the soapy water to the wall using a large flat paint brush (150mm). Starting from the bottom will help the water break the surface tension, allowing it to penetrate the wallpaper.

STEP 4 When the wall is thoroughly wet, leave the water to soak in and penetrate the wallpaper so that it will soften the paste that was used to stick it to the walls. You may need to wet it a second time if it is hard to remove or use a wallpaper scourer to help with water penetration.

STEP 5 Using a stripping knife, you can now remove the paper. If the wallpaper is still hard to remove you may need to either soak the walls again or allow more time for the water to soften the paper. Remember to let the water do the work. Clear away the wallpaper as you go.

PREVIOUSLY PAINTED WALLPAPER

If you need to remove lining paper or patterned wall coverings that have been painted, you may find it more difficult to wet in. The paint coating forms a seal, making it hard for the water to penetrate the paper. It can be removed either by using a steam stripper or by scoring the surface of the paper with a stripping knife and then wetting in with hot soapy water at least twice before proceeding with hand soaking.

REMOVING WALLPAPER BY STEAM STRIPPER

Some wallpaper/wall coverings are hard to remove by normal soaking – for example washable papers, papers that have been painted, and multi-layered papers. A steam stripper will help with removal of any type of surface covering from walls and ceilings, including emulsion and other water-borne paints.

Steam strippers consist of a water tank attached to an enclosed element much the same as the one you would find in a kettle. As the water is heated it turns to steam, which travels along a flexible hose onto a perforated plate. When the plate is laid against a surface, steam penetrates deeply into the wall covering, softening the paper and the adhesive. The wall covering can then be easily stripped from the surface.

DISPOSAL OF REMOVED PAINT AND PAPER

The wallpaper paste that was used to stick the paper up in the first place will be sticky again when the paper is removed, so you need to clear it up as you go to prevent trip hazards, and also to stop pieces of paper sticking to your boots and being trodden onto surrounding areas. Dispose of waste in polythene refuse bags.

Refuse bag

Steam stripper

Here are some safety precautions for using a steam stripper:

- Make sure the steam stripper has a PAT certificate.

- Never let the water level drop too low or dry up completely, and take care when re-filling as steam can scald.

- Make sure that the hose is not kinked, as this will stop the flow of the steam.

- As when stripping paper by hand, clean up as you work.

Storing tools and equipment

It is important to store your tools and equipment neatly and correctly to make sure they stay in optimum condition for use. It will also save you a great deal of time if you know where everything is.

- All equipment should be clean and dry before storing, and steam strippers and other electrical equipment should be allowed to cool down before being put away.

- Knives with ferrous metal blades are liable to rust if they come into contact with moisture.

- Filling knives are very sharp and should be stored in a special pouch to prevent accidents and keep the blade from getting damaged. A damaged blade will make marks on the surface when de-nibbing.

- Combustible materials should be stored in a cool, dry place.

- Dust sheets and covers should be dry before storing, and cleaned regularly to prevent contamination.

- Make sure that lids of containers are clean and sealed properly to prevent leakage and drying out of the contents.

Electrical equipment must be cooled before storing

RECTIFYING SURFACE CONDITIONS AND DEFECTS

Ask any painter and decorator for the secret of a perfect finish and you'll hear just one answer – preparation. Skimp on this, and the finish you put on top will not last as long or look as good. So far in this chapter you have looked at preparing timber products, metalwork and trowelled finishes for decoration. This section looks in detail at the type of defects you are likely to encounter, and how to produce a sound surface ready for applying the finishing coats.

HEALTH AND SAFETY

Some of the surface conditions and defects that decorators have to deal with can be hazardous to health if precautions are not taken. Properties may have been rendered unsound by fire, flood, or neglect, so carry out a risk assessment before you start work. Signs and barriers should be erected to warn people of the dangers. Particles from surfaces covered with mould, lichen and moss, or smoke damage can enter your body through your eyes, nose, mouth and skin, so make sure you are wearing the correct PPE. Take care to dispose of all debris safely and to keep your work area clean to help prevent cross-contamination. Check that load-bearing surfaces are safe before you walk on them. In older properties it is likely that asbestos was used in the construction, so make sure that this has been checked.

ADDITIONAL TOOLS AND MATERIALS

You may need a few extra tools and materials in addition to those already mentioned.

Proprietary stain block

STAIN BLOCK

This is a water-borne primer for use on interior walls and ceilings. It stops the migration of stains through the paint finish and can also be used to seal and bind dry, friable and powdery surfaces such as plaster, limestone and distemper. It is useful for covering up hard-to-conceal stains such as ink, scuffs and fire and water damage. Before use the surface must be cleaned of defective or poorly adhering materials, efflorescence, dirt, grease, wax and so on. Once you have applied it with a brush or small roller it should be allowed to dry before further paint finishes are applied.

STABILISING SOLUTION

Stabilising solution used to seal powdery surfaces

This was previously mentioned as a primer for trowelled surfaces. It will seal porous surfaces and can be used on its own, or covered with further paint systems. Before use the surfaces should be cleaned of any loose, powdery material and scraped free of moss and lichen.

REMOVING SURFACE DEFECTS WITH CLEANING AGENTS

Some substrates will be covered by **impermeable** coatings such as wax polish or silicone that will need to be removed before further paint systems can be applied. The surface will need to be wiped with a solvent, usually methylated spirit, and then decontaminated with clean water. Dirt, dust and grease may only need washing down with sugar soap or detergent.

Impermeable

Not allowing fluids to pass through

TYPES OF SURFACE CONDITION AND DEFECTS

Surface defects will have an impact on your overall finish, so it is important to treat each defect correctly to produce a sound surface, ready for decoration.

EFFLORESCENCE

The fine white powder that forms on the surface of bricks can be part of the aesthetic charm of a brick building, so often this defect is left untreated. The salts that appear on the brick surface can be brushed off, but they may keep reappearing. The surface will need to be observed over a period of time to ensure that the efflorescence has been checked. If the surface is decorated efflorescence can form on the paint film, causing it to flake and peel.

When there is no more evidence of white powder forming on the surface the area will need to be primed using an alkali-resisting primer and allowed to dry thoroughly, before giving the surface a light rub down with fine abrasive paper ready to receive finishing coatings.

Efflorescence on brickwork

CHALKING

Chalking is where a paint surface breaks down and becomes loose and powdery. It is caused by the weather, so it usually occurs on outside walls. The powdery surface needs to be stripped down using a stripping knife before being rubbed down with abrading paper. It will then need to be primed with one or two coats of stabilising solution. Once the primer has dried, lightly rub down using a fine to medium abrasive. Make good (fill), and allow the filling to dry before rubbing down with fine abrasive to give a smooth surface ready for finishing coatings.

INDUSTRY TIP

For information on moss, lichen and mould growth see pages 139–140.

Chalking on a paint surface

FLAKING

Flaking is primarily due to poor adhesion, where the paint film lifts from the surface and breaks away in the form of brittle flakes. Moisture is often the cause, and it may be present in the surface

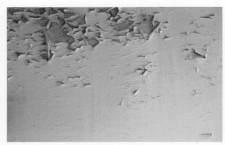

Flaking paint

before it is painted, or may find an entry into the surface after painting through open joints or building defects. This can then be drawn out by heat or sunlight, causing the paint film to lift. Flaking may also occur when the surface is loose or powdery. The presence of rust on metal surfaces or loose and crumbling plaster will cause flaking.

Timber
Remove the defective paint coating using liquid paint remover or burn off with a hot air gun (see pages 146–148). Once the film has been removed, seal any knots and give the surface a rub down with medium abrasive. Apply primer and allow it to dry before giving a final rub down using a fine abrasive, ready for undercoating.

Metal
Scrape off flaking paint down to a solid surface with a scraping knife. If you come through to bare metal it will need spot priming to seal the area. If you have a large area to cover it can be stripped with liquid paint remover and then decontaminated with clean water. Allow it to dry before applying the appropriate primer.

Plaster
Scrape off the flaking paint with a scraping knife. If the surface below is powdery it will need coating with stabilising solution before making good.

RUNS

An example of a run

Runs are defects on a painted surface that happen when paint has been applied too thickly or unevenly. The paint flows downwards and stands proud of the remainder of the surface. Some surfaces may only need a light rub down with fine abrasive to remove any bits or nibs before repainting. However, if the surface is very bad it will need to be rubbed down using a wet abrasive such silicon carbide (wet and dry).

BITTINESS

This is when bits of grit, fluff and other foreign bodies contained in the paint spoil the appearance of the finished paint film. Examples of this happening are when the lid of a tin of paint has not been put back on properly or a surface has not been dusted off after rubbing down. Straining the paint before use will help to avoid bittiness on painted surfaces. It requires the same treatment as for runs.

CURTAINS OR SAGS

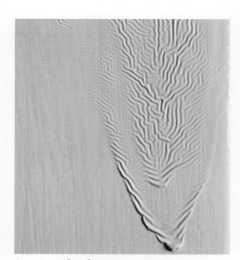

An example of sags or curtains

Similar to runs, this is a defect that occurs in paint coatings particularly when applied to a vertical surface – it is a result of uneven application. It takes the form of a thick line of paint like a draped curtain. Curtains or sags should be treated in the same way as runs.

DISCOLOURATION

This is where the pigment colour changes or becomes paler where paint has been exposed to strong sunlight over a period of time. It can also occur behind wall hangings such as pictures and mirrors. Some colours are lightfast and are less likely to discolour than others. Exposure to chemical atmospheres can also cause discolouration, with an example being the nicotine in cigarette smoke. Discolouration of paintwork usually means it is time to re-decorate!

An example of discolouration

BLEEDING

Bleeding is the action of any material in penetrating and discolouring the paint coating applied on top of it. There are many substances that may bleed and stain into new coatings including red paint, **bituminous** products, marker pens and nicotine. If paint is applied over bituminous products the surface coating rapidly develops brown stains, and the drying of the paint is impeded. Knots and resin exudation will also spoil the paint finish. It is often very difficult to remove the offending coating completely so the area should be sealed with shellac knotting or aluminium primer.

Bituminous

A word to describe a sticky black or brown substance made from petroleum, often known simply as 'tar'

WRINKLING (ALSO KNOWN AS SHRIVELLING OR RAVELLING)

This is a defect in a gloss film which takes the form of wrinkles that appear during the drying process. It is usually caused by an unduly heavy or liberal application of varnish or enamel, and the surface skins over when the material underneath has not dried hard. It is usually best to remove the surface coating by burning off using an LPG blowtorch or a solvent paint stripper. If paint stripper is used, the surface will need decontaminating with clean water before the surface coatings are applied.

SLOW- OR NON-DRYING SURFACE COATING

This can be caused by paint being applied too thickly, poor atmospheric conditions during drying or insufficient drying time between coats. Cold conditions with lack of air movement can be avoided by applying gentle heat, but take care because excessive heat can cause wrinkling.

INDUSTRY TIP

Do not confuse slow-drying paint with anti-theft paint. This is a specially formulated paint that remains tacky and is used on exterior surfaces, such as drainpipes, to prevent burglary.

CISSING

This term describes when a coat of paint or varnish refuses to form a continuous film and leaves the surface partially exposed. The main cause of this is when paint is applied over a greasy surface that has not been washed down or de-greased.

All previously coated surfaces need to be free of grease and oil before they are painted, but the term de-greasing usually refers to bare metal. See page 136 for instructions on cleaning and de-greasing.

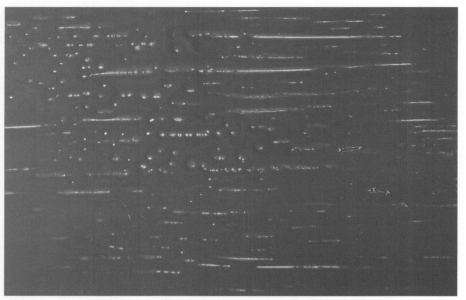

Cissing

CRAZING AND CRACKING

This defect occurs in paintwork and is usually due to the application of a hard-drying coating (oil paint) over a softer coat (paint that has not fully dried) so that the top coating is unable to keep pace with the expansion and contraction of the previous coat as it dries. If crazing or cracking has formed on the surface there is no remedy except to burn off the defective paint.

Another cause of cracking or crazing of paintwork is allowing paste or glue size to stray onto the painted surface and dry there. Always wash off any paste or size as you go.

Crazed paint surface

BLISTERING

This is a defect in painting where the paintwork lifts away from the surface in bubbles due to lack of adhesion.

Here are some of the causes of blistering:

- moisture introduced when a surface is painted during wet, foggy or misty weather – this usually affects metal as well as timber

- moisture introduced when a surface has been washed down and painted before it had time to dry

- resin exuding from knots

- moisture contained within the substrate, such as new plasterwork that has been painted before it had time to dry out, or unseasoned timber, or where timber has not been primed (to stop moisture soaking into the timber)

- paintwork that faces direct sun light (south facing) can blister due to the heat.

To treat blistering strip off loose paintwork until a solid edge is achieved, using a stripping knife, then spot prime bare surfaces. If the surface is badly affected it may need to be completely stripped. To strip timber surfaces, burn off using an LPG blowtorch or hot air gun (see pages 145–147).

To strip metal surfaces, use liquid paint remover (LPR). For more about LPR see page 148.

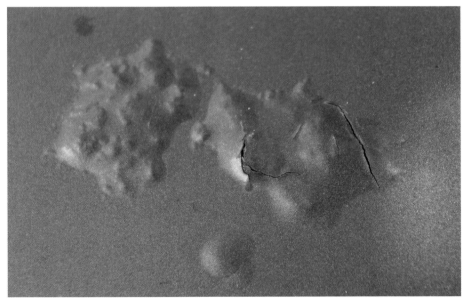

Blistering of paint

To avoid loss of gloss to facades, only paint outside in dry weather

LOSS OF GLOSS

How glossy a paint film looks depends on the proportions of oil or resins to pigment used to formulate it. Materials used to make paint vary, so some paints are matt, while others have a semi-gloss (eggshell/satin) or a high-gloss finish. Loss of gloss occasionally occurs on a painted surface soon after the finish has been applied. The most likely reason is that the surface it was applied to was too porous.

All paints, enamels and varnishes gradually lose their gloss after having been exposed for some time. The repeated use of strong alkaline solutions and scouring powders during household cleaning will in time destroy the binder of the paint and cause loss of gloss.

When painting outside, remember that damp weather or rain can affect a gloss finish so it is advisable not to apply gloss finishes too late in the day, especially in autumn.

If a surface has been affected by loss of gloss it will need repainting.

SAPONIFICATION

This is a soft sticky paint film caused by alkali contamination, which sometimes exudes a brown soapy liquid. If this occurs over a small area it can be sealed with two coats of knotting solution, but if the saponification covers a larger area the surface should be sealed using alkali-resisting primer and allowed to dry thoroughly before making good.

CONTAMINATION

This is a general term for anything that may adversely affect the condition of a substrate and that will need removing before you can proceed with finishing coatings. The following table describes how to deal with the most common contaminants.

Contaminant	Methods of removal
Dirt	Warm water with detergent or sugar soap. Surface dirt can be removed by dusting or vacuuming.
Grease	May be removed with detergent in warm water, sugar soap or proprietary cleaner and then rinsed with clean water. Stubborn grease can be removed with white spirit.
Silicone	Dried silicone may peel off – otherwise remove with white spirit.
Wax polish	Remove with white spirit.
Carbon/smoke damage	If the surface is sound, wash down with sugar soap and warm water.

REPLACING OLD AND DEFECTIVE PUTTY

When you are removing old paint from window frames, some of the putty may be damaged and will break away. Before replacing the putty the timber will need to be primed (see pages 124–126). Once the primer has dried any defective or missing putty can be replaced.

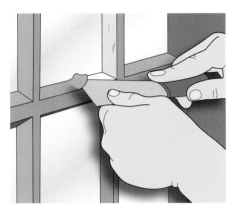

STEP 1 Remove any loose or defective putty from the glass using a small stripping knife or shavehook. Give a light rub down with a medium abrasive and dust off the area. Prime any bare timber and allow it to dry.

STEP 2 Take a small amount of putty and work it in your hands until it becomes a stiff dough. Roll the putty between your fingers to make a sausage shape, then push the putty into the rebate with your thumb.

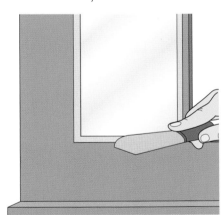

STEP 3 Smooth the putty by using a putty knife along the edge of the glass and remove any excess with the putty knife.

STEP 4 Paint the putty as soon as it is hard enough to withstand the pressure of a paint brush.

INDUSTRY TIP

If putty is too dry and crumbles when broken even after working it, add a small amount of raw linseed oil and continue to work the putty between your hands until it is soft. If the putty is so sticky that it does not leave your hands cleanly, add a little whiting, and then continue to work the putty between your hands until firm.

RE-GLAZING TIMBER FRAMES (WINDOW OR DOOR PANELS)

To fit glass into a frame rebate it needs to be sandwiched between two layers of putty.

STEP 1 First, you need to get the putty to the right consistency. Work the putty by kneading it between your fingers for a few minutes.

STEP 2 Roll it between your fingers to make a long sausage shape, and then push the putty (bedding) around the frame rebate firmly with your thumb.

STEP 3 Offer the pane of glass up to the rebate and press it in around the edges to make good contact. Continue to put light pressure on the glass until the excess putty oozes out and the bedding putty is between 2mm and 4mm thick. Warning: do not push the glass from the centre, as it is likely to break.

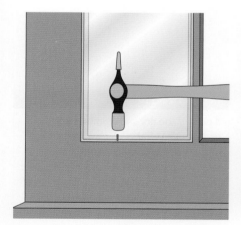

STEP 4 Tap glazing springs into the rebate to hold the glass firmly while the putty sets, using a pin hammer. The glazing springs must be flush with the glass.

STEP 5 Apply the face putty to the remainder of the rebate using your thumb.

STEP 6 Smooth the putty using a putty knife, running the flat edge of the knife along the glass. The top of the putty should be just below the top of the rebated edge, so that when it is painted the paint will just touch the glass, sealing the gap.

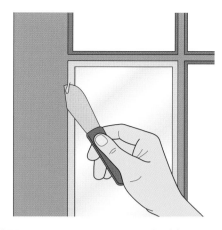

STEP 7 Remove any excess bedding putty with a putty knife.

STEP 8 Paint the putty as soon as it is hard enough to withstand the pressure of a paint brush. This should be done within two weeks, as otherwise it may crack up or even be eaten by birds.

REPAIRING AND MAKING GOOD SURFACES

The final step in preparing a surface for decoration is to repair and make good the surface. You are aiming to achieve a blank canvas on which to apply paint or wallpaper. As you have probably realised by now, the preparation can take longer than the finishing coats.

PLASTER FINISHES

Cracks appear in plaster for various reasons: due to age, movement and settlement; as a result of drying out in heat or crumbling through moisture. If the cracks are small they may be treated as described on page 139. Excessive moist heat, for example as a result of using a steam stripper for removing wall coverings, may cause the plaster to blow, meaning that it will peel off in layers. A small area can be filled with powdered or ready-mixed filler, but a larger area may need to be re-plastered by a qualified technician.

DRY ABRADING

You have already seen the types of dry abrasives used for making good substrates ready to receive paint systems. For high surfaces you may need to use a pole sander.

All substrates will need rubbing down ready for filling or receiving a paint coating. The grade of abrasive that is used will depend on the condition and type of surface. Metal can be rubbed down in any direction, but timber will need rubbing down in the direction of the grain.

Plaster, brickwork and rendering should be rubbed down dry with a fine abrasive, as a coarse abrasive will damage the surface.

Dry abrading with a pole sander

INDUSTRY TIP

Use sanding blocks for abrading, because your hands will otherwise become dry and damaged, with splinters. Don't forget to apply barrier cream and wear gloves if possible.

Tack rag

A cotton gauze textile, impregnated with a non-drying resin which makes it 'sticky'. It is used to remove fine residual dust from a surface before any paint is applied

Tack rag

All surfaces should be dusted off before painting and metal should be wiped using a **tack rag**. Work areas should be clean and dust free, as dust particles on the paint surface will cause bittiness.

WET AND DRY ABRADING

Wet and dry abrading is done where you want a first-class paint finish. It is used on previously treated timber to remove nibs, runs, cissing and other application defects to achieve a glass-like finish. This is particularly important on doors. It is not used on metal, plasterboard or plastered or trowelled surfaces.

STEP 1 Cover the surrounding area with waterproof dust sheets and secure them in place. Put out a wet floor sign to warn people that the surface may be slippery. Gather the equipment and PPE you will need, particularly rubber gloves and overalls. You will also need a bucket with warm water and a little detergent, wet and dry abrasive and a rubber sanding block.

STEP 2 Wrap the wet and dry abrasive around the sanding block and dip it in the soapy water. Using soapy water helps the abrasive to glide over the surface. Starting from the top, on a small area at a time, rub down with the abrasive in a circular motion. Continue on to the next small area, dipping the block in the water frequently.

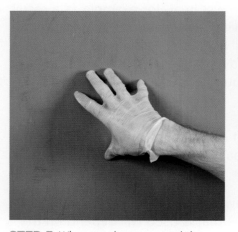

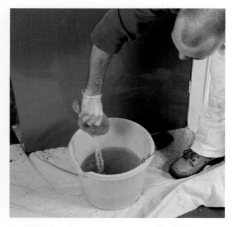

STEP 3 When you have covered the whole area, check all over for lumps, bumps and rough edges with your fingertips (as they are more sensitive than your hand), repeating as necessary until the surface feels as smooth as glass.

STEP 4 When you are satisfied that the surface is uniformly smooth, rinse with clean water – you may have to change the water several times. The surface will need to be dry before painting, so while you are waiting clean up the work area and your tools.

SCRAPING

Where abrading or dusting off is not sufficient to remove defects and nibs – the surface will have to be removed using a stripping knife. This may be used on its own, with a hot air gun or with liquid paint remover. Scraping is also used to remove wallpaper, as described in Step 5 on page 150.

FILLING

You may come across a number of other defects, such as protruding nail heads, which are usually caused by a carpenter or joiner not punching nails below the surface when securing timber. They will need to be punched in below the surface using a nail punch. Once you have dealt with protruding nails they can be filled – along with any other nail holes, dents and cracks – with a suitable filling agent before painting.

Here are some terms relating to filling that you may come across:

- **Flush filling**: Applied so that the filling material is level with the surface being filled.

- **Proud filling**: Applied so that the filling material comes slightly higher than the surface and can be rubbed down level.

- **Back filling**: Where a hole or crack is too large to be filled in one go, this is a first filling which falls short of the level of the surface. This is allowed to dry before more filling material is added for a flush or proud finish.

Types of fillers and stoppers

The most popular fillers have been described, but there are many others on the market. Look back to pages 118–119 to remind yourself about stoppers, single-pack and two-pack fillers, and plastic wood filler. Some stoppers are coloured to match the colour of the surface you are filling and flexible fillers are available to fill areas that will suffer some movement. Ready-mixed filler is useful for small jobs but is more expensive than mixing your own. Most filler is suitable for use on interior surfaces, but you can also buy filler specifically for exterior use. These are all applied using a filling knife or a putty knife. Putty is also a type of filler, used mainly for embedding glazing in frames. For the method of application, see pages 159–161.

Filling open-grained timber

Open-grained timber may need filling in order to produce a smooth surface for painting. Once primed with the appropriate primer it can be filled using two-pack filler. (Single-pack filler would produce a softer finish which might not be strong enough to withstand abrading and the surface scratch marks would show through.) If the area of open grain is small, it is possible to fill in that area alone, but a large area will require face-filling. This means that the whole of an

Nail punch

Flush filling

Filling that is level with the rest of the surface

Proud filling

Filling that projects above the surface and will need to be rubbed down when dry to make it level with the rest of the surface

FUNCTIONAL SKILLS

In a small group, research and discuss the different types of fillers available. Each of you should take a different type and research the following:

- What is it made of?
- What is it used for?
- How much does it cost?
- What colour is it?
- What are the safety instructions for using it?

Present your information to the group and discuss your findings.

Work on this activity can support FE (2.1.2).

area, for example the face of a door, will need covering with a thin layer of filler. Be careful not to over-fill the area and carefully abrade using a fine grade of glass paper or wet and dry.

WETTING IN

This term is used to mean not only wetting in of wallpaper before stripping it off, but also when raking out or undercutting is done. You will need to wet in the cracks and holes before applying filler, and this helps the filler stick to the surface. You may use a diluted solution of PVA or water to do this.

RAKING OUT

Timber that has been affected by damp can rot away and go soft and mushy. This needs to be raked out using a shavehook before being allowed to dry out completely.

Raking out timber affected by wet rot

Some previously painted surfaces may be affected by wet rot, which can occur in damp timber such as timber frames. Wet rot is a fungus that feeds off the cellulose in the timber, causing it to very gradually lose strength and break up. Before you can work on an area affected by wet rot, all moisture will need to be removed. Once it has dried out the timber will be treated as follows:

Use a shavehook to remove rotten timber

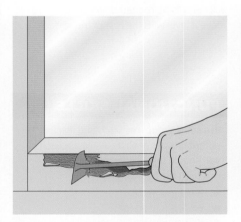

STEP 1 Defective timber can be raked out using a scraper or shavehook. Allow the surface to dry out.

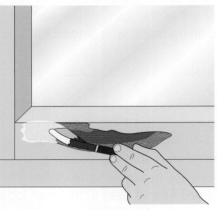

STEP 2 Using a clear wood preservative, flood (thoroughly cover) the exposed timber. Allow it to dry and then spot prime the affected areas with wood primer.

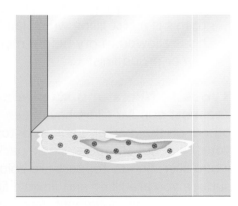

STEP 3 Fix wood screws (non-ferrous) into the timber to support the area and give the filler something to stick to.

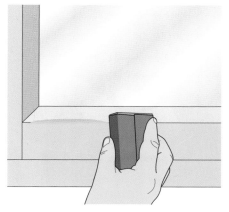

STEP 4 Apply a coat of two-pack filler and allow it to dry.

STEP 5 Apply a second coat of filler to the surface and allow it to dry. Use abrading paper to rub down the filler so that it is flush.

Note: If the surface has been affected too badly, the timber may need to be cut back and replaced by a carpenter.

UNDERCUTTING

Undercutting is similar to raking out, but you make it wider at the base to give a larger area to retain the filler or stopper.

CAULKING

Some surfaces are prone to shrinkage and movement, so cracks and holes filled with powder filler or plaster surfaces may split open. In these cases, caulking is used. Caulk is a waterproof filler and sealant used to fill cracks and gaps. It is also called painter's mastic. Mastic is an acrylic type of caulk and is applied using a mastic gun (also known as a skeleton or caulking gun) that holds and dispenses the mastic from the tube.

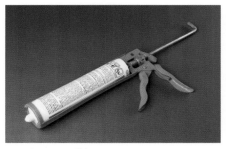

Mastic or caulking gun

Mastic (or caulk) is applied around door and window frames and around the edges of ceilings and walls. Excess mastic can be removed using a filling knife. When mastic is dry it feels like rubber. It can expand and contract with any movement or temperature change and can be painted or wallpapered over.

MAKING GOOD SURFACES AFTER REMOVING WALL COVERINGS

Once you have removed all of the wallpaper from plasterboard or plastered surfaces, you will need to make the surface ready to receive the new coating. This is called making good because it will give you a good, sound surface to work on.

STEP 1 Wash down the walls to remove any excess paste, using clean warm water and a sponge. You may need to change the water several times. Leaving paste on the walls may cause problems such as cissing (see page 155) when you are filling or painting.

STEP 2 You will need to wait for the walls to dry before making good. While you are waiting, clear the remaining removed wallpaper from the floor. It is important to remember to work safely – wallpaper can be a hazard, as the paste is both sticky and slippery.

STEP 3 Once the walls have dried, rub them down using a medium-grade abrasive and then dust off the wall area ready for filling.

STEP 4 Mix the filler to the right consistency – it should be like whipped cream. Use a spot board (a 350mm square of plywood) to mix on. Only mix as much as you need at a time because once mixed, the filler will start to set. Transfer the filler to a painter's hawk and then wash off any excess filler from the mixing board, ready to be used again.

STEP 5 With a filling knife, start to fill holes and cracks. Hairline cracks may need cutting open or raking out using a stripping knife, as the filler will only lie on top of the crack and will not stick to the plasterwork. Never use a filling knife to rake out, as this will damage the blade and result in a poor-quality finish.

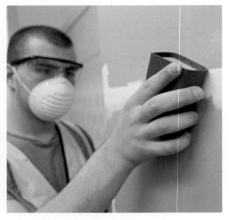

STEP 6 When the filler has dried, rub down and dust off before re-decorating. Check to see if the filling needs second filling, and if so repeat the same process.

INDUSTRY TIP

Remember that your finished work is only as good as your preparation. There is no point in skilfully applying paint coatings if the preparation is of a poor standard. Your work will look shoddy and may not stand the test of time.

MAKING GOOD PLASTERBOARD

Plasterboard is very porous and will soak up any moisture, causing it to go soft or blister. Applying a coat of sealer to the surface will stop moisture penetrating the surface. When plasterboard is used on walls, there will usually be joints where the sheets of plasterboard butt together, and these will need making good so they cannot be seen. They will need taping and then filling so that the joints do not break open. As with new plasterwork, the surface of the plasterboard should never be rubbed down with abrasive paper. This will not only scratch the surface but will also lift the paper surface of the plasterboard sheet, severely damaging the finish. Gently use a filling knife to remove surface nibs.

Tape and then fill the joints between plasterboards

Plasterboard that has been wallpapered may need to be stripped off. The method for this is the same as for removing wallpaper from a plastered wall, but it is important not to over-soak it because it will blister.

Once all of the making good has been done, and the surface rubbed and dusted down, it is time to continue with painting or wallpapering.

INDUSTRY TIP

When stripping off wallpaper from a plasterboard surface, do not dig into the surface face, as this will let water and moisture soak into the plasterboard, damaging the surface and making extra filling work necessary before decoration.

FUNCTIONAL SKILLS

With the aid of this chapter, make a list on a spreadsheet of all the things you will need to prepare surfaces for decoration. Separate the items into three categories – tools, materials and equipment – and sort the columns alphabetically.

Work on this activity can support FICT2 (6.A1).

Case Study: Emily and Finley

Emily and Finley were asked to strip heavy embossed wallpaper from a large room, so they decided to use a steam stripper to save time. They covered the floor with polythene sheeting and moved the furniture to the middle of the room. The paper had been painted over several times, so Finley scored the paper first while Emily started from the bottom corner, moving the steam stripper over the surface. It was slow going, but once they were finished they started clearing up. They noticed that the heat of the stripper had pulled some of the plaster away from the wall, which would then have to be made good once dry. They mixed up the filler to the correct consistency to patch up the defective plaster, but it was hard work because the filler was setting too fast as the walls were still warm. They were beginning to wonder whether using the steam stripper had saved any time at all! Once dry, they gave the walls a final rub down and cleaned the work area before painting.

The next day they painted the prepared wall. As the paint dried it started to craze. What had they done wrong?

Using the steam stripper did not help because excess moisture can cause plaster to lift. If you must use a steam stripper on plaster, make sure that the stripping pad is not left on the surface for too long. However, Emily and Finley's biggest mistake was that they did not wash down the walls after removing the paper, so there was still adhesive on the walls. They had to strip off the paint and seal it before they could continue.

Work through the following questions to check your learning.

1   Which one of the following timbers is a softwood?

   a   Oak.

   b   Spruce.

   c   Beech.

   d   Mahogany.

2   What substance is found in MDF?

   a   Zinc phosphate.

   b   Ferrous oxide.

   c   Urea formaldehyde.

   d   Methylated spirit.

3   Which one of the following materials is **best** used for exteriors?

   a   Hardboard.

   b   Softwood.

   c   Chipboard.

   d   Hardwood.

4   Which one of the following forms part of first fix in construction?

   a   Architraves.

   b   Dado rails.

   c   Skirting boards.

   d   Rafters.

5   Decayed timber affected by wet rot will have to be removed before replacing. What is this process called?

   a   Breaking out.

   b   Cutting out.

   c   Raking out.

   d   Scraping out.

6   What is a needle de-scaling gun used for?

   a   Stripping wallpaper from walls.

   b   Removing paint from metal surfaces.

   c   Cleaning out a steam stripper.

   d   Removing old mortar from brickwork.

7   What cleaning agent should be used to wash down a previously painted surface?

   a   Sugar soap.

   b   Methylated spirit.

   c   Diluted bleach.

   d   White spirit.

8   Which one of the following could be made of gypsum plaster?

   a   Hand rails.

   b   Window frames.

   c   Door furniture.

   d   Ceiling rose.

9   Which one of the following is liable to rust?

   a   MDF.

   b   Iron.

   c   Wood.

   d   Brick.

10 Resin exudation on timber should be coated with which one of the following?

   a   Liquid wood.

   b   Aluminium primer.

   c   Two-pack filler.

   d   Stabilising solution.

11 If external brickwork is subject to excessive moisture, this could result in the

  a spread of wet rot

  b spread of dry rot

  c growth of mould and fungus

  d growth of moss and lichen.

12 Which one of the following is **least** likely to bleed through a paint coating?

  a Bitumen.

  b Pencil marks.

  c Nicotine.

  d Red paint.

13 Which one of the following is an application defect?

  a Crazing.

  b Cissing.

  c Blistering.

  d Runs.

14 Brickwork can be affected by which one of the following defects?

  a Corrosion.

  b Efflorescence.

  c Wet rot.

  d Shrinkage.

15 Which one of the following must **always** be worn when removing old paint from a surface using liquid paint remover?

  a Steel toe-cap boots.

  b Respirator mask.

  c Ear defenders.

  d Hard hat.

16 On ferrous metal, the formation of rust will

  a strengthen the metal

  b weaken the metal

  c fireproof the metal

  d stabilise the metal.

17 A reason for protecting your work area before removing a wall covering is to

  a keep yourself clean

  b prevent electric shock

  c protect your eyesight

  d reduce slipping hazard.

18 What is the **best** way of removing a paint coating from a window frame?

  a Electric hot air gun.

  b LPG burning-off torch.

  c Liquid paint remover.

  d Steam stripper.

19 Failure to remove old peeling paint coating prior to repainting could result in

  a bleaching

  b chalking

  c wrinkling

  d flaking.

20 Shellac or aluminium sealer can be used to rectify

  a bleeding

  b cissing

  c blistering

  d curtains.

Chapter 4
Unit 216: Applying paint systems by brush and roller to complex areas

Painters and decorators are known as the finishing trade because they come in when all the other trades have finished, adding colour, decoration and protection to the surfaces. No building – whether a home, a factory, a shop or a hospital – is complete until it is decorated. This chapter will give you an understanding of the tools, materials and equipment you will use to apply paint coatings to simple and complex areas, and how to clean, maintain and store them correctly. The last chapter stressed the importance of preparation in achieving a high standard of work, but the thing people notice is the final result.

By reading this chapter you will understand:

1 How to prepare domestic and commercial work areas and protect surrounding areas.

2 How to prepare and apply water-borne and solvent-borne coatings by brush and roller in line with manufacturer's instructions to complex areas.

3 How to clean, maintain and store brushes and rollers in line with manufacturer's instructions.

4 Conditions for storing paint materials.

5 How to store materials in accordance with COSHH data sheets.

Cutting in

PREPARING DOMESTIC AND COMMERCIAL WORK AREAS AND SURROUNDING AREAS

When working in domestic and commercial areas you will need to be able to apply paint finishes to complex areas, but that does not mean that all the work you do will be complicated. Any job will consist of straightforward tasks that you will find relatively easy, and more difficult tasks that you will need to practise to build up your skills. Before starting work you will need to prepare the area to make sure that you, your colleagues, the general public and all adjacent and surrounding areas are protected from danger and damage. Make sure that a risk assessment has been carried out. In this section we will consider what you need to do and the tools and materials required to make areas ready to receive paint systems.

ENVIRONMENTAL HEALTH AND SAFETY REGULATIONS

As you have read in the chapter on health and safety, the way you work is governed by certain regulations. It is important that you keep them in mind while working. Many of the materials that you will be working with are considered hazardous to health and need to be treated with caution (see COSSH in Chapter 1). Be particularly aware of the dangers of cuts, abrasions and burns that may become infected when working with hazardous materials, and the dangers of inhaling dust particles. All paints contain vapours that are known as volatile organic compounds (VOCs).

VOLATILE ORGANIC COMPOUNDS

VOC label

These are vapours that evaporate into the air from everyday products at room temperature – from chemical substances such as cleaning products, cosmetics and paint. VOC emissions contribute to air pollution and affect the air we breathe. The paint industry is trying to reduce emissions and many low-odour paints are now being produced. The European Parliament has set maximum VOC levels for different paints and varnishes (EU Directive 2004/42/EC) and has ruled that containers should have a VOC content label so that the consumer can compare products and choose an alternative if they want. You can also ask your supplier for a copy of the data sheet (COSHH).

PROTECTIVE PERSONAL EQUIPMENT (PPE)

Barrier cream

Whether you are preparing the area or painting, you will need to wear the correct PPE. You will need a high-visibility jacket and a hard-hat when working on a building site or industrial unit, along with protective gloves, dust masks, goggles and steel toe-cap boots. Remember to protect your hands with barrier cream to prevent dermatitis and rashes caused by contact with chemical solutions.

PROTECTING WORK AREAS BEFORE AND DURING WORK

Before starting work it is very important to remember that anywhere that you need access to will need protecting from damage or spillage. Items that will need protecting are described below.

Domestic areas

- Flooring such as carpets, rugs, tiles, wooden finished floors, patio floors, etc.

- Access walkways to the work area.

- Ceiling light fittings.

- **Door furniture** such as locks, handles and hinges.

- Curtains and rails.

- Sofas and chairs.

- Tables and any other furniture.

- Computers, TVs and other media, including wall-mounted items.

- Wall lights and fittings.

- Patio areas.

- Plants and plant pots if working outside.

Commercial areas

Some or all of the above domestic items will need the same protection in commercial areas, but there may be additional considerations.

- *Machinery*: You may need to move machinery or protect it from damage or spillage.

- *Temperature control/weather*: There may be strict regulations governing the required temperature in commercial areas. Internal areas may need to be cooled or heated to keep machinery and equipment working or foodstuffs at an optimum temperature. External weather conditions such as extreme cold, rain or mist may affect the progress and finish of the job.

- *Ventilation and lighting*: Ensure that protecting areas still allows for adequate ventilation and light.

- *Access*: Can you gain access when you need to, and can you get equipment and materials in easily? Can you get to running water to wash equipment, dilute paint and so on? Are people going to need to use the area you are working on, and will that cause any danger to you or them, for example when working on stairs or in hallways?

Protect floors using dust sheets

Door furniture

Anything attached to the door, eg handles. knobs, locks, letterboxes, fingerplates and hinges

Remove curtains before decorating

■ *Public areas*: In domestic or commercial environments the property may be accessed by visitors. You may have to put up barriers to prevent people entering your work area for their own safety. In commercial premises work may still be taking place in adjacent areas, so extra care will be needed to ensure that surrounding work areas are not compromised.

Make sure that you use notices such as 'Wet paint' and 'Wet floor' where necessary. (See Chapter 1 for more information.)

Safety barrier tape

Wet paint sign

Wet floor sign

TOOLS, MATERIALS AND EQUIPMENT

The work area needs to be protected as soon as you start to prepare surfaces for decorating, so you will have already prepared it when you removed any old paint systems or wall coverings and repaired and made good all surfaces. One of the most common sheet materials used by decorators is a dust sheet. Dust sheets can protect against paint and paste splashes, as well as small particles made when rubbing down, or small spillages. Using professional-quality dust sheets not only gives a good impression about the standard of your work but also ensures that the areas are adequately protected.

INDUSTRY TIP

It is no good carefully sheeting up the living room where you are painting but forgetting about the route to that room from your van outside, or to the kitchen from where you need to fetch water. If it is impossible to protect the whole area, you may need to wear disposable shoe covers and remember to remove and replace them every time.

MASKING TAPE

Masking tape is a self-adhesive paper that comes in 55m lengths and may be 12mm, 19mm, 25mm, 38mm or 75mm wide. It has a variety of uses. Interior tape is used mainly for masking items that cannot be removed and stored, but can also be used for taping down dust sheets to wooden floors or carpets to stop them moving and hopefully prevent tripping accidents. It can also be used to protect narrow surfaces from paint or paint remover. The longer masking tape is stuck to a surface the harder it adheres, so care must be

Masking tape comes in various widths

taken when removing it. It is available in different strengths of adhesion – so for example a seven-day masking tape will be safe to leave on for seven days and will still peel off without damaging the surface. A low-tack masking tape can be used for signwriting and borders, as it does not adhere as strongly to surfaces and is less likely to pull off the underlying paint. Waterproof masking tape can be used for exterior work such as masking up door furniture, window frames and fascia boards, and particularly to cover surrounding areas when painting rendered, brick or pebbledashed walls.

Use a low-tack tape on painted surfaces

Applying and removing masking tape

When using masking tape to protect areas that are not to be painted, for example to form a straight line or for sign-writing, you will need to smooth it down with your fingertips to ensure the edges are sealed. If a seal is not made the paint is likely to seep through. If, when painting an area, the coating gets on to the masking tape it can form a continuous paint film when hard dry (see page 195), so the masking tape will need to be removed while the paint is still tacky. Pull the tape away downwards from the leading edge to ensure a crisp line.

Removing masking tape

SCREWDRIVERS

You will need a selection of screwdrivers to remove light fittings, switches and door furniture:

- *Pozidriv*: Similar to a Phillips screwdriver but with more points of contact

- *Cross-head*: For cross-head (or Phillips) slotted screw heads

- *Slotted*: For straight-slotted screws.

Screwdrivers

Screwdriver bit and head view: Pozidriv (P2), Phillips (PH) and slotted

PLIERS, PINCHERS OR CLAW HAMMERS

These tools are used to remove picture hooks from walls.

Pliers

Pinchers

Claw hammer

BROOMS, DUSTPANS AND BRUSHES, AND SHOVELS

These are very important tools for a painter, and not only for clearing up when you have finished – you may also need to clear the area before you start work.

PROTECTIVE SHEETING

You will need to lay protective sheeting to protect areas as detailed above from damage. There are a range of different materials to choose from, which are covered below.

Twill

A woven material

Cotton dust sheets

The best quality dust sheets are cotton **twill** sheets. They are generally used to protect floors and furniture, and come in different sizes. They can be folded to give better protection. You can buy dust sheets in a narrow width made especially for treads and risers on staircases. They also come in different weights, from lightweight to heavy-duty, and some have a protective waterproof backing.

The table below describes the advantages and disadvantages of using cotton dust sheets.

Cotton twill dust sheet

Advantages	Disadvantages
■ When new or clean, they give a very professional image. ■ When used to cover the floor they will remain in place when walked on (in some places they may need taping down with masking tape). ■ They are available in different sizes.	■ They are expensive to buy and clean. ■ They can absorb chemicals such as paint stripper. ■ Paint spillage may soak through them. ■ There is a risk of fire when burning off old paintwork.

Polythene/plastic dust sheets

Polythene dust sheets can be used in the same way as cotton dust sheets, but are waterproof and can be thrown away after use. They can be used under cotton dust sheets to protect electrical equipment. The added weight helps to ensure that the plastic sheeting stays in place.

The table below describes the advantages and disadvantages of using polythene/plastic dust sheets.

Advantages	Disadvantages
■ They are inexpensive to buy. ■ Paint spillage will not soak through them. ■ They do not absorb chemicals such as paint stripper.	■ They do not look as professional as cotton dust sheets. ■ They do not stay in place as easily as cotton dust sheets. ■ When wet they can become slippery. ■ As liquid does not soak in, but lies on the surface, there is a danger of treading paint onto unprotected areas.

Tarpaulins

Tarpaulins are made from a number of different types of material, including:

- PVC-coated nylon

- rubber-coated cotton

- heavy cotton canvas

- nylon scrim.

The most common size used by decorators is 6m × 4m. Because tarpaulins can protect against moisture they are best used when washing down a surface or stripping off old wallpaper.

Tarpaulin

Drop cloths

These are made of heavy-duty cotton canvas and are hard wearing, durable and reusable. You can also buy eco-friendly drop cloths made of recycled cotton, and waterproof versions coated with butyl or PVC. When using a drop cloth, make sure the coated side is underneath.

Adhesive plastic covering

This is used to cover flooring. It comes on a roll and can be disposed of after use. The advantage of this is that it does not require additional taping to secure it.

Adhesive plastic covering

Storing protective sheeting

- Cotton dust sheets and other protective sheeting should be given a light shake once finished with (although not near wet paint!) and folded up ready for use. If sheets are wet or damp they should be allowed to dry before being folded and stored to prevent mildew forming on the sheets. All protective sheeting should be stored on shelves off the floor. It is important to keep sheeting clean and dry, because it will be used to protect floors and furniture another time. If necessary, sheets should be sent away for cleaning.

- Sheeting such as tarpaulin, PVC-coated nylon, rubber-coated cotton and heavy cotton canvas should be stored in the same way as cotton dust sheets. Rubber tarpaulin can be wiped clean using a sponge and warm water and allowed to dry before it is folded and stored.

- If protective sheeting is not used for some time it will need to be checked for damp. If there are signs of damp, unfold it and air-dry before re-folding and storing it.

THE PREPARATION PROCESS

- Where possible, portable items should be stripped from the room and stored during the painting and decorating process. You may be responsible for re-instating these items, in which case you may need to label them so you know where they go.

- Remove all moveable items from the room and store them in other rooms, making sure that access routes are not blocked. Furniture or office equipment that is too large to be moved should be relocated to the centre of the room and covered with protective sheeting.

- Office equipment such as computers and printers that cannot be removed from the room must be covered carefully and unplugged if possible (check with the client first).

- Take care, if working in kitchens, that hazardous surfaces such as gas and electric hobs are not turned on, causing a fire hazard.

- If the carpet is to be lifted, roll it up with the underlay and place them in the centre of the room. Cover with protective sheeting.

- Remove all curtains, nets and blinds, and carefully fold them. If possible, store them in another room to prevent any damage. If there is more than one window you may need to label them so you know where to hang them at the end of the job.

- Remove all curtain rails and fittings, and store them in a safe place together ready for refitting.

If possible, remove all furniture from the room

- Switch off the electricity supply at the mains before loosening light fittings and switches (do not leave them loose when you are away from the work area, as this could be dangerous when the mains is turned back on).

- Remove all ironmongery (furniture) from windows and doors to be painted.

- Mask up where needed (remember, do not leave masking tape on longer than necessary).

- Cover floors with dust sheets and secure with masking tape.

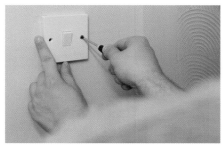

Loosen electrical fittings

If you are working outside you will also need to consider the following:

- Protecting flower beds. If you need to access doors or windows from the outside, make sure than you do not damage plants and ornaments. Cover with light polythene dust sheets if necessary to stop paint or debris falling on plants and pathways.

- Terraces or patios may need protecting, not just from paint and debris but also from steps or scaffolding. Use tarpaulin to protect the ground, as it is waterproof and harder wearing than cotton dust sheets.

- PVC guttering and pipes can be removed if required by unclipping them from the retaining clips, so that you can paint behind them.

- Make sure that there is no danger to the public and householders, and use warning signs where necessary.

PREPARING AND APPLYING WATER-BORNE AND SOLVENT-BORNE COATINGS TO COMPLEX AREAS

Before starting any job you will need to do your own risk assessment, not only to make sure that you and those around you are safe, but also to make sure that your finished work will be of a high standard.

Have you ever stopped to think why it is necessary to paint anything? When asked, many painters and decorators don't really know! Most people say that it is to make things look nice, and that answer is not wrong, but making something look nice is not *all* a painter and decorator does.

Pipes are painted for identification purposes

REASONS FOR APPLYING PAINT SYSTEMS

There are four reasons why a paint coating would be applied to a surface. To help you remember these, you can use the word **DIPS**.

Each letter stands for one of the reasons for painting:

- **D**ecoration
- **I**dentification
- **P**reservation
- **S**anitation.

DECORATION

We all have our own tastes – what we like and do not like – but the reason for decoration is to make something look nice. You might not like the colours that the client has chosen, but you still have to apply them to the best of your ability. With experience you might be able to advise them if you know that colours do not work together. There is a whole science surrounding the use of colour, and some colours are said to make people feel different emotions. For example, pale blue can be calming, red can make you anxious and sunny yellows can make you happy. Red walls would not be ideal in a hospital, and white or pastel colours in a nightclub would not make for a very cosy setting. More information on the use of colour can be found in Chapter 7.

More information on the use of colour can be found in Chapter 7.

ACTIVITY

Start to take notice of the paint colours around you: in shops, offices, classrooms, doctors' waiting rooms, your own home … Are the colours appropriate for the area? If you could change the colour, what would you change it to – and why?

Colour cards

IDENTIFICATION

Different colours or types of surface coating can be used to identify areas or components. For example, pipework may have a British Standard (BS) colour painted on it to identify whether it is carrying gas, water or other liquids. Such industry standards ensure that all manufacturers use the same colours for identification and that mistakes are not made.

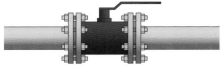

Pipe contents	RAL code
Gas	RAL 1004
Fire fighting	RAL 3000
Air	RAL 5012
Combustible liquids	RAL 8001
Acids and alkalis	RAL 4001
Water	RAL 6010
Other liquids	RAL 9005
Steam	RAL 9006

Pipeline identification colours – British Standard BS 1710:1980 (Part 1)

PRESERVATION

Painting can stop metal corroding and wood from rotting, particularly when exposed to weather. An exterior door that has not been painted or that has lost its paint coating will rot and need replacing, which will cost far more than regularly maintaining the door with paint or varnish. Corroding metal can also cost lives, if it causes a structure to collapse.

SANITATION

Coating substrates with paint prevents germs and dirt penetrating a surface, which makes it much easier to wash and keep clean. This is particularly important in hospitals and shops, and in manufacturing or where people are working with food.

PAINT

Now that you know why paint is used, consider what paint is and the different types available. There are two main types:

- water-borne paint means that the liquid part of the paint is water

- solvent-borne paint means that a chemical has been used instead of water to dissolve the other components.

When paint is applied to a surface, the water or the solvent, depending on the type of paint being used, will evaporate into the air, leaving behind a solid film that forms a protective and decorative layer on the surface.

Water-borne paint consists of three main elements:

- *Thinner*: This is either the water-borne or solvent part of the paint that dissolves the other components so that it is possible to apply the paint to the surface.

- *Form-filler or binder*: This is a resin that forms the film of the paint. The binder determines how long it will last and the type of finish (eg, gloss, eggshell, flat).

- *Pigment*: This gives colour to the paint and is also responsible for the paint's ability to cover the surface.

Pigment is used to colour paint

Oil based paint contains a fourth element known as the drier, which speeds up the drying process. Paint may also contain a dispersant or dispersing agent, which helps to keep the pigment wet so it does not settle into a hard lump at the bottom of the can, and emulsifiers to keep the elements of the paint stable.

Paint dries in the following ways:

- *Evaporation*: The water or solvent turns into a vapour in the atmosphere, and disappears.

- *Coalescence*: This applies to water-borne paints in which the binder is a polymer dispersed in water. When the water evaporates, the polymer particles **coalesce**. When all the water evaporates, the polymer particles form a uniform film.

- *Oxidation or chemical reaction*: As the liquid part of the paint evaporates, a chemical change takes place as oxygen combines with the resin and oils to form a dried paint film.

There are many factors to consider when using paint, as different conditions may affect your finished work. These include:

- *External*: Rain, snow, sleet, overcast conditions, wind, storms, sea mist, pedestrians, vehicle traffic, pollution.

- *Internal*: Dust, grease, damp, poor light conditions, occupation (is part of the area being used?), public areas.

- *Location*: Rural areas, industrial areas, coastal areas.

All paint relies on temperature to enable water and solvents to evaporate into the atmosphere so that the material can dry. If the conditions are not good, problems can occur during drying.

If it is too warm, the following may happen:

- Applied paint becomes too thin and does not cover the previous coating.

- The paint may dry too quickly while you are applying it, due to the solvent evaporating during the oxidation process.

If it is too cold, the following may happen:

- The paint will not dry.

- It may be difficult to apply the paint.

- The paint may become too thick to apply.

- Condensation may form on the painted area.

- Surfaces may be affected by frost.

Coalesce

Particles merging to form a film, particularly in water-borne coatings – the drying process is also known as coalescence

INDUSTRY TIP

Always read the manufacturer's instructions before using paint, as some paints give off vapours that can be harmful to health. Remember to wear your PPE.

INDUSTRY TIP

Some paints give off fumes as they dry. Make sure that your work area is well ventilated.

If it is too windy, the following may happen:

- Paintwork may be coved in dust/debris, affecting the standard and quality of the completed work.

- Access equipment (ladder, scaffolding towers) cannot be used safely.

- There may be damage to property during the application of the paint material (eg paint splattering on cars and flower beds below).

- It becomes unsafe to use burning-off equipment.

If it is too wet, the following may happen:

- The film finish may be impaired (loss of gloss, **flashing**).

- Paint may not adhere (stick) to the previous coat of paint.

- It may become unsafe to work.

- It may delay the completion of the job.

Flashing

A defect that occurs in flat and eggshell finishes and looks like glossy streaks or patches

Always make sure that the work area is well ventilated if you are working inside, not only when rubbing down or painting but also when burning off, because as the paint softens it starts to give off fumes again.

PAINT COATINGS

Undercoats are designed to give a sound base for the finish. A finish coat (top coat) is the coat of paint that will be seen at the end of the job. There are many types of finishing coat, and choosing the best one for the job often comes down to personal taste. The different undercoats and finish coats are described in the following table.

Opacity

The ability of the pigment in paint to obliterate or hide the existing surface colour

Undercoat/finish coat	Description	Method of application	Uses
Oil based undercoat	A heavily pigmented oil based paint that dries to a matt finish and comes in a variety of different colours. It has good adhesion to the primer and good **opacity**. Paint brushes and equipment are to be cleaned with solvent (white spirit).	Brush, roller or spray	Used over previously painted surfaces, timber, plaster, concrete and metalwork. It gives body and colour to a paint system and can be used over all primed surfaces both inside and outside.

Undercoat/finish coat	Description	Method of application	Uses
Matt emulsion	A water-thinned paint suitable for painting ceilings and walls. It is easier to apply than oil based paint. Matt emulsion dries to a flat/matt finish. One advantage is that small imperfections do not show, as no light is reflected. Paint brushes and equipment are to be cleaned with water.	Brush, roller or spray	Mainly used for walls and ceilings – suitable for use over plaster, plasterboard, hardboard, brickwork, cement, rendering and wallpaper.
Vinyl silk emulsion	Similar to matt emulsion paint, but with less opacity, and dries to a sheen finish. Paint brushes and equipment are to be cleaned with water.	Brush, roller or spray	The same as matt emulsion, but dries to a sheen finish which can be easily wiped down and is harder wearing, making it more suitable for bathrooms, kitchens, hospital and schools.
Gloss finish	Interior and exterior decorative paint used as the main protective coating in the decorating trade. It dries to a very high-gloss finish. Excellent flow when laying off. Very good flexibility, allowing the paint to expand and contract when dry. Good weather resistance. Paint brushes and equipment are to be cleaned with solvent (white spirit).	Brush, roller or spray	A decorative finish for interior and exterior surfaces. Can be used on all woodwork, plaster and metalwork.

Undercoat/finish coat	Description	Method of application	Uses
Eggshell/semi-gloss finishes	An interior decorative paint that dries with a sheen, also known as a silk or satin finish. As this is a solvent-borne paint it will dry to a harder finish than vinyl silk paint. Paint brushes and equipment are to be cleaned with solvent (white spirit).	Brush, roller or spray	Decorative finish for interior surfaces including ceilings, walls, softwoods, hardwoods and metal surfaces.
Masonry paint	A durable paint used for exterior walls (not timber surfaces) that have good opacity, and is also alkali resistant. The finish is not only tough, but durable and flexible. Paint brushes and equipment are to be cleaned with water.	Brush, roller or spray	Used to protect surfaces against the weather while also giving a good decorative finish. Used on new and old cement rendering, concrete, brickwork, pebbledash and other types of masonry.
Low-odour eggshell	A water-borne coating for interior use, which dries to an eggshell finish or a soft semi-gloss finish. Paint brushes and equipment are to be cleaned with water.	Brush, roller or spray	Decorative finish coat for all interior surfaces. Used where there is poor ventilation (in toilets, kitchens, etc) so it has low odour and is non-toxic. Requires no undercoat and dries quickly so that a second coat can be applied when required.

THIXOTROPIC PAINT

Thixotropic paint has a jelly-like structure which breaks down to a thin liquid if the paint is stirred, shaken or exposed to heat. The structure of the paint can also be broken down if over-worked by brush or roller during application. It will revert to its original state if it is left for a while. The advantages of using thixotropic paint are that it does not require stirring before use, and it is therefore easy to apply without dripping or splashing. There is also less likelihood of runs and sags occurring. The two main drawbacks are that the paint

Sweat

A defect in which paint or varnish develops tackiness or thickens when it is left standing for long periods

tends to **sweat** when stored, especially in warm conditions, and it thins rapidly if using in sunlight. The defect can often be overcome by shaking or stirring the paint and then allowing it to revert to its high viscosity.

ACTIVITY

Take a small amount of water-borne paint and the same amount of thixotropic paint and then stir and strain the paints. Compare the two consistencies. Check the liquids at short intervals to see if the consistency changes. Try painting a small area with each of the paints and compare their coverage and ease of use.

Thixotropic paint

Wood staining on floorboards

CLEAR FINISHES AND WOOD PRESERVATIVES

Paint does not always need to provide colour. For example, timber needs painting in order to preserve it, but it is often important to let the grain of the wood show through. For this purpose a variety of clear, non-pigmented finishes, glazes and wood preservatives are used, as shown in the table below.

Material	Description	Method of application	Uses
Emulsion varnish	A milky white material that provides a clear washable surface when dry. It can be thinned using water. Grease and food-stain resistant. Washable and resistant to mild chemicals. Non-toxic. Paint brushes and equipment are to be cleaned with water	Brush, roller or spray	Used as a protective coating on wallpaper.

Material	Description	Method of application	Uses
Polyurethane varnish	Clear surface coating available in gloss, matt or eggshell finish. If you need to thin it, use the manufacturer's recommended solvent. Water, chemical and heat resistant. Good adhesion. Paint brushes and equipment are to be cleaned using manufacturers' recommended solvents (instructions vary).	Brush or roller	Used for protecting new and stained timber. Used to protect paintwork, furniture and special decorative finishes such as marbling and graining. Although hard wearing, it is not really suitable for exposed exterior surfaces.
Oil–resin varnish	A liquid coating which, when dry, becomes a clear and protective film. Hard wearing and suitable for external use. Water and weather resistant. Dries to a high-gloss finish. Paint brushes and equipment are to be cleaned with solvent (white spirit).	Brush or roller	Used for protecting new and stained timber. Used to protect paintwork, furniture and special decorative finishes such as marbling and graining. Suitable for external use.
Quick-drying varnish	A fast-drying, high-quality varnish that is easy to apply and has a very low odour. During application it has a milky white appearance, but when dry it forms a clear finish. Available in high-gloss or satin finish. Paint brushes and equipment are to be cleaned with water.	Brush, roller or spray	Gives good protection and decoration for interior timber and re-coating a previously coated surface that is in good condition.

Material	Description	Method of application	Uses
High build wood	A highly durable **micro-porous**, **translucent**, semi-gloss finish which comes in a variety of colours (wood tones). Will form a very flexible film once dry that can withstand changes in timber without cracking (contracting or retracting). Paint brushes and equipment are to be cleaned with solvent (white spirit).	Brush or roller	The flexible micro-porous properties of high build wood stain make it particularly suitable for the protection and decoration of exterior timber surface such as window frames and doors.
Universal preservative	Although universal preservative is similar in consistency to stains and varnish, it is a clear liquid and is solvent borne. It takes a relatively long time to dry (16 to 24 hours) under normal conditions. Contains fungicide. Paint brushes and equipment are to be cleaned with solvent (white spirit).	Brush or roller	Usually applied to new softwood that has not been treated with a preservative and suitable as a coating for weathered timber surfaces. On old timber the surface needs to be sound. Stir well before use and apply one generous coat, paying particular attention to the end grain and joints.
Protective wood stain	A specially formulated protective wood stain. Paint brushes and equipment are to be cleaned with solvent (white spirit).	Brush and lint-free rag	This can be used on both exterior and interior surfaces, on softwood and hardwood as a decorative treatment. Not to be used on painted or varnished timber. Apply two coats of the wood stain by brush and lint-free rag. Allow to dry overnight between coats.

Micro-porous paint

A paint that leaves a breathable film that allows moisture and air to be released but prevents moisture, like rain, getting in

Translucent

Allows light to pass through, but prevents images from being seen clearly

PAINT ADDITIVES

Following are some examples of liquids or oils that can be added to paints for various reasons.

Anti-frothing agent

This is an additive that reduces the surface tension of a solution or emulsion, and so helps to stop froth and bubbles forming and breaks up foam that has already formed. Painting with frothy paint will show in the final paint finish. Commonly used agents are insoluble oils, dimethyl polysiloxanes and other silicones, certain alcohols, stearates and glycols.

Biocides

These are added to keep bacteria from spoiling paint during storage, or to keep fungi and algae from growing on the applied paint.

Water

Water is the liquid medium for water-borne paints. Paint can be thinned by adding water, but care must be taken to follow manufacturers' instructions, as over-thinning the paint will result in poor coverage.

Prevent growth of algae by adding biocides to paint before application

Extenders

These are materials that have little or no opacity when mixed with vanish or oil, and that are incorporated into paints for a variety of technical reasons, such as to prevent the settling of heavy pigments, to harden the film, to increase the body and to arrest the flow of the paint. It can be useful when painting a large area to add some extender to allow you to finish the job without altering the pigmentation of the paint.

PAINT SYSTEMS

The table below gives some examples of the order of paint used for paint systems.

Paint system	First coat	Second coat	Third coat	Fourth coat
New, unpainted surfaces to be painted with oil based or water-borne paints	Primer/sealer	Undercoat	Gloss	
	Primer	Undercoat	Eggshell	
	Sealer	Emulsion	Emulsion	
	Emulsion	Emulsion		
	Special primer	Undercoat	Top coat	Top coat
	Sealer	Stain	Varnish	
Previously painted surfaces	Undercoat	Gloss		
	Undercoat	Gloss	Gloss	
	Undercoat	Eggshell	Eggshell	
	Emulsion	Emulsion		
	Acrylic undercoat	Acrylic gloss		

APPLICATION TOOLS FOR SURFACE COATING

There is a wide selection of brushes and rollers on the market, used to apply paints, stains and clear coatings. The following will give you an understanding of which tool to use for a particular job.

In Chapter 3 you looked at the tools and equipment required for preparing surfaces for decoration, and the importance of buying good-quality tools and equipment was highlighted. The same can be said of the tools and equipment needed for applying surface coatings.

BRUSHES

There are five parts that make up a brush.

- *Handle*: Usually made of a hardwood such as beech, and sealed to make handling and cleaning easier and to stop water soaking into and damaging the wood. It can also be made from plastic.

- *Ferrule/stock*: This is a metal band that holds the filling and the handle together.

- *Epoxy/setting*: An adhesive which cements the filling by its roots into the stock.

- *Filament/filling*: Usually natural bristle or synthetic man-made hairs, such as nylon.

- *Spacer*: A small wood, plastic or cardboard strip that creates a reservoir to carry paint.

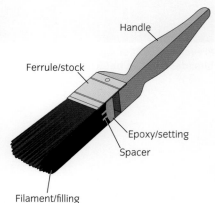

Handle

Ferrule/stock

Epoxy/setting

Spacer

Filament/filling

The parts of a brush

ACTIVITY

Take a 75mm brush, a 25mm brush and a foam roller and practise applying gloss paint to a panel door with each of them, **cutting in** around the mouldings. Check your work for runs, fatty edges and misses.

Cutting in

The process of producing a sharp neat paint line between two structural components in a room, such as a wall/ceiling, architrave/wall, etc

TYPES OF BRUSH

Natural bristle brushes are usually made from pig, hog or boar hair and are particularly suitable for applying oil based paints. Synthetic or man-made bristles are more springy and are better suited to applying water-borne paints.

Paint brushes, whether they are natural or synthetic, come in different sizes for different jobs. Although as you gain experience you may develop a preference for a particular size or type of brush, the chart below gives examples of brush sizes used for specific tasks.

Brush size	Use
12mm	Used for difficult-to-reach areas, eg between two architraves on wall areas or for cutting in around window panels, skirtings, angles and edges of mouldings.

Brush size	Use
25mm	Can be used as above and for general cutting-in work, eg the edges of walls and ceilings when using rollers. This is also known as a sash tool.
50–75mm	For applying paint coatings to medium-sized areas and doors, etc.
100mm	For applying paint (usually water-borne) to flat areas such as small ceilings and walls.
125mm and upwards	For applying water-borne paints to large surface areas and applying adhesive to wallpaper.

The following table shows some of the different types of brush you may come across.

Type of brush	Description
Flat paint or varnish brushes 	Available in pure bristle or synthetic hair versions, the cost of these brushes varies according to the quality and the quantity of the filling. They can be used for applying most types of paint and varnish coatings to a variety of surfaces, including doors, window frames, ceilings and wall areas.
Washing-down brushes 	These are relatively cheap two-knot or flat brushes, available in one size only and used for washing down with sugar soap or detergent.
Flat wall brush 	These are available in a wide range of varying qualities and are either man made or pure bristle. The quality is dependent on the weight and length of the filling. They are used to apply emulsion to large flat areas, eg ceilings and walls, and also to apply adhesive to wallpaper.

Type of brush	Description
Two-knot brush 	These are available mainly in pure bristle. The knots are usually bound in copper wire, as it does not rust. They are used to apply water-thinned paints to rough surfaces such as cement, rendering and brickwork. They are also used to apply cement-based paints, as the bristles are not attacked by alkali in the cement, and for washing down surfaces when using a cleaning agent such as sugar soap.
Cement paint brush (block brush) 	These have man-made filling or coarse white fibre that has been set in a polished wooden handle. Cheaper block brushes are available in plastic. They are inexpensive brushes for applying masonry finishes and cement paints to a rough surface such as cement, rendering or brickwork.
Fitch 	These are available with pure bristle or synthetic filling, which is usually white, set in a round or flat ferrule. These brushes are used for fine, detailed work in areas that are difficult to reach with a paint brush.
Radiator brush 	These have a bristle filling attached to a long wooden handle or a wire handle that can be bent to fit into awkward areas. They are used to apply paint to areas that are difficult to reach with a paint brush, particularly behind pipes, radiators and columns.

ACTIVITY

Practise holding different-sized brushes, and find a style that is comfortable for you. Can you paint with either hand? This may be an advantage on difficult to reach areas.

ROLLERS

A paint roller is an application tool used for painting large flat surfaces rapidly and efficiently. It typically consists of three parts: a roller frame or cage, attached to a yoke that forms the handle, and a roller cover or sleeve. The roller cover absorbs the paint and transfers it to the painted surface. The roller frame is reusable.

Applying paint to a large flat surface may be quicker using a paint roller. Specially shaped rollers are also available for painting corners, but sometimes it can be easier to use a paint brush. The standard type of roller used by decorators is a cylinder roller. It consists of a straight cylinder with a fabric cover or sleeve.

Choosing a roller will depend on the type of coating being used and the type of substrate to be painted. The many types include very smooth for applying finishing paints to flat doors, and lambswool for applying paint to textured surfaces such as pebbledash – it is important that you to select the appropriate roller for the job. Some new types of roller contain paint within the cylindrical core that is released onto the surface when pressure is applied. When working on ceilings or high walls an extension pole attached to a roller may reduce the need for scaffolding.

Mohair rollers
Rollers made from natural mohair are very expensive, but synthetic mohair rollers are now available and these are more affordable. Short-haired rollers are used for applying gloss paint to a smooth surface, medium are for applying emulsion, and long-haired rollers are used for pebbledash.

Short-pile lambswool rollers
Lambswool roller sleeves are made from the wool of a sheep, and are used to apply water or oil paint to a smooth surface such as plaster, plasterboard or metal.

Long-pile lambswool rollers
These have a much deeper **pile** which is suitable for applying water-borne paints to brickwork and pebbledashed surfaces.

Woven long-pile rollers
All woven rollers are made of synthetic filaments. Long-pile rollers are used mainly for applying emulsion and masonry paint to pebbledashed surfaces. They come in 330mm widths, so become very heavy when loaded with paint. All woven rollers are very similar to lambswool rollers, but they are much cheaper and can be thrown away after use.

Woven medium-pile rollers
These are used for applying emulsion, primer, rust-protection paint and varnish to small surfaces, or to semi-rough surfaces.

Roller cage

Mohair roller

Pile

The soft projecting surface of a fabric consisting of many small threads

Woven medium-pile roller

Polyester long-pile rollers

These are synthetic fabric rollers that have a highly absorbent 18mm pile. They are used for applying water-borne coatings such as emulsion and masonry paint to rough areas.

Polyester medium-pile rollers

These do similar jobs to the long-pile ones, but have a 12mm pile.

Woven short-pile rollers

The 6mm deep pile is used for applying emulsion, primer, rust-protection paint and varnish on small surfaces.

Mini rollers

Small rollers

Small 100mm rollers can also be bought in long-, medium- and short-pile versions, and can be made from a natural or synthetic material. They are used for applying paint to small areas such as flush doors, door panels, door furniture and small wall areas. They can also be used for applying paint behind a radiator.

Roller scuttle

This is used for large areas to save time loading up a roller tray.

Sheepskin roller sleeves and roller scuttle

Extension pole

Extension pole

An extension pole can be fitted to a roller frame to reach high walls and ceilings.

THE DRYING PROCESS

Sometimes referred to as the most interesting part of a painter's work, the drying process is where a film of paint changes from a liquid to a solid. There are three main ways in which paints dry:

- *By evaporation of the solvent*: As paint dries, the solvent evaporates into the atmosphere.

- *By oxidation of the oil content*: This is a chemical process in which substances take up or combine with oxygen.

- *By polymerisation*: This is change in the structure of a medium, in which molecules fuse together to form a solid film. The paint does not rely on an oxygen supply, as drying is caused by chemical reaction.

Paint may dry by just one of these methods, or more likely by a combination of the three. Traditional oil paint, for example, dries partly by the evaporation of the solvent and partly by the oxidation and polymerisation of the oil, while cellulose paint dries entirely by the evaporation of the solvent.

Drying paint

DRYING TIME

This is the length of time between the application of a coat of paint and the point at which it achieves a certain degree of hardness. There are certain terms that indicate the degree of hardness achieved by the paint film.

- *Flow (dry dust free)*: The stage of drying when particles of dust that settle on the surface do not stick to the paint film.

- *Set (dry tack free)*: The stage of drying when the paint no longer feels sticky or tacky when lightly touched.

- *Touch dry (dry to handle)*: The stage of drying when a paint film has hardened sufficiently so the object or surface painted may be used without marring it.

- *Hard dry (dry to recoat)*: The stage of drying when the next coat can be applied.

- *Thorough dry (dry to sand)*: The stage of drying when a paint film can be sanded without the sandpaper sticking or clogging.

SEQUENCE OF PAINTING A ROOM AREA AND COMPONENTS

Before you start to apply paint coatings you need to consider the sequence of the task to make sure that you keep the edge of the paint wet and that you do not mark your completed work or spill paint onto it. If you are working in an area inhabited by people, you may need to amend your schedule to work around them. You should be familiar with painting straightforward flat areas, but here is a reminder of the sequence to follow:

- It is good practice to start by painting the ceilings, working from one end of the room to the other. When cutting in it is advisable to extend the paint 15–25cm on to the top of the wall to give you a nice line to cut in to. Once the coating has dried the ceiling can be re-coated.

- The wall areas are next, and should be coated one wall at a time. If you are using brushes you may need a 25mm brush for cutting in and a 150mm brush for the rest. Start at the top, following the diagram on page 200. If you are using a roller and brush, cut in a straight line where you have overlapped the paint from the ceiling and then paint the edges before filling in with the roller. Do not re-coat until the first coating has fully dried.

- Next will come doors, windows and **linear** work (skirting boards, door frames, picture frames or dado rails). Most will require two coats. The sequence of painting panelled doors is on page 203.

- This is the correct sequence, but with experience and taking into account different circumstances on different jobs, you may paint all the areas with one coat first and then start again with the ceiling, then the walls, and linear work with a second coat.

PREPARING PAINT FOR USE

Once the surface is prepared and you have chosen the paint system to apply there is still some work to do before you start to paint. The covering you are going to use will usually come in a large container, so the paint will need to be **decanted** into a paint kettle, a roller tray or a bucket.

DECANTING PAINT

If the container of paint has not been used before:

- Remove any dust from the lid of the paint container. The container may have gathered dust by being stored near someone rubbing down.

- Open the lid using a paint tin opener. Never use the edge of a paint scraper or filling knife, as the blades are easily damaged.

- Stir the paint with a paint stirrer or palette knife until all the sediment is dispersed and the required consistency is achieved.

Linear

Relating to straight, often narrow, lines

> **INDUSTRY TIP**
>
> Never use paint directly from the manufacturer's container, as any **contamination** can ruin the whole batch of paint.

Contaminate

To pollute or infect

Decant

To transfer a liquid by pouring from one container into another

Paint decanted into a roller tray

Palette knives   Paint stirrers

- Pour the required amount of paint into the paint kettle or roller tray.

- With your brush, remove any paint that may have gathered in the rim of the paint container and then wipe clean using a rag.

- Replace the lid of the paint container so that the remaining paint does not become contaminated.

If the containers of paint have been previously used:

- Remove any dust from the lid of the paint container, and open it as above.

- The air trapped inside the container when the lid was last replaced may cause a skin to form on the surface of the paint. If there is a layer of skin present, it can be removed by cutting the skin away from the edge of the inside of the container. Lift out the skin intact if possible and dispose of in a waste bin.

- Search the paint for lumps and debris by straining. Place a paint strainer on a paint kettle and pour the required amount of paint through the strainer to remove any bits of skin or contamination present from the last time the container was opened.

- Remove the strainer and clean or dispose of it as appropriate.

- Clean the rim of the container as before and then replace the lid.

Traditional strainers will need cleaning after each use, or they will clog up when the paint dries. Single-use disposable strainers are available but work out more expensive. For a cheaper option you can use old tights or stockings to strain the paint and then dispose of them afterwards.

The **viscosity** of the paint will have to be checked to make sure it is the correct thickness to apply to the surface. Paint that is too thick will be hard to apply, leaving fatty edges and excessive brush marks. Paint that is too thin will not give sufficient coverage to obliterate the previous coating and the colours may bleed through. Check the manufacturer's instructions before thinning out paint – water-borne with water, and oil based with white spirit. There is a debate among

Old paint tins need to be opened with care

Viscosity

How thick or thin the paint is – this will affect how the paint flows, the ease of application and the suitability for a particular surface

professionals about whether paint should ever be thinned out, as manufacturers produce paint to the correct opacity. Thinned paint will not give the same coverage and the paint film may break down. The thickness of the paint is affected by temperature, so if it has been stored in a cold place it may just need bringing up to room temperature before use.

USING A PAINT KETTLE

The aim of a decorator should be to transfer paint to surfaces without getting covered in the stuff. Although you should always be wearing overalls, you should endeavour to work as cleanly as possible, as wet paint has a habit of transferring itself to places where it should not be. Follow these tips to minimise paint transference:

- Only pour as much paint as is needed into the paint kettle.

- Use only one side of the kettle so you have a clean side and a paint side.

- Load the brush with paint and use the side of the kettle to remove any excess.

- When breaking from work, lay the brush across the top of the kettle with the bristles lying on the paint side of the kettle so the handle rests on the clean side.

- If you are stopping for a longer time, stand the brush in the paint kettle with the handle against the clean side.

- When you resume work, wipe off the excess paint (on the paint side of the kettle) before continuing.

PAINTING LARGE AREAS

When painting large areas, such as ceilings and walls, there are a number of things that must be considered:

- *What is needed to reach the work areas?* If you are working on a ceiling or a high wall you may need some form of scaffolding to reach the work area, or you may be able to manage with a pair of steps. The important thing is to plan how you are going to reach the whole area to be covered, because once you have started you will need to keep the edge going so that paint will flow into itself and not leave fatty edges.

- *Is the surface flat or textured?* This will determine what tools and equipment you will need to carry out the painting.

- *What is the drying time of the paint?* The manufacturer's instructions on the back of the paint container will tell you how quickly the paint will dry. If the drying time is quick and you have a

Rest the bristles across the paint side of the kettle

ACTIVITY

Practise using paint from a kettle and keeping one side of it clean. It will soon become second nature to you, and you will work much more cleanly.

Scaffold tower

large area to paint, you may need a second person to help. The instructions will also tell you how long you will need to wait before giving the surface a second coat.

■ *Is the work area to be painted manageable by one decorator or will it require more than one person?* Remember that you will need to keep the edge wet to ensure you produce a solid paint film by eliminating brush strokes. You may need to work with a partner to achieve this.

■ *Is the surface porous or non-porous?* This may affect the drying time, the consistency and the amount of paint required.

■ *What should you use to apply the paint?* For small areas such as doors, window frames and pipes you may need only a brush, but for larger areas you may need a roller for the large area and a brush for cutting around the edges. If two are working on the same area one may cut in and the other may apply the paint using the roller.

■ *Where should you start?* When painting large areas, plan where to start and where you will finish to ensure that the edge does not dry off before the next application of paint. Look at the area that is going to be painted and remember that you will need to keep the edge wet, so whether it is a ceiling, wall or door always start at the narrowest part.

APPLICATION OF PAINT COATINGS TO CEILINGS AND WALLS

It is important to apply paint in the correct way to ceilings and walls. The methods and techniques you will need to use to ensure a good finish are detailed below.

Painting a ceiling wearing overalls and gloves

Cutting in

Refract

To deflect light from a straight path

Opaque

Not transmitting light – the opposite of transparent

CUTTING IN

When you are painting an area with a large brush or roller it can be difficult to get into the corners and around obstructions. Before you start you will need to use a small brush to make a neat line around door frames, windows, mouldings and internal angles. Professional decorators rarely use masking tape to cut in around windows and other obstacles, as it is time consuming and paint sometimes seeps under the tape anyway. You will develop the skill to paint straight lines neatly, although it may take a while to have the confidence to paint freehand. Practice makes perfect!

Once you have cut in the edges you can then fill in the area with a large brush or roller.

WATER-BORNE PAINTS

When applying water-borne coatings such as emulsion paint to ceilings or walls by brush, work in stages as illustrated below. However do not lay off in the conventional way, as you would when painting a door, for example (see page 202). Cross-hatching is the best process to use when applying emulsion, to minimise the effect of brush marks (tramlines) created by the brush.

When matt emulsion dries, the light is **refracted** and does not run down the brush marks, thus making the paint appear more **opaque** and matt.

Vinyl silk emulsion highlights defects of both the surface and the brush marks, but it is easier to keep clean and can be wiped over with a cloth.

If you are using oil based paint on ceilings you will need to follow the same process as for applying a coat of paint to walls.

In order to keep the wet edge to a minimum in terms of both time and area you will need to work on small areas at a time by mentally dividing the wall into small squares.

This is the sequence for one decorator applying paint to walls:

One decorator paints sections 1–6.	5	3	1
	6	4	2

Example area 2.5m × 5m

If two decorators are working on a large wall, one would cut in while the other decorator filled in with a roller. This is the sequence for two decorators working together applying paint to a ceiling:

One decorator paints sections 1–3 above.	3	2	1
At the same time as the second decorator paints sections 1–3 below.	3	2	1

Example area 2.5m × 5m

As before, keep the edge wet. The size of the brush you use will depend on the area that is being painted, but remember that you are aiming to keep the edge wet and apply an even coat.

When using brushes and rollers on large surfaces such as ceilings and walls:

- cut in the edges first at the ceiling or wall line
- cut around obstacles such as electrical fittings and any fixtures
- use a suitable size of paint brush for the cutting in.

APPLICATION PROCEDURES

The following sequence is for applying oil based paints by brush to non-complex areas.

STEP 1 Apply the first application of coating to the surface using the cross-hatch method. Work in areas of approximately 300mm square along the surface and then continue down or across the surface. You will find that you make mistakes when applying the paint, for example putting it on too thickly or not brushing it out evenly, but don't worry – the more you practise, the fewer mistakes you will make.

STEP 2 The next step of the paint application requires you to lay off the applied paint in the short direction, overlapping each brush stroke by a third of the width of the brush. The paint will flow into itself and make an invisible join.

STEP 3 When applying the paint, you will need to apply light pressure to the brush to make the bristles work the paint to an even application.

STEP 4 The final stage requires you to lay off in the final direction, lengthways. You do not need to load any more paint onto the brush for the **laying-off** process.

> **INDUSTRY TIP**
>
> Close windows and doors when applying paint to large areas. This will help to slow down the drying time through lack of ventilation. This slows up the evaporation rate of the solvents and gives a longer wet-edge time. Warning: Wear a respirator when doing this, as some paints may give off harmful fumes.

Laying off

Finishing off an area of paintwork with very light strokes of the brush in order to eliminate brush marks

APPLYING OIL BASED AND ACRYLIC PAINTS BY BRUSH TO DOORS

Here are some factors to consider when applying paint coatings to doors:

- Is it an external door? External doors are often made from hardwood to help protect them from the weather, and should be coated with an oil based paint. Remember that paint will dry quicker outside.

- Is it an internal door? Internal doors are more likely to be made from softwood and not be affected by bad weather, so they can be painted using either oil based or acrylic paint.

- Is the surface flush or panelled?

- Is the surface PVC or metal?

- Are there any glazed (glass) areas?

The traditional sequence of painting a flush door starts at the top left-hand corner and ends at the bottom right, as shown on the diagram.

If you are painting a door that opens towards you into the room, you will need to paint the edge with the lock and fittings on. When you are painting a door that opens away from you, you will need to paint the hinge edge. Paint the edge before the face of the door, as once the face has been painted there may be a build-up of paint on the edge, which will be less noticeable when the paint has dried.

Remember: Always rub down between coats to remove nibs and so on, and then use a dusting brush to remove any fine dust remaining on the surface.

Sequence for painting a flush door

Panelled doors

When painting or varnishing a panelled door follow the sequence in the diagram, starting at the top left panel to help prevent fatty edges forming. Remember to lay off following the direction of the grain.

PAINTING LINEAR WORK

All rooms have some form of linear work, consisting of some or all of the following surfaces:

- door frames

- skirting boards

- mouldings

- dado rails

- picture rails.

When painting these surfaces, use a small cutting-in brush and make sure that the surfaces are not overloaded with paint, as this could result in runs and sags, spoiling the finished look. These complex areas require careful painting, as they are often decorative and will really stand out in the completed room.

APPLICATION OF COATINGS TO WINDOWS

Although in recent years PVC windows have been fitted to new buildings and used to replace old decayed timber windows or rusty metal windows, you will still come across many different types of timber or metal windows that will need painting. As there are so many different designs, all with different types of openings, window painting is one of the most time-consuming jobs that a painter has to carry out when decorating properties both internally and externally. There are many different designs and it can take some time to master the sequences for each one, but the principles are similar for each of them.

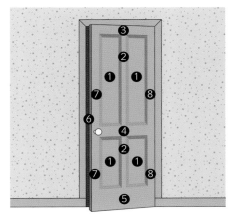
Sequence for painting a panelled door

> **INDUSTRY TIP**
>
> Panelled doors consist of horizontal members ('rails') and vertical members ('stiles' on the outside of the door or 'muntins' in the centre).

Painting a skirting board

Bay window

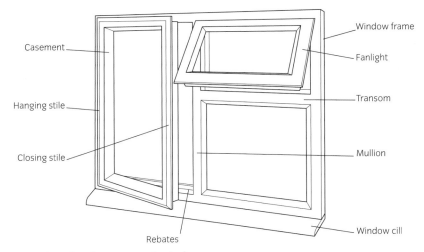

Window frame

Casement

Fanlight

Transom

Hanging stile

Closing stile

Mullion

Rebates

Window cill

Component parts of a casement window

Rebate

A rectangular area removed from the corner of a timber section. Used to locate a pane of glass while a frame rebate locates a window sash

The following is the painting sequence for standard opening windows:

1 Open the windows and paint all the frame **rebates**.

2 Paint fanlights, cutting in around the puttied areas.

3 Paint the hanging stiles.

4 Paint the closing stiles.

5 Paint the mullion.

6 Paint the transom.

7 Paint the window frame.

8 Finish by painting the window cill.

9 Allow to dry fully before closing the windows.

Painting sequence for a sash window

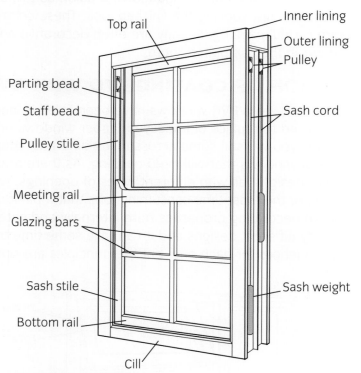

Component parts of a sash window

The following is the painting sequence for the internal window:

1 Slide the outer sash down a little and raise the inner sash, leaving a gap at the top and bottom.

2 Paint the glazing bars and the surface of the inner sash, including the top surface of the meeting rail and the underside of the bottom rail.

3 Paint the parts of the outer sash that are visible.

4 Slide the outer sash until it is almost closed, and lower the inner sash (grip it from the outside so you don't touch the wet paint).

5 Complete the painting of the outer sash, omitting the top rail.

6 To paint the pulley stiles, pull the sash cord away from the surface so that you can paint behind them. Avoid painting the sash cord, as this will hinder the smooth running of the sash window. Paint the pulley wheel plate (the metal surround) but not the pulley itself.

7 Paint all remaining liners and shutters.

8 Finish by painting the cill.

The following is the painting sequence for the external window:

1 Reverse the sashes by sliding the outer sash up and the inner sash down.

2 Paint all visible surfaces except the top surface of the top rail. The pulley stiles can be painted at the same time if not already painted.

3 Return the sash windows to an almost closed position and complete the painting of the inner sash and the pulley stiles.

4 Paint the cill.

PAINTING A STAIRCASE

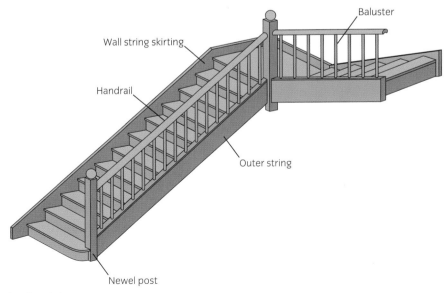

Parts of a staircase

Transparent

Easily seen through, like clear glass

Wood stain

Cover the floor with dust sheets and secure them with masking tape. After the preparation has been completed, apply paint in the following order:

1 Balusters (also known as spindles), starting from the top.

2 Outer string.

3 Newel post.

4 Handrail.

5 Wall string skirting.

FERROUS AND NON-FERROUS SURFACES

If the surface needs priming, use the appropriate primer followed by an undercoat and a finishing coat.

The method for applying paint is the same for all surfaces.

1 Lightly rub down with fine abrasive.

2 Dust off.

3 Apply the coating and lay off to form an even coat of paint.

VARNISHING OR STAINING TIMBER SURFACES

Although this can be a specialist job, you may be called on to varnish a timber surface such as a door or a skirting board. On surfaces that are to be covered with opaque paint the undercoat and primer will not show through the finishing coats, but this is not the case with translucent or **transparent** coverings. Stains and varnishes protect timber surfaces without obscuring the beauty of the grain. It is therefore important that these surfaces are prepared in a different way from wood that is painted.

Wood stains

Wood stains can be used on exterior and interior timbers, and when applied they soak deep into the timber surface to emphasise the grain of the wood. They come in a variety of colours, from natural wood shades to vibrant colours intended to change the appearance of the timber. They can be sealed with clear varnish or polish after applying.

Before applying the wood stain, make sure the surface is dry, then lightly rub down using fine silicon carbide paper, with the grain. Remove dust and apply the stain with a brush and a lint-free cloth. Lay off following the direction of the grain so that the wood stain flows and forms an even finish.

Varnish

This is a transparent liquid that is applied to a surface to produce a hard protective transparent coating. Varnish may be clear, but it is also available already stained to make wood colours.

When applying varnish, the object is to produce an even level film free from runs, sags and pinholing and with no dust or bittiness. It is important to apply the varnish firmly and confidently. If the coating is rubbed out too thinly and is bare in places, it will be impossible to obtain an evenly distributed film and this will result in runs and a poor appearance. Previously varnished surfaces should be lightly rubbed down to de-nib, then dusted off and the surface wiped over with a tack rag. Knots should not be sealed with knotting solution, as it will show through the varnish. Some surfaces will require more preparation and will need sanding, then wet abrading using silicone paper.

Varnishing wood

APPLICATION AND POST-APPLICATION DEFECTS

As decorators we aim to produce a perfect finish, but you may still make mistakes that need correcting. Chapter 3 lists many of the common defects you may find when preparing previously painted surfaces. These and other defects are looked at here in a little more detail, with a focus on what causes them and how to avoid making them in the first place.

- *Cissing*: Take care not to pick up grease on the bristles of the brush, as this can cause cissing. Check also that there is no grease on the substrate. If an area has cissed, allow it to dry before wiping off, and then de-grease before repainting.

- *Orange peel*: This is the texture left by certain roller sleeves when applying paint to the surface. Make sure that the pile on the roller is not too thick for the job – however, most rollers will leave a slight orange peel effect. If a smooth, flat finish is required it is best to use a brush.

- *Ladders and excessive brush marks*: These are paint defects where the laying-off brush lines can be seen after the final laying-off process has been completed. When laying off, use light brush strokes so the paint flows into itself. To rectify these defects you will need to wait until the paint is thoroughly dry, not just touch dry. The surface will then need to be wet and dried before re-coating (see abrading in Chapter 3, pages 123–124). Try not to break through the surface of the paint film when rubbing down, or you may have to undercoat the area again.

- *Runs*: A defect caused by over-application of paint, which at first sags and then turns into runs before drying. Paint needs to be applied evenly and laid off so that the paint flows into itself. Rectify in the same way as ladders.

A run defect

An example of bittiness

Arris

A sharp external edge, such as the edge of a door

An example of a miss

Crazed paint surface

■ *Sags and curtains*: Similar to runs – rectify in the same way as ladders.

■ *Excessive bits and nibs*: These could be caused by the paint not being strained, or by the surface not being dusted down properly after rubbing down. They may also be caused by other tradespeople doing their job or just walking by if there is dust on the floor. If the paint is the problem, stop and strain the paint – the problem will not just go away. Dust off the surface if necessary, and make sure you don't paint while someone is sweeping up around you. Bits and nibs on the surface will have to be thoroughly rubbed down once completely dry before you apply the next coat.

■ *Fat edges*: This is an application fault in which a thick ridge of paint occurs on a corner or **arris**. It can be avoided by laying off at the corners with an almost dry brush. This can be a problem when painting doors, as paint tends to build up on the edges.

■ *Ropiness*: Also known as ribbiness or tramlines. This occurs when paint does not flow evenly, and is usually caused by faulty workmanship. It could happen as a result of applying the paint unevenly or over-brushing the paint until it starts to set (not keeping the edge alive/wet).

■ *Misses*: These are areas which have been missed when applying paint, generally through carelessness. When dry, the area will have to be re-coated and then checked to make sure the area is uniformly covered. If not, re-coat.

■ *Roller skid marks and roller edge marks*: These are usually caused by overloaded rollers skidding over the surface, and the edges not being sufficiently laid off.

■ *Irregular cutting in*: Poor cutting in skills can result in irregular lines that will need repainting to produce a neat finish. This is particularly noticeable when using two different colours.

■ *Paint splatters and specks on surrounding areas*: This could be because you were over-vigorous with your brush strokes or the brush was overloaded. Make sure that surrounding areas are protected before starting work. Remove splatters with the appropriate solvent – water for emulsion, white spirit for gloss paint.

■ *Crazing and cracking*: This occurs in paintwork and is usually due to the application of a hard-drying coating (oil paint) over a softer coat (paint that has not fully dried) so that the top coating is unable to keep pace with the expansion and contraction of the previous coat as it dries. If crazing or cracking has formed on the surface there is no remedy except to burn off the defective paint.

■ *Flaking and peeling*: This is where the paint film lifts from the surface and breaks away in the form of brittle flakes. It is caused by applying paint to moist or loose, powdery surfaces. Remove the defective surface down to a smooth finish and then ensure that the surface is dry and stable before coating.

■ *Cratering or rain spotting*: Craters in the surface of a dry paint surface can be caused by rain, condensation or heavy dew falling onto the wet paint surface before it is dry. If it is likely to rain, avoid painting any exposed surfaces. Avoid painting in damp, humid atmospheres. You should never apply paint to an external surface if it does not have time to become touch dry before dew starts to rise.

■ *Yellowing*: This is where paint, usually white, gradually yellows over time. It is caused when linseed oil or phenolic resin (oil) based paints receive little or no light, for example if they are behind pictures or furniture, or inside cupboards. These areas will require re-decoration with a non-yellowing paint coating.

■ *Blooming*: This is a whitish appearance on the surface of varnish and can sometimes be accompanied by loss of gloss. It is caused by:
  □ applying paint in cold damp conditions
  □ applying paint in humid conditions
  □ water being absorbed into the paint coating – always ensure that the surface is dry before applying paint
  □ pollutants in the atmosphere – if work is being carried out where pollution is likely, wipe over the surface with white spirit and allow it to dry.

■ *Fading*: This is loss of colour on a painted surface, which may be due to exposure to sunlight, ageing or exposure to the weather. Colours that fade with the action of sunlight are known as **fugitive colours**. They tend to fade more in flat finishes than when protected by a gloss medium.

■ *Retarded drying*: This is when paint takes a long time to dry. This is caused by humidity (moisture) in the air, which retards evaporation of solvents from the paint. The drying of paint can also be impeded if it is colder than 10°C. Direct sunlight will dramatically increase the paint temperature (and thus the speed of drying), with dark colours absorbing the heat much faster. Wind and air movement speeds drying because as air passes over the wet paint it helps the solvents in the paint to evaporate.

■ *Grinning*: This is a term used when a coat of paint has not obliterated (obscured) the surface to which it has been applied. This may be due to the paint being applied unevenly or too thinly, or the dramatic colour difference between the surface colour and the new colour. You may have to apply several coats before a satisfactory finish is achieved.

FUNCTIONAL SKILLS

Design a letterhead for your decorating company and make an estimate for painting a staircase and a hallway in a small detached house. In a group, or with your tutor/supervisor, discuss how you decided what to charge and how relevant those charges are to the current market.

Work on this activity can support FEE3 (W.2), FICTE3 (6.Ai) and FM2 (C2.2).

Fugitive colours

Colours that fade when exposed to light. Some colours that are reasonably stable when used at full strength develop fugitive tendencies when mixed with white to create a lighter shade

This wall will need several coats to avoid grinning

CLEAN, MAINTAIN AND STORE BRUSHES AND ROLLERS

As with all tools and equipment, there is little point in buying good-quality paint brushes and rollers if they are not cleaned and stored properly.

CLEANING BRUSHES AND ROLLERS

Tools that have been used for oil based paint will need cleaning with a different solvent from tools used for water-based paint, but the aim is the same – to remove all of the remaining paint from the filling and stock of the brush. This is the process:

1 Identify the type of paint that has been used, and whether it was oil based or water-borne paint (you may not have been using the brush yourself).

2 Pour excess paint from the kettle or roller tray back into the paint container, and wipe the brush on the container to remove as much paint as possible (some decorators use a piece of board to wipe their brush on).

3 Wash in the correct solvent: for oil paint use white spirit or the manufacturer's recommended cleaner, or use water for water-borne paint.

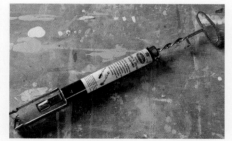

Paint brush spinner

CLEANING OIL BASED PAINT BRUSHES

1 Pour the cleaning agent (white spirit) into the paint kettle and use a vigorous pumping action to remove paint from the stock. Repeat until there is no evidence of any colour coming from the brush.

2 Spin the brush between your two hands to remove as much of the solvent as possible (paint brush spinners can help with this job).

3 Wash in warm soapy water until a clean lather is obtained and then rinse thoroughly in clean water.

CLEANING WATER-BORNE PAINT BRUSHES

Follow the same process as for oil based paint, but rinse in cold water until the water runs clear and then wash in warm soapy water. Rinse in clean water and then mop up excess water with a rag before storing.

Cleaning brushes used for water-borne paint

CLEANING ROLLERS

These take longer to clean than paint brushes, and the longer the pile the more time consuming they are. Using cheaper roller sleeves that can be thrown away at the end of a job can be more cost effective. It is important to consider the time it will take to clean roller sleeves, as this can have a significant effect on the time it takes to complete a job. Painting a door with gloss paint may seem quicker with a mohair roller but you will also need to use a brush for cutting in, and at the end of the process the mohair roller will need scrupulous cleaning in large amounts of white spirit.

The process for cleaning rollers is similar to that for cleaning paint brushes, but remember to use white spirit for oil based paint and water for water-borne paint. When rollers are clear of all paint residue, remove as much moisture as possible by spinning the roller. Some colleges and industrial sites use a waste management system (commonly branded as Safetykleen), which provides a constant flow of solvent to clean brushes, rollers and equipment quickly and efficiently. It is essential to wear gloves and goggles when using this machine.

If you cannot clean up your brushes and rollers at the end of the day they can be **steeped** in water or solvent until you can clean them properly. Do not leave them too long, as the liquids will evaporate and the brushes and rollers will dry out, making them unusable. For short breaks you may wrap rollers or brushes in a plastic carrier bag or plastic film to keep the surface moist.

Steeped

Soaked in liquid

INDUSTRY TIP

Always check that tools are clean before use. Kettles, buckets and roller trays should be wiped out before use to remove dust particles.

INDUSTRY TIP

Remember to wear rubber gloves and goggles to protect your hands and eyes from paint and solvents.

CLEANING OTHER EQUIPMENT

Used kettles, roller trays and roller buckets should have any excess paint wiped back into the paint container and should be washed with the appropriate solvent. Once they have been cleaned and dried they can be stored in a dry area, as damp may cause metal to rust and wood to rot.

STORING PAINT BRUSHES

Clean paint brushes should be stored in a cool, dry place. Excessive heat may cause the bristles and setting material to shrink, resulting in loose ferrules and bristles. In damp conditions damaging mildew may develop on the bristles.

Never store the brushes with the filling downwards, as this will bend the bristles and ruin the brush.

A brush keep is used to store brushes in a wet state. It works by solvent being contained in a bottle with an evaporating wick. The fumes from the evaporating solvent replace the air in the brush keep, preventing the brushes from drying out.

Paint brush keep

STORING ROLLERS

Rollers should be stored in moderate temperatures where they cannot be contaminated by chemicals, oil or grease. If possible, hang them up so that the air will flow around the roller sleeve. If you cannot hang them up stand them upright, as storing them on flat surfaces may crush the pile.

STORE PAINT AND MATERIALS IN ACCORDANCE WITH COSHH DATA SHEETS

The materials used by painter decorators need to be treated carefully to ensure everybody's safety, and this section looks at ways to keep risks to a minimum. In order to work safely with substances that can be hazardous to health, it is important to know what the risks are. COSHH (Control of Substances Hazardous to Health) data sheets are available for the substances you will be using.

The data sheets will provide the following information:

- what the product is
- what it is used for
- identification of hazards
- information on the composition of ingredients
- first-aid measures
- fire fighting measures
- accidental release measures
- handling
- storage.

This information should be on the label of the product, but if it is missing or the product has been decanted into another container the data sheets will be available online or from the manufacturer.

Example of COSHH data sheet for decorator's caulk

FUNCTIONAL SKILLS

Use the internet to research two-pack epoxy solvent floor paint. Find the COSHH data sheet and write a short report on how to use the product, and the health and safety considerations including first aid and transport and storage instructions.

Work on this activity can support FE1 (1.3) and FICTE3 (4.A).

INDUSTRY TIP

It is not advisable to decant hazardous substances into new containers. Carefully read the instructions for storage, and if you have any leftover product that cannot be stored follow instructions for how to dispose of it.

DISPOSAL OF WASTE

Great care must be taken when disposing of hazardous waste. It should never be poured down the sink. Try not to buy more paint than you need for a job, and consider applying another coat if you have some left over. Empty emulsion tins must be washed out and can then be disposed of in the household waste. You can now buy proprietary paint solidifiers, which are small beads that absorb the paint, turning it into a solid mass that can be disposed of in the household waste. Check with your local authority for how to dispose of oil based paints and varnishes. Rags and cloths that have been used to apply chemical solvents should be allowed to dry and then be disposed of carefully, as they can be a fire risk.

STORING PROTECTIVE SHEETING

Ensure tarpaulin is dry before folding and storing

- Cotton dust sheets and other protective sheeting should be given a light shake once finished with (although not near wet paint!) and folded up ready for use. If sheets are wet or damp they should be allowed to dry before being folded and stored to prevent mildew forming on them. All protective sheeting should be stored on shelves off the floor. It is important to keep sheeting clean and dry because it will be used to protect floors and furniture another time. Send sheets away if they need cleaning.

- Sheeting such as tarpaulin, PVC-coated nylon, rubber-coated cotton and heavy cotton canvas should be stored in the same way as cotton dust sheets. Rubber tarpaulin can be wiped clean using a sponge and warm water and allowed to dry before being folded and stored.

- If protective sheeting is not used for some time it will need to be checked for damp. If there are signs of damp, unfold and air-dry it before re-folding and storing.

CARE OF PPE

Clean work boots after use

It is very important that your own PPE is kept clean and in good condition. Check it daily to make sure that it will do the job it is intended to do.

Safety/steel toe-cap boots
After use wipe away dirt and grime with a cloth, as some solvents may harm the leather. Clear the treads and clean as required.

Hard hats
These should be cleaned at least once a month, or as or as often as necessary to remove oil, grease, chemicals and sweat. Soak the hat in a mild solution of soap and hot water, rinse with clean water, wipe and let the air dry it. Sunlight can damage the hat, so check it for cracks or splits and replace it if necessary.

High-visibility jackets
Wearing a high-visibility jacket is meant to make it easier for other people to see you, so you must keep it clean. Wiping it clean with a damp rag should be sufficient.

Use mild soapy water to clean goggles

Goggles

There are lots of jobs that you will be carrying out that will require you to wear goggles (rubbing down, washing down, cleaning solvents from brushes, etc). Wash goggles in mild soapy water to keep the lenses free from grease and dirt.

Protective gloves

Make sure that there are no tears or splits in rubber gloves, as solvents and chemicals may seep through and harm your skin (they can cause rashes and dermatitis). Cotton or latex gloves are good for light work. Wash cotton gloves regularly, or wear disposable latex gloves. Remember always to apply barrier cream, even when you are wearing gloves.

Dust mask

Your dust mask will need changing regularly depending on the type of work you are doing. For example, when you are doing heavy rubbing down or sanding, the mask will need changing more often than during light rubbing down.

For more information, refer back to Chapter 1.

INDUSTRY TIP

Remember not to smoke around highly flammable materials.

Deteriorate

To make or become worse

Flash point

The temperature at which a material gives off a vapour that will ignite if exposed to flame. Chemicals with a low flash point are labelled as highly flammable

INDUSTRY TIP

Be careful how you lift items from storage areas. Look back at the guidance on manual handling in Chapter 1.

INDUSTRY TIP

Always check the manufacturer's instructions for storage.

STORAGE OF PAINT MATERIALS

New or partially used materials, tools and equipment will need to be stored correctly for safety and to ensure that they do not **deteriorate**. They should be stored in such a way as to protect your own health and safety and that of others. Many chemicals used by decorators have a low **flash point**, and if they are kept in conditions that are too hot they are likely to explode or catch fire.

The storage area should be dry, well ventilated and frost free all year round. There should be no risk of materials coming into contact with naked flames such as gas heaters, boilers, etc, as many of these materials are flammable. For the same reason you should never smoke in a storage area.

■ The storage area should be fitted with sturdy racking, and large and heavy materials stored on the bottom shelves. Never store powder filler or textured finishing materials on concrete floors, as they can remain cold and damp even in warm weather and will be unfit for use. Small containers of filler that have been opened can be stored in airtight plastic containers.

■ Oil based paints (undercoat, gloss and varnish) and water-borne paints (emulsions and masonry paints) should be stored on shelves and clearly marked with the labels turned to the front, and used in date order.

Inverted

Turned upside down

■ Oil based materials should be **inverted** at regular intervals to prevent settlement of the pigments and separation of the ingredients. Check that the lids are on firmly first.

- Some water-borne paint products such as emulsions and acrylics have a limited shelf life and should be used before their use-by date.

- Fattening is where the paint in partially filled containers becomes very thick, making it hard to apply. The paint should either be thinned before use (but remember the danger of the pigment not providing sufficient coverage), or disposed of.

- When receiving a delivery of new paint materials, make sure that the old stock is brought to the front to be used first and the new stock stored behind it. This is known as stock rotation, and it helps to ensure that old stock is not left to go out of date.

- Livering – some paints are liable to this defect, where the paint thickens to a jelly-like condition (like raw liver) by oxidation during storage.

- Skinning – to avoid this defect, see instructions for decanting paint on pages 196–198.

- Two-pack paints are specialist paints used for cars and aircraft which dry to an extremely hard finish. You may also come across a two-pack epoxy solvent floor paint. These paints are extremely toxic and must be handled with care. Ensure that they are stored upright with the lid firmly closed, away from heat and flame.

- Never stack materials so high that there is a danger of them falling. Also, never over-reach yourself if you are trying to get a product from a high shelf, as you don't want it falling on you or covering you from head to toe in paint!

- Appropriate fire extinguishers should be on hand in case of a fire. (See fire extinguishers and their uses in Chapter 1, page 39.)

- Make sure that lids and caps are closed tightly to limit the escape of VOCs into the air.

Dispose of any paint that cannot be used

Case Study: Shaun and Gareth

Shaun and Gareth were commissioned to paint the outside of an office building in late October. They had estimated that the work would take five days with two painters working on the job.

On the first day they sheeted the work and surrounding areas, and put out barriers and signs to warn people that work was taking place. The first two days of preparation were uneventful, but on the third day when they were painting under the eaves, the guttering and the fascia boards, the wind started to pick up. When they returned the following morning they found that all the painted areas were covered in dust and debris, so they had to be rubbed down and repainted. It was now cold and drizzling with rain but they continued with glossing the windows. By the end of the day the paint was still not dry, but they had to close the windows before they left for security and to prevent the rain getting in.

By the next morning the paint had set, and unfortunately the windows had stuck fast. It was still very cold, but dry, so they decided to leave the windows for the time being and carry on glossing the doors. Coming back for what should have been their final day they realised that the paint on the doors was dull and flat. It had lost gloss because of the autumn dew falling before the paint system was completely dry. They had to return two weeks later when the weather had improved to repaint the windows and doors, costing them time and money.

Work through the following questions to check your learning.

1   When working with water, which one of the following will require special attention in an office environment?

   a   Radiator.

   b   Desk.

   c   Shelf.

   d   Computer.

2   Which part of the brush is used to apply the paint?

   a   Frame.

   b   Stock.

   c   Filament

   d   Spacer.

3   A lambswool roller is unsuitable for applying gloss paint to a flat surface because

   a   the texture would be too heavy

   b   it would take too long

   c   the roller lines would show

   d   it would stop the surface drying.

4   Strongly coloured painted surfaces exposed to direct sunlight may over time experience

   a   bleeding

   b   flaking

   c   fading

   d   cissing.

5   Which solvent would you use to thin oil based primer?

   a   Methylated spirit.

   b   Acetone.

   c   White spirit.

   d   Cellulose thinner.

6   What substance evaporates when emulsion paint dries?

   a   Acetone.

   b   Water.

   c   Methylated spirit.

   d   Cellulose thinner.

7   When completing linear work in a domestic area, which one of the following should be painted last?

   a   Architraves.

   b   Picture rails.

   c   Dado rails.

   d   Skirting boards.

8   What is the likely outcome of applying a gloss finish onto a base undercoat of the wrong colour?

   a   Runs.

   b   Grinning.

   c   Sags.

   d   Fat edges.

9   How should a synthetic filament brush be stored after cleaning?

   a   Wrapped in an oiled rag.

   b   Suspended in oil.

   c   Laid flat in a dry place.

   d   Suspended in water.

10   What is meant by stock rotation?

   a   To store the paint upside down.

   b   To ensure that older stock is used first.

   c   To move stock around in the cupboard.

   d   To mix paint with a mechanical stirrer.

11 Why is polythene sheeting sometimes used under cotton dust sheets when protecting furniture?

   a   To protect the polythene sheeting.

   b   To prevent dust transferring through.

   c   To prevent the sheets from slipping off.

   d   To save time when sweeping up.

12 Which one of the following is generally the **best** sheeting for covering office equipment?

   a   Tarpaulin.

   b   Adhesive plastic.

   c   Plastic sheet.

   d   Cotton twill.

13 Careless application of solvent-borne gloss by roller can cause which one of the following defects?

   a   Blooming.

   b   Crazing.

   c   Cissing.

   d   Skid marks.

14 Why would you use a synthetic filament brush when applying water-borne paint to a window cill?

   a   The filament is easier to clean after use.

   b   The brush marks produce a good texture.

   c   The filament brush is cheaper.

   d   The brush marks are less visible.

15 Which one of the following identifies the **best** reason for removing masking tape carefully after painting has been completed?

   a   To save time cleaning up.

   b   To stop the paint being lifted off.

   c   To reuse the masking tape.

   d   To prevent the surface from discolouring.

16 Which one of the following surfaces coatings allows timber to 'breathe'?

   a   Gloss paint.

   b   Eggshell paint.

   c   Silk emulsion.

   d   Micro-porous paint.

17 Which one of the following paint types would **not** be stirred before use?

   a   Gloss.

   b   Thixotropic.

   c   Silk emulsion.

   d   Micro-porous.

18 A common problem associated with gloss paint drying in hot and dry conditions is

   a   rapid drying

   b   loss of gloss

   c   cissing

   d   crazing.

19 The **first** part of a panelled door to be painted is the

   a   stiles

   b   rails

   c   muntins

   d   mouldings.

20 How should materials with low flash points be stored?

   a   Away from other paints.

   b   At specific temperatures.

   c   Outside only.

   d   In direct sunlight.

Chapter 5
Unit 217: Applying standard papers to walls and ceilings

This chapter will extend your knowledge of standard papers hung to ceilings and walls. In addition to the types of foundation and plain papers that you will already be familiar with from Level 1, this chapter will cover the use of embossed papers, blown vinyl papers, standard papers (washable and vinyl), ready-pasted papers and borders.

The invention of wallpaper allowed us to bring colour, pattern and texture into our rooms, and provided us with the opportunity to change our decor on a fairly regular basis. The use of wallpapers dates back to medieval times, when they were introduced to provide a cheaper alternative to the expensive textiles that typically covered the walls. Originally paper was hand made in small squares decorated with patterns and then stuck together to form an all-over pattern. As you will see in this chapter, processes and techniques have moved on a long way since then.

By reading this chapter you will know:

1 Methods used in wallpaper production.

2 How to select and prepare adhesives.

3 How to apply papers to ceilings and walls.

4 How to store materials.

METHODS OF WALLPAPER PRODUCTION

This section looks at some of the different methods of wallpaper production you may come across.

PRODUCTION METHODS

Mill

A paper mill is a factory for manufacturing paper

Paper production

Paper is made from wood pulp that is run through a **mill**. Chlorine and oxygen are added along with water to bleach the pulp and enable it to become one continuous flat stream. Synthetic fibres are sometimes added to give additional texture and strength. A roll of paper from the mill is 1.65m wide and typically more than 6,000m long. It weighs about one ton.

Before paper is transferred to the printer, each roll is cut into 530mm widths that are 10m long. This is a typical size for a standard roll of wallpaper. It is possible to make longer rolls if necessary. Wood pulp sheets may be coated with china clay to allow for good, even absorption of colour, and/or titanium dioxide which provides more opacity. This is the basic method for producing a single-layer paper (called a pulp) that is suitable for printing as a simplex paper. For more complex papers – ingrains, duplex, embossed, blown vinyl and vinyl coated papers – there are additional processes required prior to the printing process in order to produce the desired paper texture or structure.

Ingrains, duplex and embossed papers are manufactured using two layers of paper. In the case of wood ingrain, chips of wood are sandwiched between the layers. The two layers give wallpaper greater strength, and are bonded together ready to be sent for printing.

EMBOSSING

Embossed papers typically consist of two layers of paper passed through soft rollers. The rollers consist of a male and a female mould that enable the formation of either a raised or relief pattern.

Dry embossing

Anaglypta and duplex embossed papers are produced by the dry embossing process, and can be printed with colour or designed to remain white, to be painted on site by the decorator. Lower-cost embossed papers can be produced using a single layer of paper, but they will obviously be thinner and therefore will have a lower relief that may be more prone to flattening when they are hung.

Wet embossing

Supaglypta or high-relief panels are produced by the wet embossing method and have cotton lint and other fillers added between the

ACTIVITY

Visit www.paperonline.org and answer the following questions:

- What is paper made from?
- Is there a process for recycling paper?

An example of embossed wallpaper

layers of paper before pressing. This method allows for a much heavier-quality product, which should ensure that the raised pattern remains in place after hanging. Hanging of this type of wallpaper is discussed in more detail at Level 3.

HEAT EXPANSION

Blown vinyl wallpaper is produced using this method. An expanding agent is added to liquid vinyl (PVC), which expands in size after it is heated to a high temperature, producing a three-dimensional effect. Within the PVC is a blowing agent, and when heat is applied to the PVC (during the production process) the PVC on the flat wallpaper expands into patterned rollers to create the blown vinyl effect in a range of patterns and textures. Vinyl is printed on a paper substrate.

Further manufacturing processes are discussed in the next section.

Blown vinyl wallpaper

PRINTING METHODS

The application of wallpapers dates back to at least the medieval period, when they were seen as cheap alternatives to costly tapestries, silks, panelling and other decorations of the time. These early wallpapers were usually hand block-printed onto squares of paper and then matched on the wall. Later papers were machine printed and at that point it became possible to manufacture wallpaper in long lengths, similar to what is still in production today.

The following information and illustrations explain the printing processes in use today to produce the wonderful range of pattern, colour and texture that is possible on modern wall coverings.

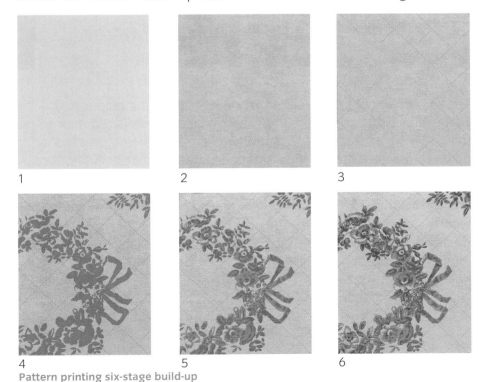

Pattern printing six-stage build-up

There are a number of print methods that can be used to get colour, texture and pattern onto wallpaper. For pattern printing it is a matter of developing a series of pattern plates that essentially overprint the pattern onto the previous print. This can be seen in the illustration showing a six-process print run. Each run will apply a different colour or pattern over the one before. Each process must be allowed to dry before the next is applied. The first coating applied is referred to as the ground.

BLOCK PRINTING

The photographs below show carved printing blocks, and the printer applying a block to the paper.

Wooden printing blocks

Printing in progress using a wooden block

The printer colours the block by lowering it onto the colour tray. Once sufficiently inked, the block is lifted and manoeuvred over to the paper by an arch lever system (crane) before being pressed down to create the print. Pins on the side of the blocks guide the printer to help position the block exactly.

The printer decides how much pressure to apply to the block, with the accuracy and strength of colour depending on how much pressure is applied to the back. After each colour has been applied the paper is hung to dry for four to five hours before the next colour is applied. Once the design is complete the printed wallpaper is lacquered for protection.

MACHINE PRINTING

The surface print machine was invented in 1839 – this is the oldest mechanised process. It provided the only mechanised means of printing wallpaper for over 100 years, but has since been replaced by the relief printing flexo machine. It was what made wallpaper available to the masses and so became much more widespread and successful than block printing.

The print cylinders in a surface print machine are made of a hard ceramic type rubber with a pattern cut out. The picture shows a surface printing machine which has multiple rollers and colours being printed at the same time.

SCREEN PRINTING

Screen printing was originally called silk-screen printing, because the stencil screens were made from silk. Nowadays nylon stencils are more commonly used. This is a simple process which produces wallpapers that have a rich depth of colour.

Surface printing machine

Flatbed screen printing (silk-screen printing)

The screen used for flatbed screen printing is a rectangular frame with a fine nylon woven mesh stretched across it. The design is transferred onto the mesh by placing a stencil of the design onto a screen coated in a photosensitive polymer. The screen is then photo-exposed under special lighting, which transfers the design onto the screen.

Screen printing table

Screen printing frame

To print the design the screen is laid face down onto the wallpaper, and inks are applied to the back of the screen and drawn across the mesh using a rubber squeegee. The ink is forced through the open areas of the mesh, printing the design onto the paper. The screen can then be lifted and moved along to the next position, where the process is repeated. This is an expensive process and it is used to produce high-end wallpapers.

Rotary screen printing machine

Rotary screen printing

Rotary screen printing was developed from the flatbed screen printing process. It prints a continuous web of moving paper, up to 3,000 metres long. It uses similar methods to the hand screen printing method described above, but it is much cheaper because it can print continuously.

FLEXOGRAPHIC PRINTING

Flexographic printing, or flexo, is a similar process to surface printing. It is a relief-type process that uses a soft rubber print cylinder with a raised printing surface. The area that is not to be printed is cut out of the roller, and the process works in a similar way to a hand-held rubber stamp. The design is transferred onto the paper by a series of 'print stations', equally spaced around the outside of a large cylindrical drum. The drum carries the paper face-out and the print stations transfer the design onto the paper.

Flexographic rubber roller

Flexographic printing machine in use

ROTOGRAVURE PRINTING

Rotogravure print machines

Rotogravure printing, or intaglio, transfers an image onto the paper surface via a hard engraved cylinder. Unlike in the flexo process, the image is recessed onto the cylinder (rather than being raised). The ink collects in the recesses and is absorbed by the paper as it passes over the cylinder. To achieve deep colours, deeper recesses are used as this means that more ink is transferred to the paper.

Rotogravure allows an essentially unlimited range of colours and shades to be used. By overlapping four transparent colours, most colours can be produced. Rotogravure printing can realistically duplicate the look of photography or art.

HEAT EMBOSSING PRINTED VINYLS

There are two types of vinyl: solid PVC vinyl and blown PVC vinyl.

Blown PVC vinyl, created by heat expansion, can be divided into two types: mechanically blown vinyl and chemically embossed blown vinyl.

Heat embossing vinyl is a way to convert a smooth plastic wall covering into one with a third dimension. The textured relief can be a smooth and light effect, such as a light sand emboss, or a heavily textured effect such as a rough emboss, which has a visual and tactile effect.

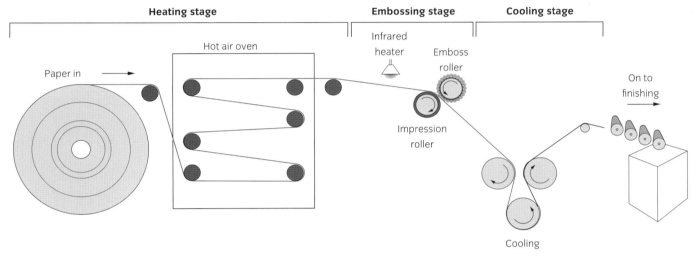

Heat embossing process

These effects are achieved by loading a print reel onto an embossing machine. The paper goes through a series of rollers that keep the paper in line and taut. The paper is exposed to a heating section that gradually warms the vinyl up to 190°C, making the vinyl layer soft. The paper is then squeezed between two rollers (the impression roller and the emboss roller), and this process transfers the relief to the paper's surface. The paper is immediately cooled so that the new shape of the vinyl is fixed.

ACTIVITY

Visit www.anstey.uk.com, a paper manufacturer's website, and download the print guide PDF (select 'Customer service'). Use it to help you answer the following questions:

- How is block printing done?
- How is embossed paper produced?

PAPER TYPES AND PATTERNS

This section looks in more detail at the types of wallpapers that you need to know about at Level 2.

PAPER TYPES

Lining paper and wood ingrain were covered at Level 1. At Level 2 you will also cover the following wallpaper types:

- simplex

- duplex

- pulp
- wood ingrain
- embossed
- blown vinyl
- washable
- vinyl
- ready-pasted vinyl
- blown vinyl
- borders.

Generic

Members of a group or type – no specific brand

Simplex, duplex and pulp are **generic** terms that refer to the initial production process of wallpapers before the application of further treatments.

SIMPLEX

This is wallpaper made from a single layer of paper. It can be produced in smooth or embossed patterns.

DUPLEX

These wall coverings consist of two pressed-together layers of paper, where the layers are usually embossed to form a pattern in relief.

PULP

This is a cheap form of simplex wallpaper – it is wallpaper produced in its simplest form from wood pulp, as described in the section on manufacture (see pages 220–221). Pulp is often used to describe thin, inexpensive printed wallpapers. These do not offer the luxury of protective layers such as vinyl, and are therefore easily marked.

Lining paper

Lining paper is a white pulp paper sold in various grades such as 800g/m^2 or 1,000g/m^2, where the number of grams per m^2 will determine how heavy and thick it is. Typically rolls are 560mm wide and 10m long – however it is possible to buy double-, treble- and quadruple-length rolls. The longer rolls can be more economical if you are carrying out a lot of lining, as waste is minimised.

Lining paper has the following common uses:

Lining paper

Porosity

The state of being porous – when small spaces or voids in a solid material mean that it can absorb liquids

- It can be used to provide a uniform surface with even **porosity** for the subsequent hanging of finishing papers.

- It can be used to line non-absorbent surfaces such as oil-painted walls, again to provide a surface of even porosity. Hanging finishing papers directly on non-absorbent surfaces could lead to defects such as springing of joints and poor drying out, leading to blistering and poor overall adhesion.

- It evens out porosity on surfaces where large areas of making good have changed the surface.

Hang lining paper using cellulose paste (see page 236 for a list of types of adhesives, such as starch paste). For thinner varieties starch ether or all-purpose paste may also be used.

Non-woven lining paper

Fibre lining paper is a non-woven material that is most suitable for covering up unsightly and poor plaster surfaces. It is extremely strong, does not require any soaking and can also be hung directly on pasted walls. Use it on surfaces such as old or poor plaster, breeze and cement blockwork, wood panelling or cement render. A good-quality heavy-duty paste should be used for all types of surfaces, and the wall should be pasted rather than the paper. All surfaces must be well prepared prior to hanging fibre lining, and when hung it can be painted with emulsion, used as a base for overhanging other wall coverings, or as a base for specialist paint effects. Fibre lining paper is used as a replacement for cotton-backed lining paper.

To hang non-woven lining paper, paste the wall using manufacturers' medium-weight ready-mixed **PVA adhesive**.

Fibre lining paper

PVA

PVA stands for polyvinyl acetate, a resin used in both adhesives and paints to provide a hard, strong film – in the case of adhesives, the film is clear and does not stain

Adhesive

In decorating and particularly paperhanging terms, adhesive is a material sometimes referred to as paste that can stick paper to ceiling and wall surfaces

Cotton-backed lining paper

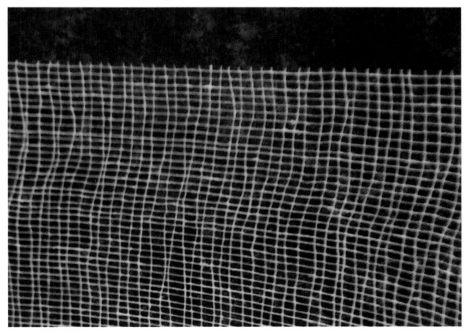

Cotton backing

Cotton-backed lining paper was developed to cover cracks and other surface irregularities. The cotton backing allows for a certain amount movement of the substrate without the crack appearing through the face of the paper. However, this has now been superseded by fibre lining papers and glass fibre preparatory papers.

If still available for hanging then hang cotton-backed lining paper as you would other lining papers, using starch or all-purpose paste applied to the cotton backing.

WOOD INGRAIN PAPER

Wood ingrain paper

Wood ingrain paper is often referred to as woodchip, and you looked at it for Level 1. It is a pulp paper made up of two layers, with small chips of wood sandwiched between them. It usually comes in 10m by 530mm rolls although, as with lining paper, it is possible to obtain double-, treble- and quadruple-length rolls for greater economy. Wood ingrain can be supplied in different grades of texture, too: fine, medium or coarse. The choice of grade really comes down to taste, depending on whether you want a more or less pronounced appearance.

Wood ingrain is usually coated with water-borne paint, or sometimes oil based paint, after hanging. Ingrain papers tend to mask irregularities in the underlying surface due to their pronounced texture.

As with lining paper, you should not over-soak the wood ingrain paper when hanging because thinner grades may tear and possibly delaminate. Delamination is described further in the section on defects (see page 238), and is when the top and bottom layers of paper separate.

Hang wood ingrain paper using starch paste or starch ether.

EMBOSSED

Embossed paper

Embossed papers are typically produced by either dry embossing or wet embossing.

Dry embossing provides a low-relief pattern suitable for ceilings and walls. Wet embossing produces a heavier high-relief pattern. Both methods mostly use duplex paper to produce the raised pattern. Paper can be produced in colour or left white for overpainting. They are suitable for both ceilings and walls.

Hang embossed papers using starch or starch ether. Do not over-fill the relief, and take care when brushing out to avoid flattening it.

BLOWN VINYL

Expanded blown vinyl textured paintable wallpaper is created by an application of liquid PVC to flat wallpaper. Within the PVC is a blowing agent, and when heat is applied to the PVC (during the production process) the PVC on the flat wallpaper expands to create the blown vinyl wallpaper, which is textured, white and paintable.

Expanded blown vinyl paintable wallpaper is used to disguise walls with cracks, lumps, bumps and even old woodchip wallpaper. The textured blown vinyl wallpaper can be painted to create a tough, hard-wearing, textured wall covering.

Hang blown vinyl using starch ether or all-purpose paste containing a fungicide. If blown vinyl is to be overlapped, as in corners for example, overlap PVA adhesive must be used because ordinary paste will not stick vinyl to vinyl. Bear in mind that blown vinyl when overlapped will produce a rather bulky appearance, so it may be best to splice the overlap to enable the bulky underlayer to be removed. This is discussed further on page 257.

Blown vinyl wallpaper

WASHABLE

This wallpaper has a paper substrate onto which the decorative surface has been sprayed or applied with an acrylic coating. The proper name for this type of paper should be acrylic-coated paper, but the inaccurate name – washable wallpaper– has caught on and is used instead. These wallpapers are classified as scrubbable and strippable, and are suitable for use in almost any area. They are more resistant to grease and moisture than plain papers, and are good for bathrooms and kitchens.

Hang washable wallpaper using starch ether or all-purpose paste containing a fungicide.

VINYL

This type of wallpaper has a paper (pulp) substrate laminated to a solid decorative surface. It is very durable because the decorative surface is a solid sheet of vinyl. It is classified as scrubbable and peelable.

Washable wallpaper

Paper-backed vinyl
Here a solid vinyl layer of material is laminated or bonded to a paper backing sheet. These wall coverings have a heat-embossed (raised) effect to register (fit) the pattern design, and provide a multitude of textural effects. They have a high-quality appearance and are durable because the decorative surface is solid vinyl. They resist moisture, stains and grease and are scrubbable and peelable, but will not withstand extreme physical abuse. Cleaning may be relatively difficult due to the raised pattern.

Fabric-backed vinyl
This wallpaper has a substrate laminated to a solid vinyl decorative surface. It is generally considered the most durable wall covering because the vinyl is a solid sheet rather than being applied in a liquid form. This type of wallpaper is ideal for consumers looking for a great degree of washability, scrubbability and durability. Fabric-backed vinyl papers are most commonly used in commercial settings.

Vinyl wallpaper

Hang vinyl papers using starch ether or all-purpose paste containing a fungicide.

READY-PASTED VINYL

This type of vinyl wallpaper has been pre-pasted in the factory with a water-activated fungicidal paste. The cut length or roll is dipped into a trough of water to wet and activate the paste.

After soaking ready-pasted paper in a trough according to the manufacturer's instructions, the paper can then be applied to the wall and smoothed down using a sponge.

BORDERS

Borders add a decorative feature to the room and are commonly used between the ceiling and the top of the wall. They can also be used around frames, or indeed to make framed feature panels as well being used at dado height. Fashion tends to dictate their use and the positioning will depend on the taste of the time. They are manufactured in rolls and generally supplied in 10m lengths – however, widths can vary greatly. As with wallpaper there is an abundance of patterns and textures available. The illustration shows a typical application.

Borders are normally unrolled on the paste table and pasted using PVA adhesive. The border is concertina folded and hung in the same way as cross-lining.

Later in the chapter the use of papers for various surfaces is discussed further, but in essence wallpapers fall into two main categories:

- *Foundation papers*: These primarily provide a base for further papers to hang on top of, which will provide the decorative finish. Some foundation papers can be painted over, such as lining paper, wood ingrain and undecorated blown vinyl or embossed papers.

- *Finishing papers*: As well as providing colour and pattern, these may also provide a surface that is washable, enabling them to be used in areas such as bathrooms and kitchens, where there will be a lot of moisture present. Embossed vinyl papers often provide a scrubbable surface that will withstand hard wear and offer water resistance. The papers will generally fall into the following categories, **pulp**, **ground**, specially treated papers, embossed and vinyl faced.

Embossed papers in particular will provide a relief texture that is suitable for covering defective substrates – they are very good at hiding underlying surface imperfections and bumps.

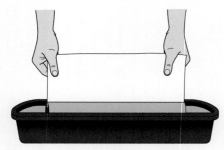

Using a pasting trough for soaking

Hanging a wallpaper border

Pulp

An untreated paper printed directly with colour print

Ground

A printed wallpaper that has had a colour applied first to provide a background

ACTIVITY

Create your own record of paper types either by using images from the internet, or by collecting/cutting different samples from your college or training centre. Arrange the samples in the order as shown in the illustrations above, giving each a title and brief details.

PATTERN AND MATCHING PAPERS

All wallpapers, except for some textures and murals, have a **pattern repeat**. The repeat is the vertical distance between one point on the pattern and the next identical point, and it is an integral part of the design. The repeat can range anywhere from 20mm – or even, occasionally, less – up to the width of the wallpaper or even more.

Pattern repeat

This is the distance between a single point on the pattern and the next point where it is repeated on the pattern

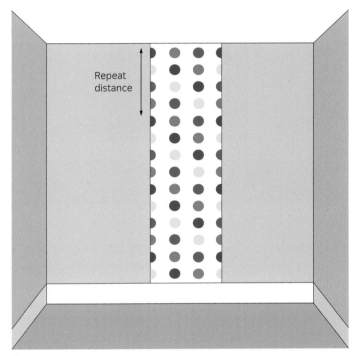

Pattern repeat

Repeat distance

Matching wallpaper pattern

It would appear that understanding **pattern match** and pattern repeat is one of the more difficult areas of wallpapering. Understanding the pattern repeat is particularly relevant when calculating how much wallpaper is required, as buying too much can be expensive, while not buying enough may mean going back to the shop and finding that the supplier no longer has any of the same batch left in stock.

Pattern match

This helps you identify where the pattern at the edge of one piece of wallpaper fits together with another roll. This could be an offset match, such as a half-drop or random match, or a straight match. The type of pattern match is given by the symbol on the packet

If the wallpaper to be hung has a pattern, find out what type of pattern match it has. There are three major types:

- *Random/free match*: In this type of pattern, the pattern matches no matter how adjoining strips are positioned. Stripes are the best examples of this type of match. It is generally recommended that you reverse every other strip to minimise visual effects such as shading or colour variations from edge to edge. Note that any random match will produce less waste, because there is no repeat distance to take into account.

- *Set/straight match*: This match has a pattern which matches on adjoining strips. Every strip will be the same at the ceiling line.

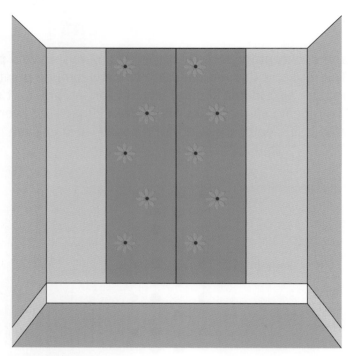

Set pattern match

■ *Drop/offset match, such as half-drop match*: Every other length is the same at the ceiling line, and the pattern runs diagonally. It takes three strips to repeat the vertical design. Every other length is identical, so when cutting it is best to number the sheets on the back to avoid confusion. It is quite common to cut paper from two rolls when dealing with drop patterns to try to minimise the amount of waste produced. Drop patterns, particularly those with a large pattern repeat distance, will certainly produce large amounts of waste when matching.

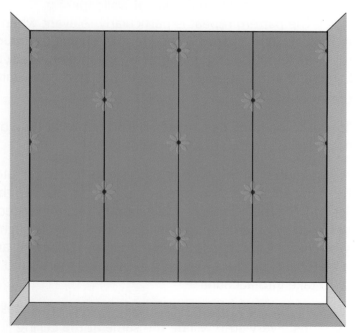

Drop pattern match

WALLPAPER LABELS

All wallpapers are labelled, and the label includes some very important details that need to be considered before hanging.

On the front of the label are the pattern number, batch number, shade number and also various symbols denoting whether the paper is, for example, washable, straight match, and so on. The back of the label contains all the manufacturer's recommended hanging instructions.

Check the batch numbers

PRE-HANGING CHECKS

- Read the label carefully before opening the roll to check that the pattern numbers and **batch** numbers match on all the rolls you are using. Matching labels in this way should help you avoid any colour or **shading** problems.

- Visually check that the rolls are not damaged.

- When opening rolls, check that there are no obvious manufacturing faults.

- It is usual to open all rolls at this point and shade them over the edge of the paste board.

- Try to locate the pattern repeat and also the suggested direction of hanging.

- Once you are satisfied that all is well, match the paper on the bench by matching the pattern edge to edge using two rolls.

Batch

The wallpaper batch is shown by an identification number, or code, that denotes when it was produced and the print details. Codes should be the same on all rolls to avoid colour differences

Shading

A process normally associated with paperhanging where the operative visually checks every roll to ensure that all rolls to be used are of the same colour and tone

INDUSTRY TIP

To avoid shading problems, batch and shade numbers should be the same on every roll, and you can also check the shading visually.

Visually check wallpaper shades and colours

Match the pattern on the bench

INTERNATIONAL PERFORMANCE SYMBOLS

The following symbols can be found in a wallpaper pattern book or on product labels. Use this guide to help you understand what the symbols mean for the best results.

Symbol	Characteristics	Symbol	Characteristics
Spongeable	Either printed with waterfast colours or thinly coated with PVA. Paste on the surface can be safely removed by gentle use of a damp sponge.	**Overlap and double cut**	Where edges cannot (or should not) be butt-jointed in the usual way, they are lapped and the two thicknesses sliced through, usually with a straight edge and a knife. The subsequent two strips of waste are pulled away, leaving two edges stuck down as a perfect butt joint. Often applies to contract materials and thicker wall coverings.
Washable	Like spongeable, but with more protection. Will withstand more wiping after light soiling.	**Peelable**	The top skin of the decoration should peel cleanly away, leaving the backing (if still secure) ready for further decoration.
Super washable	Like spongeable, but well protected with PVA. Suitable for wet areas such as bathrooms and kitchens.	**Offset match**	This is sometimes called a half-drop or drop pattern – the match is obtained by halving the repeat.
Scrubbable	Normally only applies to vinyl wall coverings used in areas with heavy wear.	**Straight match**	The pattern matches straight across the width.
Good lightfastness	This means that the wall covering should retain its original colour for a considerable amount of time, but can't be guaranteed on any permanent basis.	**Free match**	No matching required – lengths can be cut straight from the roll without wastage.

ACTIVITY

Answer the following questions:
- What is a pattern repeat?
- What is a pattern match?

Symbol	Characteristics	Symbol	Characteristics
Moderate lightfastness	Beware! This product may well fade or discolour in areas of direct sunlight.	**Design repeat distance offset** $$\frac{50}{25}\,\text{cm}$$	The circumference of the printed rollers, half of which represents the wall covering drop (where applicable). This is very important information for calculating the number of lengths available from a roll and will give the total quantity you will need.
Adhesive to wallcovering	This needs to be pasted, as it is not a ready-pasted or paste-the-wall product.	**Direction of hanging**	This can be found (rarely), on the selvedge of wall coverings that have been untrimmed, or it may be on the reverse of some products. In other respects, on a label it will mean 'don't reverse the lengths'.
Ready-pasted	To be hung after immersion in a trough of clean water according to the instructions.	**Reverse alternate lengths**	Mostly applicable to plain effects, and necessary to minimise the risk of side-to-side shading.
Paste the wall	Applicable only to Novamura, some textiles and some wide-width wall coverings. Always check the type of adhesive and the method of application.	**Co-ordinated fabric available**	This does not necessarily mean an exact matching fabric even when the design is the same, as colours may vary because of the different printing techniques.
Strippable	Should peel cleanly from the wall in a dry state.	**Wet removable**	This will not dry-peel.

FUNCTIONAL SKILLS

Find a wallpaper information label online or at your college or training centre. Copy the information about the name of the paper and the shade or batch number. Also copy the symbols relating to this specific wallpaper and write down what they mean.

Work on this activity can support FE E3 (R.2).

ACTIVITY

Answer the following questions:
- What is a batch number?
- What is shading?

SELECT AND PREPARE ADHESIVES

This section looks at the types and uses of various adhesives. In general terms adhesives are considered in terms of their water content, as this has the most impact when you come to select an adhesive for a particular surface or paper.

TYPES OF ADHESIVES

The types of paper studied at Level 2 are relatively lightweight, and the following types of adhesive are suitable for use with them:

- *Starch paste*: This is typically supplied in powder form and is based on organic starches extracted from maize, corn, wheat and so on. It is easy to prepare and should be used when freshly made. It can be used on all types of paper providing that it contains fungicide. If no fungicide protection is indicated, it is best not to use it for vinyl papers because of the potential for mould growth under the surface of the paper.

- *Cellulose paste*: This will generally produce the thinnest of pastes and is therefore only really suitable for lightweight papers such as lining papers and other lightweight foundation papers.

- *Cellulose paste moderated with starch ether*: This is suitable for all types of paper, including lightweight vinyls. It usually contains fungicide to reduce the possibility of mould growth occurring.

- *Ready-mixed adhesive (medium weight)*: This is typically a PVA-based adhesive. It can be supplied in light, medium and heavy grade depending on the type of wallpaper to be hung. It is designed to roller or brush directly from the tub for speedy application – no mixing or dilution is required. The super-smooth, easy-spread adhesive has strong grab and easy slide for perfect wallpaper hanging.

- *Border and overlap paste*: This is PVA resin-based adhesive supplied in tubes and plastic tubs. It is commonly used for sticking overlaps of vinyl wallpaper, as well as fixing borders.

- *PVA*: As described above, ready-mixed adhesives and border/overlap adhesives use PVA resin to provide a strong bond with the surface. Papers hung with PVA are often quite difficult to remove because of this strong bond – however, it is essential when hanging heavyweight materials.

The table opposite shows the advantages and disadvantages of common wallpaper adhesives.

The adhesive you use will depend on the surface and type of paper

Adhere

To stick to a substance or surface

Type of adhesive	Water/solid content	Advantages	Disadvantages
Starch paste	Medium solid – low water	■ Relatively slow setting ■ **Adheres** well to surfaces	■ Easily stains the face of the paper ■ Encourages and supports mould growth if not fungicide protected
Cellulose paste	Low solid – high water	■ Fairly transparent and therefore less likely to stain the face of papers	■ Has less adhesion than starch paste ■ When cellulose paste has been standing around for a long period of time it will become thin and unusable
Cellulose paste modified with starch ether (all-purpose paste)	Medium solid – medium water	■ Fairly transparent ■ Mixes easily to a smooth paste ■ Better adhesive properties than cellulose	■ Can mark the face of papers more than cellulose
Ready-mixed adhesive (medium weight)	High solid – low water	■ No mixing ■ Easy to apply ■ Suitable for hanging all types of lining papers and wallpapers	■ More expensive than other types of adhesive
Overlap adhesive	High solid – low water	■ Ready mixed ■ Easy to apply	■ Need to ensure any excess is properly cleaned off as it will show as shiny marks if left

Consistency

Related directly to the viscosity of a coating, which can be altered by the addition of thinners or solvents

Mixing paste

INDUSTRY TIP

When mixing paste it is best to create a swirling effect in the bucket of water and then to sprinkle the dry adhesive into the centre while continuing to stir.

CONSISTENCY

Incorrect preparation of pastes and adhesives can lead to difficulties when hanging the wallpaper. When mixing pastes, particularly in powder or flake form, it is essential to get the **consistency** right and also to avoid lumps. If the paste is lumpy it will be difficult to flatten out when pasting and it will be likely to show as lumps or blisters in the finished job. It is important to follow the manufacturer's instructions and adjust the consistency of the paste to suit the various types of paper. Do not over-thin the paste, as this is likely to cause problems after pasting such as over-stretching, over-soaking and possibly delamination of duplex papers. Thicker/heavier wallpaper will typically require a much thicker adhesive.

Paperhanging in warm rather than hot rooms will tend to enable pastes to dry more quickly, usually providing a better result – bubbles and blisters are less likely to remain, as the paper will dry evenly. In some cases working in too cold an atmosphere can lead to slow drying, and consequently, uneven drying out.

If pastes are stored overnight, ensure they are covered to avoid contamination from dust and debris that may settle on the top. If pastes are kept for too long they can become stale and unusable. In particular cellulose pastes become thin, and starch pastes can also thin and start to smell.

DEFECTS

The table describes some common defects associated with pasting wallpaper.

Defect	Cause
Blisters	Can be due to using adhesive that is too thin, which in turn will lead to over-soaking. The paper will then blister when hung, as it is likely to be still expanding on the wall. Some of the blisters may remain after drying.
Delamination	Delamination of duplex or two-part papers can occur particularly if the paper has been allowed to over-soak or has been pasted with paste that is too thin. The paste applied will soak through the first layer, softening the paper manufacturer's adhesive used to laminate the two layers together. Once this happens then the two layers can separate.

Defect	Cause
Stretching	This is usually caused by over-soaking, or by application of paste that is too thin. The paper continues to expand and if this occurs with pattern papers the pattern will not match up, as lengths will have stretched differently.

Cellulose modified with starch ether is probably the most popular choice for decorators for general hanging of papers, including lining papers and wood ingrain, because of its good adhesive and low marking properties.

Other pastes can be considered, and more recently the use of 'all-purpose' pastes has caught on. These pastes provide all the benefits of starch and cellulose pastes. The thickness of the paste can easily be adjusted according to the type of paper being hung. They can be supplied in powder form for self-mixing, or ready mixed in tubs. Tub-based pastes are often used with rollers when pasting.

Do follow correct procedures when disposing of any waste product to avoid contaminating the water course.

ENVIRONMENTAL AND HEALTH AND SAFETY REGULATIONS

It is extremely important to be aware of the environmental and health and safety regulations when mixing and using pastes and adhesives. In particular it is important to ensure that COSHH Regulations are followed and that the correct PPE is worn.

CORRECT PPE

Although most paperhanging activities will take place in a closed-room environment, compliance with PPE and site requirements is necessary in order to gain access across a site or within a refurbished property. This means wearing a safety helmet, hi-viz jacket, safety boots, gloves and goggles on some building sites as standard practice. It is usually permissible to remove these while actually paperhanging, but always check with your supervisor or site agent first.

In many cases, though paperhanging tasks will take place without a hard hat, safety boots and goggles, gloves and barrier cream may well be used. A number of pastes and adhesives contain fungicide to reduce the likelihood of mould growth and this can irritate skin, and even lead to skin conditions such as dermatitis. Ensure that you wash your hands, especially before eating food, to avoid **absorbing** or **ingesting** any product, which could lead to stomach irritation or upset.

Use barrier cream to avoid developing skin conditions

Absorb

To take something in – in this case harmful products through pores in the skin

Ingest

To take into the body or mouth in the act of swallowing or absorption

Overalls with a bib or a paperhanger's apron are extremely useful not only as protective clothing but to enable you to carry a small number of tools, particularly a hanging brush and shears, in the pockets.

PRODUCT DATA SHEETS

Manufacturers have a legal duty under health and safety legislation to provide information about their products, and it is important to obtain a safety data sheet for each product used. Always ensure that you follow the manufacturer's instructions and carry out a risk assessment from the information provided to determine what the hazards are and how they can be reduced. Advice on first aid measures, such as how to deal with any ingestion of the product, protective equipment required and methods of disposal of waste products, will be covered by the manufacturer's data sheet.

WASTE DISPOSAL

In general terms pastes are not described as hazardous – however, waste materials should not be allowed to enter drains, soil or bodies of water but should be collected and disposed of in the appropriate skip on site or in the correct area of the Local Authority recycling centre. Additionally disposal of waste products will need to be carried out in accordance with the proper requirements for segregation of potentially hazardous materials.

COSHH AND WORK AT HEIGHT REGULATIONS

Regulations that need to be considered include COSHH, particularly in relation to the handling of materials such as fungicidal paste. If any of the work is to be carried out at height then the Work at Height Regulations 2005 (as amended) will have to be adhered to, so be sure that you that you have assessed the risks and are working safely. See Chapter 8 for more information on the Work at Height Regulations.

APPLYING PAPERS TO CEILINGS AND WALLS

There are a number of considerations when applying paper to ceilings and walls. The following section looks at the access equipment required as well as the tools and equipment you will use and the methods and techniques you will need to know about.

Product data sheets will include first-aid information

ACTIVITY

Source a wallpaper adhesive data sheet either by finding one at your college or workplace or by searching online, and use it to help you answer the following questions:

- What safety precautions should you take when mixing the adhesive?
- Does it contain anything to inhibit mould growth?

PREPARATION

To ensure good preparation of the underlying surface it is usual to apply a size coat prior to hanging foundation papers. Sizing will help the paper adhere better, and will allow for good movement when hanging so that the paper slides into position and forms good **butt joints**. For more information on preparing surfaces for decoration, go to Chapter 3.

Butt joint

Edges of lengths of paper that touch without a gap or overlap

ACCESS EQUIPMENT

You are likely to need to apply wallpaper above ground level. A sound knowledge of the Work at Height Regulations 2005 (as amended) will enable you to correctly select the access equipment required for each task. It is probable that you will use one or more of the following items at some stage in the papering process:

- hop-ups
- steps
- trestles
- lightweight staging
- tower scaffolds to enable access to higher areas.

The selection of equipment will often depend on space, height and following correct procedures as defined in the risk assessment and method statement. In many domestic interiors lack of space and the need for a low-risk approach will often dictate the use of hop-ups and lightweight staging.

STEPS AND PODIUM STEPS

The use of steps and podium steps will be limited to small areas when working on ceilings, but will often be used for papering walls.

Hop-up

Platform steps

Podium steps

LIGHTWEIGHT PLATFORM AND TRESTLES

Trestle

Trestle scaffold in use

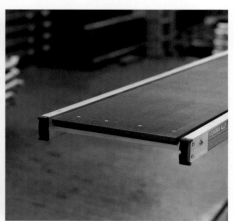

Lightweight staging

Lightweight platforms can be used with hop-ups or trestles to produce a platform of varying lengths. Handrails can be fitted depending on your particular set-up and whether the risk assessment identifies them as a requirement.

TOWER SCAFFOLD

Tower scaffolds may be used where space allows. They will need to be used with guard rails to guard against falling. They can be adapted to enable longer working platforms to be attached by using towers at each end of the run. It may be possible to utilise a cut-down version of this structure for work at a lower height.

STAIR SCAFFOLD

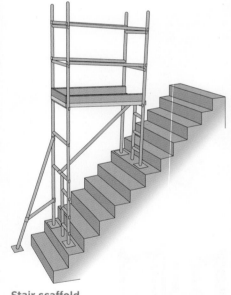

Stair scaffold

The model shown here features a walkthrough frame, enabling the user to gain access to the inside of the scaffold to go up and down the ladder when required. A stair scaffold should be used on all staircases to enable safe access to both ceiling and wall. This equipment stands clear of the walls to allow the lengths of paper to be dropped through and finished off.

Further information and details about the regulations and safe working practices can be found in Chapter 8.

TOOLS AND EQUIPMENT

The most commonly used tools are a paperhanging brush, shears and other trimming equipment such as trimming knives with retractable or snap-off blades. Vinyl papers are often smoothed down using wide spatulas made of hard plastic to provide the required pressure for removing air pockets.

Laser levels are very useful for providing horizontal lines for cross-lining and also for hanging borders. Equally they can also be used to produce vertically plumbed lines. As described at Level 1 the

A range of wallpapering tools

following tools and equipment will also be required to complete your tool kit:

- tape measure
- folding rule
- plumb bob
- spirit level
- sponges
- pencil
- paste brush
- buckets
- rubbish containers/bags
- metal straight edge
- chalk and line
- troughs
- paste table.

ACTIVITY

Answer the following question:

Why should a stair scaffold be used for staircases instead of a ladder and scaffold board?

For further information refer to Chapter 8 or the Work at Height Regulations 2005 (as amended).

USE OF PAPERS

Foundation papers and finishing papers are used to produce various effects. Foundation papers can be used as part of the preparation process, while finishing papers will create a visually pleasing finished effect.

FOUNDATION OR PREPARATORY PAPERS

Papers such as lining papers and ingrains are described as **preparatory** papers, and their primary use is to ensure that there is a defect-free substrate available for hanging finishing papers or for applying paints. As described earlier in the chapter, lining papers are used as a **foundation** for either painting or for finishing papers.

In the case of hanging lining papers it is usual to hang horizontally, which is termed cross-lining. Hanging in this manner helps to avoid joints lining up in the layers of paper.

Lining papers should also be used on gloss-painted walls after suitable preparation, to enable the finishing paper to stick to the surface. Glossy surfaces offer poor adhesion, and without lining it is likely that the finishing paper would lift and peel away. The gloss surface should be abraded (preferably wet) to remove as much of the shine as possible. This abrasion will also provide a good key for

Preparatory

In the context of paperhanging, this refers to the preparation of a surface for further treatment

Foundation

In the context of paperhanging, this means providing a suitable base for further treatment, such as hanging finishing paper over the top or for paint application

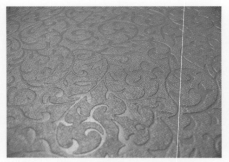

Embossed paper can be hung and then painted

FUNCTIONAL SKILLS

Using an online dictionary or one from your library, look up the words 'accentuate' and 'accent' from the passage to the right and explain their meanings in the sentences in which they are used.

Work on this activity can support FE1 (1.2.2).

ACTIVITY

Using wallpaper pattern books either online or from another source, identify patterns that will demonstrate the principles of making a room appear taller or wider. Attach the pattern to a sheet of paper with your own drawings to show the effect.

the paper to adhere to. Hang the paper horizontally as a foundation for finishing papers, or vertically if you will be applying paints as the finish.

Undecorated blown vinyl and embossed papers are also used as foundation papers, as they are usually painted over after hanging. Wood ingrains are also used in this way. Each of these types of paper affords the opportunity of disguising rough and uneven surfaces, as their textured finish tends to disperse the light effect and avoids accentuating the defects beneath.

FINISHING PAPERS

As the term implies, finishing papers are used to provide an effect through a coloured, visually textured or patterned finish. Finishing papers will include those listed earlier in the chapter, such as the various types of vinyl, embossed papers, printed pulps and grounds. Borders are also used to give a finished effect to the edges of areas and provide a visual impact or accent.

Patterned and textured papers can provide a variety of designs and colours that enable you to achieve interesting and visually appealing effects in a way that plain colours do not. Finishing papers can change the appearance and visual dimensions of rooms. Patterns with a diagonal or horizontal emphasis can make rooms appear wider, and similarly patterns with a vertical emphasis can make rooms appear taller.

Vertical patterns make a room appear taller

Horizontal patterns make a room appear wider

HANGING TECHNIQUES AND PROCESSES

The processes described below will, in principle, be the same for hanging foundation, plain and most patterned papers. Some papers, particularly specialist types, will require special hanging instructions, and some of these will be dealt with in the Level 3 syllabus.

A number of factors will need to be considered before you start paperhanging, including the following:

- the amount of paper required
- starting and finishing points relative to the source(s) of natural light or the feature wall

- hanging method (horizontal or vertical)

- paper selection

- type of paste required

- pasting method to be used

- wall and ceiling features such as doors, features/obstacles, internal and external angles, sockets/switches/ceiling roses, borders and window reveals.

Before starting work try to ensure that the room is cleared of furniture or that it has been arranged in the middle of the room. This will be particularly important when papering a ceiling. Cover any items left in the room and lay a dust sheet in the area of the paste board.

PAPERING WALLS

The following section deals with the process to follow when papering walls.

STARTING AND FINISHING POINTS

The starting point in many rooms will be to hang the first length away from the light – ie a window or other source of daylight. Working away from the light in this manner will minimise shadows appearing along the edges of the joints and therefore they will be less noticeable.

In some instances it may also be desirable to consider any features such as fireplaces or feature walls in order to achieve the best effect. Note the idea of **centring** over the fireplace to try to get an even pattern appearance.

The finishing point in many cases will be above the doorway to enter the room. The main idea, particularly when using patterned papers, is to find the area where the loss of pattern will be least noticeable.

There will be a number of occasions when you may need to mark starting lines, and these include the first drop to be hung after internal and external angles. It will also be necessary to provide a horizontally levelled line when cross-lining. This line will be marked approximately one length down from the ceiling line to ensure that all following lengths remain horizontal. Cross-lining is recommended when papering over excessive making good, over solvent-painted surfaces that offer little adhesion and to even up the porosity of the surface before hanging the finishing paper. The lining paper will be hung horizontally to the vertical finishing paper.

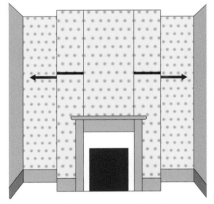

Centring wallpaper over a fireplace

Centring

Setting out a wall to create a balanced or even effect for the pattern. Working out from the centre should enable this

INDUSTRY TIP

Don't assume that a paper comes off a roll in the direction it should be hung. Look at the design to make sure you hang it the right way up.

MARKING LINES

Few walls are truly square or perfectly vertical. To overcome this, and avoid your pattern going out of alignment, it is essential to mark a vertical pencil line against a plumb line or long spirit level adjacent to where the first length is to hang.

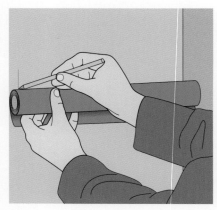

STEP 1 Measure the width of a roll or use a roll of paper to mark the wall, one width away from the corner (less 10mm) to allow a slight overlap onto the return wall or chosen starting point.

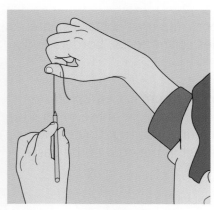

STEP 2 Allow the plumb bob to swing freely until it is at rest, before putting a pencil mark down the wall behind the string.

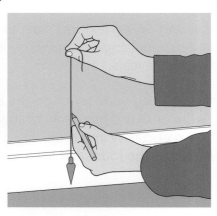

STEP 3 Using a plumb line, lightly pencil some guide marks from ceiling to skirting.

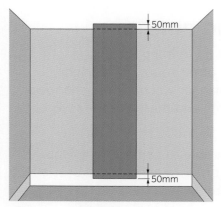

50mm

50mm

STEP 4 Measure your first length, allowing an extra 50mm at the top and bottom.

STEP 5 Cut all lengths of paper on the table ready for pasting.

Repeat the process on every wall.

MEASURING AND CALCULATING QUANTITIES OF ROLLS OF WALLPAPER

Before starting the paperhanging project it is important to calculate how many rolls of paper will be required so that you can buy enough before starting the job. There are a few methods used by decorators to calculate the paper quantity, but the area and girthing methods are shown here.

Area method

This method makes use of knowing the area of a roll of paper being used and dividing the total area to be papered by that figure. The following calculations illustrate this method.

Example

Area of roll of paper: 10m long × 0.525m wide = 5.25m²

Example room dimensions: 4.5m long × 3.5m wide × 2.1m high.

You can calculate the area of the walls in a similar way.

To calculate the area of the room it is useful to add together the distance around the room (often referred to as the perimeter) and then multiply by the height to give the total area.

In the example shown, the calculation will be as follows:

Area of the walls:

(4.5m + 3.5m + 4.5m + 3.5m) = 16m (perimeter)
× 2.1m (height) = 33.6m²

To work out how many rolls you need you then divide the area of the walls by the area of a roll of paper:

33.6m² ÷ 5.25m² = 6.4 rolls of paper

This total should always be rounded up to the next full number, so in this case seven rolls will be required.

This method of calculation will be perfectly adequate for calculating non-patterned wallpapers such as lining paper and wood ingrain, but for patterned papers more accurate methods should be used.

To make this a more accurate figure the total area of items such as doors and windows would need to be deducted as well as an allowance made for pattern repeat.

Girthing method

An alternative method of calculation known as the girthing method can also be used, and is shown in the following illustration.

Using the measurements in the example room above, we will work out how many rolls of paper are needed.

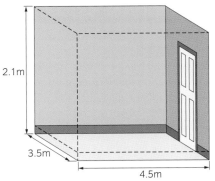

2.1m

3.5m

4.5m

Room dimensions

Example

For example purposes we will presume that our rolls of paper have the following dimensions:

Roll length: 10m

Roll width: 0.5m (500mm)

And the room has the following dimensions:

4.5m long × 3.5m wide × 2.1m high

So our calculation is as follows:

Step 1

Add together all the sides of the room to get the perimeter:

$$4.5 + 3.5 + 4.5 + 3.5 = 16\text{m}$$

Step 2

Divide the perimeter by the width of a roll of paper to calculate number of lengths = 16m ÷ 0.5m = 32 lengths required

Step 3

You now need to know how many lengths can be cut from a roll. To do this, you need to know the room height, with 100mm wastage for each length. This means that you are now measuring a room height of 2.2m, rather than the original 2.1m. Divide the length of one roll by the new room height to find out how many lengths can be cut from one roll.

$$10 ÷ 2.2 = 4.5$$

Round *down* to get the number of lengths per roll: 4.

Step 4

Divide the total number of lengths required by the number of lengths in one roll – in this example it will be: 32 ÷ 4 = **8 rolls**

In many cases neither method shown will make sufficient allowance for waste, particularly when applied to drop patterns. For many domestic rooms of a standard 2.3m height, it may only be possible to cut three lengths from a roll. In the example given this would mean buying an extra three rolls, as 11 rolls would be required. However, the girthing method is probably the more accurate of the two methods described here.

As described on page 232, this waste can be minimised when cutting from two rolls.

CALCULATING QUANTITIES FOR CEILINGS

Quantities of paper for ceilings are normally calculated using a method that involves calculating how many lengths can be cut from a roll. Then divide the width of the room by the width of the roll of paper to work out how many lengths are required.

Example

Using the room sizes from the last illustration:

Length of roll of paper divided by length of room = 10m ÷ 4.7m (added 100mm for cutting at each end) = 2.1 lengths, therefore this will be 2 lengths per roll

Width of room = 3.5m ÷ 0.5m = 7 lengths required. Allow 8 lengths (best to allow extra length for any variations to room width due to room being out of square)

If 8 lengths are required and we can cut 2 lengths from a roll, then:

$$8 ÷ 2 = \textbf{4 rolls required}$$

INDUSTRY TIP

A more practical way of following this girthing method would be to mark the number of lengths around the room using a roll of wallpaper or a tape measure set at 525mm, and divide that total by three. Three is the average number of lengths cut from one roll of wallpaper, particularly when using patterned wallpapers. You do need to consider the height of the room to be sure of the number that can be cut.

INDUSTRY TIP

It is quite common practice to order an extra roll to allow for waste.

FUNCTIONAL SKILLS

Using the following dimensions, calculate how many rolls of wallpaper are needed for both the ceiling and walls using either one width or length measurement. As in the previous examples, ignore any aspects of pattern or allowance for doors and windows.

Room size = 6.2m long × 3m wide × 2.3m high.

Work on this activity can support FM1 (C1.9).

Answers: 5 rolls for ceiling if hung in 3m direction, 6 rolls if hung in 6.2m direction, and 10 rolls for 4 walls.

INDUSTRY TIP

Always measure twice before cutting lengths of wallpaper to ensure you don't make any mistakes.

CUTTING AND PASTING METHODS

We looked in detail at the various cutting types at Level 1, but this topic needs to be revisited at Level 2. Perfecting the skill of using paperhanging shears is extremely important. This will require lots of practice to ensure that you cut straight and true each time without tearing the paper.

Shears can be used for all cutting activities, including cutting around obstacles. You will need to keep them sharp to cut accurately around obstacles.

Using trimming knives accurately and well will also require practice. They are particularly useful for cutting against edges and around obstacles. Safe use is always important when using sharp tools to ensure that you do not cut yourself. If you are using knives with retractable blades, do ensure that the blades are fully retracted when they are not in use – this is especially important if you store them in your paperhanging apron. When using trimming knives with snap-off blades you will need to take the same precautions, and in addition the snapped-off blades must be stored in a specially designed container.

One further tool that is sometimes used for cutting, particularly around obstacles, is the casing wheel. However, it has become less popular and is now almost impossible to source. It is used in a similar way as a knife but the wheel is rolled around the obstacle, cutting as it goes. These have largely been replaced by knives as they are difficult to keep sharp or re-sharpen.

PASTING METHODS

There are a number of possible pasting methods, including pasting the paper on the bench using a brush or roller, pasting the wall using a brush or roller, applying paste using a pasting machine, or using a wallpaper pasting trough for ready-pasted papers. The pasting-the-wall technique is only suitable for those papers where the manufacturer has specified this method of application.

Pasting using a brush

This is a tried-and-tested method employed for pasting papers or walls. Care must be taken to ensure that the correct amount of paste is applied, and of all the methods this is probably the slowest in terms of speed of application.

Pasting using a roller

This is a relatively modern approach to pasting and will enable a speedier application of the paste. Again, care is needed to ensure that the correct amount of paste is applied.

Paperhanging shears

Snap-off trimming knife

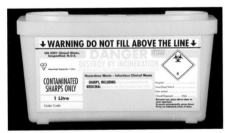

Sharps box

Pasting using a brush

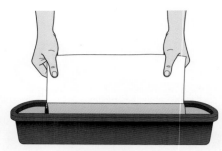

Using a pasting trough

Pasting machine

Pasting the paper

Pasting using a pasting trough

This method is only suitable for ready-pasted papers. The wallpaper has a dried paste coating applied at the manufacturing stage, before sale. The cut length is rolled and immersed in a trough that contains water, allowed to soak and then pulled from the trough. Excess water is allowed to drain off before the paper is hung on the wall.

Pasting paper using a pasting machine

Paste is mixed and poured into the machine trough. The machine roller guides are set to the correct pressure and the wallpaper is pulled through, allowing paste to be applied automatically to the face of the wallpaper. This is the quickest method of application.

PASTE, FOLD AND SOAK PAPER IN LINE WITH MANUFACTURER'S INSTRUCTIONS

Apply paste up through the middle of the length of paper and paste out towards the edge of the paste board, first towards the top edge and then pulling the paper across down towards the bottom edge (nearest you). Once the length of paper on the paste table has been pasted, begin folding the paper, ensuring that the edges are square when folded to stop them from drying out. Make sure that no paste gets onto the face of the paper or onto the paste table (from where it may be transferred to the face of the paper). Depending on the length of paper being pasted, you may choose to use either the end-to-end folding technique, or the concertina folding technique. Typically end-to-end folding is selected for folding papers for standard height rooms when hanging them vertically. Concertina folding is the method selected when hanging horizontally, for example when cross-lining. This method is also used when hanging ceiling papers and can be employed for extremely long vertical lengths such as on staircases. This method makes it easier to handle smaller folds when opening out and following the remainder of the hanging process.

Once the paper has been pasted, it should be allowed to soak for an appropriate length of time according to the manufacturer's instructions.

Under-soaking

If paper is not soaked enough this can lead to it having air bubbles underneath once hung – also known as blistering. This defect occurs because the paper is still trying to expand, and as it will be stuck in some places the paper will push outwards to form bubbles or blisters.

Over-soaking

If the paper has been allowed to soak for too long it will have over-stretched, and some of the paste may have started to dry. When paper over-soaks it will also be much harder to handle and will tear more easily. Duplex papers such as wood ingrain may delaminate when over-soaked. This is where the top layer separates from the bottom layer.

For more about these defects, see pages 258–260.

FOLDING

Concertina fold

End-to-end fold

These images show both concertina and end-to-end folding. Typically concertina folding is used for lining papers, ceiling papers and extra-long lengths such as those on a staircase.

End-to-end folding is used for most standard-sized rooms, and makes it easier to mark papers that require cutting for width. This will be required when hanging to a corner, and each side of the corner will require cutting to width.

INDUSTRY TIP

Marking the top of the paper on the reverse with a pencil will ensure that you don't hang a piece upside down. This can easily happen with a plain paper.

INSTRUCTIONS FOR PAPERING WALLS

The following steps outline the basic process of papering walls.

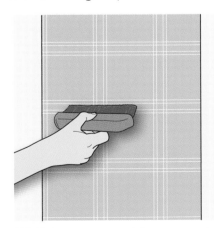

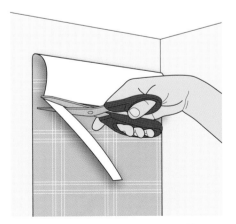

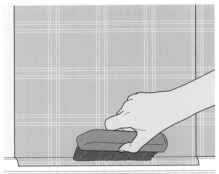

STEP 1 Having pasted the paper and allowed it to soak, in line with the manufacturer's instructions, hang the top fold against the plumbed line and brush out from the centre, working down.

STEP 2 When the paper is smoothly brushed down, run the outer edge of your scissors along the ceiling angle, peel away the paper, cut off the excess along the crease, then brush back onto the wall.

STEP 3 At the skirting, tap your brush gently into the top edge, peel away the paper and cut along the folded line with scissors or blade as before, then brush back.

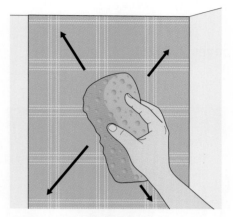

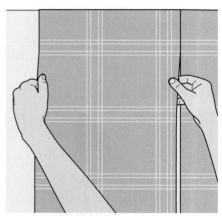

STEP 4 Using a sponge and a bucket of clean water, make sure you remove all of the paste from the surface of the paper.

STEP 5 Cut the next piece, allowing for pattern repeat, and paste and soak as before. Hang the piece, butting it up to the first, taking care to match the pattern. Do not overlap.

Papering around electrical fittings

Be very careful when applying wallpapers over, under or around electrical switches, sockets and similar items. It is recommended that you turn off the supply at the mains before carrying out this task, as it possible to receive an electric shock as a result of the wet metal shears coming in contact with live areas.

- Smooth the wallpaper down very gently over the fitting and then, for square shapes, pierce the paper in the centre to mark the corners and make diagonal cuts from the centre to each corner. Some decorators prefer to slightly unscrew the fitting so that the wallpaper can be tucked just behind.

- Press the wallpaper firmly around the edge of the fitting, lightly mark the outline and trim away the surplus.

- For circular objects such as ceiling roses and light fittings, make a series of cuts to produce a star shape.

- Press down around the outline, mark and trim in the same way.

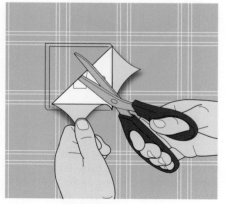

Making diagonal cuts

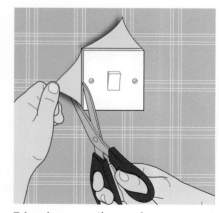

Trimming away the surplus

Papering behind radiators

Ideally, you should drain the radiator and take it off the wall so that you can paper behind it. If that is not possible, first turn off the heat and wait for the radiator to cool. Paste the strip of paper to the wall above the radiator, then slit it from the bottom edge so that you can smooth it down on either side of the radiator's fixing brackets. Press the paper in place behind the radiator, using a dry radiator paint roller.

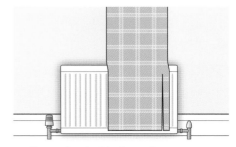

Wallpapering behind a radiator

Papering around corners

Allow a minimum of 5mm to turn into the corner. Turning as little as possible will minimise the amount of pattern lost. Sufficient turn should be allowed, however, for the corner to be possibly out of plumb.

When applying paper to corners, ensure that the return piece is plumbed so that the paper hung on the return wall will remain vertical.

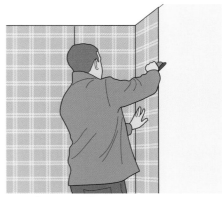

Papering around a corner

Papering around windows as the starting point

Decorators use a number of methods for papering around windows, and the following is a typical example used to get a good result.

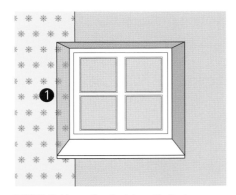

STEP 1 Hang the first length that goes into the recess and make cuts, top and bottom, to allow the spare piece to be brushed into the recess.

STEP 2 Join the next piece above the window and turn under the recess, then trim off the excess.

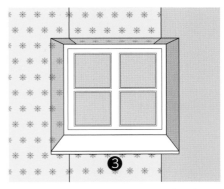

STEP 3 Join the next piece under the window and trim off the excess. Continue hanging the short lengths at the top and bottom of the window to fill spaces until the other side of the window is reached.

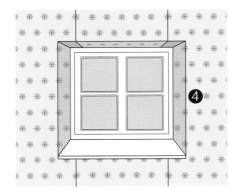

STEP 4 Hang the final length for the other side of the window as in Step 1. Ensure that this length is checked for plumb, as hanging around obstacles can set the paper out of plumb.

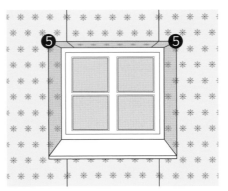

STEP 5 Cut and paste under the head of the window, slightly over-sized, to allow for laying under the edge of the paper already hung.

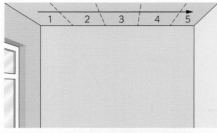

Work away from the natural light source

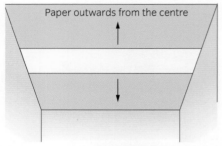

Paper outwards from the centre

Hang paper from the centre of the ceiling

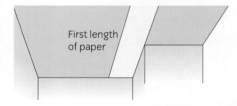

First length of paper

Hang the longest piece of paper first in odd-shaped rooms

PAPERING CEILINGS

Papering ceilings involves some considerations that are different from when you paper walls.

STARTING POINTS

When papering ceilings, in most cases it will be best to hang lengths working from the natural light source. Using this method minimises the likelihood of any overlapped edges appearing when viewed from across the room.

When hanging patterned papers to ceilings it may be desirable to centre the paper to enable an even pattern effect across the whole ceiling.

For odd-shaped or L-shaped rooms, it may be preferable to hang the longest length first and work away from there.

In some cases economy of cutting and hanging will determine the direction of hanging. This should be considered as part of the planning process when you are calculating the quantity of paper required (see page 248).

MARKING OUT

Mark out a starting point using a chalk line

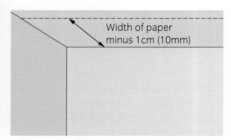

Width of paper minus 1cm (10mm)

Measure a width of paper out from the wall

As with walls, it is particularly important to get the first length of paper absolutely straight. Ceiling/wall junctions are not usually true enough to use as a guide. It is better to mark a chalk line and then position the first length along it.

INSTRUCTIONS FOR PAPERING CEILINGS

The following steps outline the basic process of papering ceilings.

INDUSTRY TIP

It is usual to carry out a trial run first to ensure that sufficient paste is being transferred to the ceiling.

STEP 1 Paste can be applied to most papers by brush, roller or pasting machine. If the brush or roller method is employed, start pasting down through the centre, then outwards to the edges. Make sure no paste gets onto the edges of the paper.

STEP 2 After each paste board length has been pasted, start folding in a concertina fashion. Try to ensure that the folds are no greater than 350mm, as if they are too wide this will make you need to stretch beyond arm's length.

STEP 3 Use a spare roll of paper or cardboard tube to act as a crutch to support the weight of the paper during the hanging process. Using this method will prevent paper from falling around your head as the length is opened.

STEP 4 Position the edge of the first length of paper against the chalk line and smooth the other edge into the ceiling/wall edge to give a 10mm overlap onto the wall. If the edge of the wall is not straight, the overlap will be uneven rather than the paper on the ceiling.

STEP 5 Brush out the bubbles with a paperhanging brush, using a sweeping action through the centre and brushing out to the edges. Continue opening each of the concertina folds while walking backwards along the scaffold. Always be aware of your footing and the edge of the scaffold platform to avoid stepping off the edge. If there is room to use a platform with guard rails, this will add extra protection.

STEP 6 Run wallpaper scissors along the ceiling/wall edge to make a sharp crease. Gently pull back the paper and cut along the crease. Brush the trimmed edge back into place, applying extra paste at the edges if necessary. Butt the next length of paper against the first.

INDUSTRY TIP

It can be dangerous to just drop waste offcuts onto the floor, as they will be a potential slip or trip hazard.

Cutting around a central light fitting

Cutting excess paper from the end

Mitre cut in a corner

Papering around electrical fittings

When papering ceilings it is quite likely that you will encounter obstacles such as ceiling roses – these will require cutting around. This will take a good deal of practice to get right while you are still holding onto the full length of paper at the same time. The star cut technique should be employed once the centre of the rose has been found with the point of the shears. Cuts can then be made from the centre outwards in a star fashion to the edge of the rose. Once this been done, push the rose through the paper, loosely press into position and then proceed with hanging the ceiling paper. Trim off around the rose using a trimming knife once the whole length has been properly smoothed into position.

HANGING WALLPAPER BORDERS

When hanging wallpaper borders it is usual to establish a level line using either a laser level or a long spirit level. These levels need to be accurately transferred around the room. Once the border has been cut for length and pasted using border adhesive, the border should be folded concertina fashion. Hang the border in a similar way as you would hang on a ceiling, by opening folds as you go. Smooth out the folds with a smoothing brush, spatula or sponge.

If you are using border wallpaper to make frames or to emphasise doorways, it is almost certain that you will want to make a mitre cut at each corner or junction. The illustration shows the border being cut at a 45° angle. Use a trimming knife to cut against a straight edge or wide-bladed scraper.

Hanging a wallpaper border

PAPERING STAIRCASES

Papering staircases presents slightly different challenges, although the actual hanging technique is the same. Not all staircases will follow the same process as shown in the illustration, but this will give you an understanding of the principles to apply to the planning process.

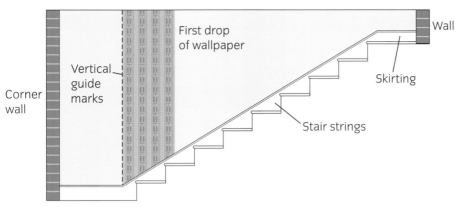

Hanging paper on a staircase

The first length of paper to be hung should be as illustrated – by selecting the longest drop and plumbing a line. Hang the first length to this line and then work away in both directions until the wall is completed.

ACCESS EQUIPMENT FOR STAIRCASES

As previously described on page 242, it is essential to use the type of equipment illustrated for papering staircases.

GOOD PRACTICE WHEN PAPERING

Read the manufacturer's instructions first.

- Follow soaking times carefully – this will prevent shrinkage – and use the correct adhesive.
- Keep the face of the paper clean, removing adhesive with a sponge and clean water.
- Take care to apply an even amount of adhesive on the paper, particularly the edges.
- Make sure the wall is properly prepared, smooth and clean. Good preparation will ensure a better finish.
- Always use a sharp knife or scissors so as not to tear the paper.
- Double cutting or splicing is often a good way of achieving a perfect, invisible butt joint. This technique is particularly useful when using thick or heavily embossed papers (ie blown vinyl), where an overlap would clearly show. To achieve this it is necessary, having overlapped the papers, to use a sharp trimming knife and metal straight edge. Holding the straight edge down the middle of the overlap and pressing just hard enough to go through both layers of paper, draw the trimming knife from top to bottom. Remove the outer trimmed excess, then lift the top layer clear and remove the trimmed excess beneath. Brush the two layers flat to the wall. Wipe off the excess adhesive that will be on the face of one edge with a clean damp sponge.

ACTIVITY

Answer the following questions:
- Where is the suggested starting point for hanging papers to ceilings?
- Where is the suggested starting point for walls?
- If there is a feature fireplace in a room, where would it be best to start?
- In all cases, where is the best finishing point for paperhanging?

DEFECTS IN PAPERHANGING

The following defects can occur through lack of care or by following incorrect methods. Rectifying some of these defects will prove extremely costly – in many cases the defective wallpaper will need to be removed before hanging again.

Defect	Cause	Prevention
Blistering	Usually caused by under-soaking or over-soaking and then careless brushing. Areas of paper that have been missed when pasting will be dry and will therefore not stick to the wall surface, leading to blisters.	▪ Ensure that manufacturers' soaking times are followed. ▪ Papers need to be properly pasted and smoothed to ensure that there are no air bubbles or excess paste.
Pattern mismatch	Can be caused by papers being initially over-soaked or lengths having varying soak times, allowing them to stretch at different rates. This can then lead to inaccurate matching of the pattern and will be most obvious at the joints as it will be difficult to match at every position on the length.	▪ Should a small mismatch occur, ensure that the pattern is matched at eye level.
Creasing	Can be caused by excessive brushing which may cause the surface of the paper to stretch, and then when trying to keep plumb there will be excess paper which is likely to crease. Also papering over very uneven surfaces can cause paper to stretch, resulting in excess paper and potential creasing.	▪ Avoid over-brushing. ▪ Take care when hanging to avoid over-stretching.
Overlaps	Can be caused by over-brushing but also likely to be due to over-soaking which can cause papers to stretch after hanging, causing overlaps. Sometimes careless use of the seam roller can stretch the paper, resulting in overlaps.	▪ Do not over-brush or allow papers to become over-soaked. ▪ Take care when hanging to avoid overlaps.
Tears	This is probably due to lack of care at some stage in the hanging process. If paste that is too thin is used this can cause over-wetting which in turn can make paper more likely to tear. Using blunt tools such as shears can also cause paper to tear. Once papers have been soaked and are ready to hang, proper care should be taken as rough handling can cause tearing.	▪ Make sure paste is the correct consistency. ▪ Ensure that tools are kept sharp and clean. ▪ Take care when hanging.

Defect	Cause	Prevention
Polished edges	In most cases this defect is caused by poor use of the seam roller. If paste is allowed to get onto the face of the paper at the edges, and is then rolled, it is likely that the seam roller will polish this area and leave shiny marks. Sometimes careless pasting can leave paste on the face of the paper edges and this also can give a polished effect when dried.	■ Use a dry piece of paper between the seam roller and the face of the paper. ■ Take care when pasting to avoid getting paste on the face of the paper.
Open joints	Uneven surfaces can make it difficult for the lengths of paper to be properly butted together. If the paper is over-stretched to make them butt, the joints can spring back and leave a gap.	■ Do not over-stretch papers to make them butt. Slide papers into position instead.
Springing of joints	Will often occur due to lack of adhesion. This can be particularly noticeable when papering on non-absorbent surfaces such as gloss-painted walls. It can also occur when papers are over-stretched and will shrink back on drying to leave an open joint.	■ Make sure gloss-painted walls are sized and lined. ■ Ensure papers are not over-brushed when hanging.
Loose or dry edges	This defect is almost always due to careless pasting techniques – edges that have been missed or have an inadequate amount of paste covering them. These dry areas will not stick to the surface and will lift.	■ Use good pasting techniques to ensure edges are well pasted.
Irregular cutting	Caused by poor technique when using cutting tools such as paperhanging shears. It is advisable to carry out a number of sessions of practice cutting before attempting to cut the real thing. The skill of cutting to a line without tearing the paper or producing irregular cuts takes patience.	■ Use the correct cutting technique to avoid jagged cuts. ■ Ensure that cutting tools are kept clean and sharp.

Defect	Cause	Prevention
Staining or surface marking	Usually caused by poor pasting technique, where either the paste has got onto the face from the paste table surface or has been allowed to wrap around the edges of the paper during application. Occasionally water stains on the existing surface can be softened by the new paste and may stain through the newly applied paper.	■ It is extremely important to ensure that the paste table is kept clean at all times, and wipe it regularly to ensure no paste is on the face of the table. ■ This can be remedied by ensuring that the water stain is adequately sealed before applying new paper.
Corners incorrectly negotiated	It is extremely important to plan, especially when hanging patterned papers, to lessen the impact of pattern loss when turning corners and going around various obstacles.	■ Starting points for paperhanging are extremely important, as are the correct application methods when dealing with corners. Refer to the application methods on pages 251–253 for more details.
Inaccurate plumbing	Inaccurate plumbing will lead to lengths of paper being out of plumb, which on patterned papers will become extremely noticeable. The pattern will start to run out of position at the top of the wall.	■ It is essential to ensure that the plumbing of the first lengths on turning corners is carried out accurately, and also to ensure that the plumb bob has stopped moving before marking. ■ Hanging lengths of paper following obstacles such as windows and doorways will also require the use of the plumb bob to establish a truly vertical starting point.
Flattened edges or embossing	Flattening of the edges or embossing of wallpaper will occur when poor brushing technique is used to smooth out the paper. This can be made worse when the paper is allowed to over-soak or the paste has been applied too thinly. Excess pressure applied in these cases will also result in flattening.	■ Do not use too much pressure when hanging embossed papers. ■ Do not allow papers to over-soak.

ACTIVITY

Study the list of defects and answer the following questions:

■ How are overlaps caused?
■ What causes flattening of embossed patterns?
■ What causes delamination of embossed papers?

STORAGE OF MATERIALS

Consideration should be given to the physical characteristics of materials when storing them, bearing in mind that that most will be badly affected by the atmospheric conditions relative to temperature, dampness or direct sunlight. In the main the products that you will be storing are made of paper or are dry powder based and are sometimes contained in cardboard packets. Any opened products will need to be properly sealed before being stored, and also bear in mind that they will have a limited shelf life before they become unusable.

Care should always be taken with the storage of wallpapers and adhesives, as they can be badly affected by damp, cold conditions. If it is too hot papers can become too dry, and if they are exposed to direct sunlight discolouration will take place, which will particularly affect patterned papers.

Always refer to manufacturers' instructions with regard to use, handling and storage. However, in most cases materials should be stored in warm, dry and secure conditions. If you buy materials in bulk it is probably a good idea to keep a stock book to track when items are removed and require replacing. With all materials it is always best to check that oldest stock is used first to ensure it is not allowed to age too much. Most materials, particularly adhesives, will have use-by dates for guidance.

In the case of papers such as lining and ingrain papers decorators will often store additional stock, as these products are often used – you will need a good racked storage system to do this. Wallpapers are best stored on racks and laid on their sides to prevent damage to their edges. Most papers are shrink wrapped in plastic to keep them clean before they are used. Paste and adhesives, similarly, should be stored in cool, dry, frost-free conditions where packets may be stored in drawers and tubs stored on shelves. If pastes are allowed to get damp they will be unusable, as they will start to become solid.

ACTIVITY

Answer the following questions:

- What kind of storage conditions should be avoided?
- What might happen to papers if rolls are stored on their ends?
- Why are most papers shrink wrapped in plastic?

Wallpaper is best stored in racks

Pastes stored on shelves

Case Study: Greg and Angelo

Greg and Angelo were in the middle of hanging a patterned paper to a lounge. This had been a bit of rush job as they were behind on the contract. As Angelo looked back over the work they had done so far he noticed that some lengths appeared to be different in colour. The difference was quite noticeable now that he looked more closely at what they had done. Some lengths appeared darker than others.

When Greg checked the labels from the rolls of wallpaper, he saw that they showed different numbers. He soon realised that because they had not checked the batch numbers before starting, they had ended up with the defect known as shading.

This proved to be a costly mistake, because some of the paper needed to be removed and paper of the same batch re-hung.

INDUSTRY TIP

Always check the rolls before starting for different batch numbers and different shades. Different batch numbers mean that papers were printed at different times and may vary in colour.

Work through the following questions to check your learning.

1   By which one of the following wallpaper manufacturing processes is blown vinyl produced?

a   Rotary printing.

b   Wet embossing.

c   Dry embossing.

d   Heat expansion.

2   Which method is used to produce Supaglypta?

a   Dry embossing.

b   Wet embossing.

c   Rotary printing.

d   Heat expansion.

3   Which one of the following methods is used to produce textured vinyl?

a   Dry embossing.

b   Wet embossing.

c   Heat expansion.

d   Rotary printing.

4   Which one of the following symbols relates to drop or offset pattern match?

a

b

c

d

5   How many layers is duplex paper made from?

a   1.

b   2.

c   3.

d   4.

6   Which one of the following types of paper will provide a pattern in relief?

a   Pulp.

b   Simplex.

c   Embossed.

d   Washable.

7   What does 'reverse alternate lengths' mean?

a   All lengths of paper are hung upside down.

b   Every second length is hung upside down.

c   Every third length is hung upside down.

d   Every fourth length is hung upside down.

8   Which one of the following symbols describes paper with good lightfastness?

a

b

c

d

9   Which one of the following pastes and adhesives is most likely to encourage mould growth?

a   Border adhesive.

b   Ready-mixed adhesive.

c   Starch paste.

d   Cellulose paste.

10   Which one of the following application methods will provide the quickest and most even application?

a   Applying paste to paper by roller.

b   Applying paste to paper by brush.

c   Applying paste to paper by pasting machine.

d   Applying paste to paper by hand.

11 Which one of the following defects could be caused by over-thinning the paste?

a Polished joints.

b Face staining.

c Springing joints.

d Over-stretching.

12 Fungicides are used in some adhesives, but which one of the following health problems can be caused by their use?

a Breathing difficulties.

b Skin irritation.

c Dizzy spells.

d Loss of taste.

13 Which one of the following papers is used as a lining for covering cracks and wood panelling?

a White lining paper.

b Vinyl wallpaper.

c Plain fibre lining.

d Standard washable paper.

14 Where is the suggested starting point for papering a ceiling?

a In a corner.

b By the door.

c By the window.

d You can start anywhere.

15 What is the name given to colour differences in rolls of wallpaper?

a Shading.

b Blending.

c Colouring.

d Matching.

16 Why should you vertically mark the starting point of the first length of paper?

a To make sure the paper is plumb.

b To make sure you have enough paper.

c To make sure you know where to finish.

d To make sure you have the correct length.

17 Star cuts are used when cutting around which one of the following?

a Door openings.

b Window openings.

c Ceiling rose.

d Chimney breast.

18 What is loss of emboss likely to have been caused by?

a Over-brushing.

b Poor matching.

c Overlapping.

d Under-soaking.

19 A dry room with low level of light is ideal for storing which of the following types of papers?

a Lining.

b Patterned.

c Wood ingrain.

d Non-patterned.

20 Wallpaper should be stored in racks to

a make it easier to count the rolls

b prevent damage to the edges

c enable you to see the pattern number

d enable you to see the batch number.

Chapter 6
Unit 218: Producing specialist finishes for decorative work

This unit covers the skills and knowledge required to produce specialist finishes, and you will draw on your experience of having prepared surfaces and painted them. You will develop your skills further by carrying out these decorative finishes, increasing your knowledge of a wider range of materials, tools and equipment.

Attention to detail, quality and cleanliness are most important, as this type of work is decorative and will be a focus for people to look at. Remember that not all painters can produce decorative finishes and you will therefore be able to offer future employers and customers added value with the skills you develop in this area of work. This will also enable you to increase your earnings.

By reading this chapter you will understand how to:

1 Produce quality finish ground coats for painted decorative work.
2 Produce broken colour effects using acrylic, oil based and water-borne scumbles.
3 Prepare stencil plates from a given design and apply stencils.
4 Produce wood and marble effects using basic techniques.

PRODUCE QUALITY FINISH GROUND COATS FOR PAINTED DECORATIVE WORK

It is possible to produce specialist finishes for decoration, and by doing so you will be able to hide or mask minor surface imperfections, match other decoration and provide something different for the customer. The advantages of these finishes are that each job is **unique**, and the colours and effects can be tailored to suit the customer's personal choice. The main disadvantages are that it can be expensive to carry out this work, as it is labour intensive; it is difficult, if not impossible, to repair damage to the finished work; and ideally you need a smooth and level surface to work on.

Although the work of preparing and **grounding out** the surface may seem to be the least productive or enjoyable aspect of painting and decorating, it is most important to carry it out thoroughly, as any imperfections may be highlighted or made more obvious by the materials used for the decorative finish.

SURFACES

The specialist finishes for which you will be developing skills are usually applied to walls, doors (eg kitchen cupboards, wardrobes) or items of furniture (eg boxes, picture/mirror frames), and the substrates will therefore normally be previously painted timber, previously painted plaster or previously painted plasterboard.

However, one decorative effect called 'glazing and wiping' requires a **high relief** wall covering to be hung to the surface (usually ceiling or wall) before the ground coat is applied. There are three main types of suitable wall covering:

- embossed wallpaper
- blown vinyl wallpaper
- Lincrusta wall covering.

It is the depth of pattern that is most important, as a shallow texture will make it harder to produce a 'glazed and wiped' effect, and it will be less effective.

Unique

The only one of its kind

Grounding out

Applying the ground coat for painted decorative work

FUNCTIONAL SKILLS

Using ICT resources, find out the manufacturing process for, and characteristics of, embossed papers, blown vinyl papers and Lincrusta wall covering.

Work on this activity can support FICTE2 (4).

High relief

Deep textured pattern

ACTIVITY

From your knowledge of various substrate types (you may wish to refer to Chapter 3), make a list of substrates on which broken colour effects would usually be used.

Embossed wallpaper

Blown vinyl wallpaper

Lincrusta wall covering

GROUND COATS

The paint that is applied to the surface on which decorative finishes will be produced is called the ground coat. It is important that it has a high-quality finish with no defects or irregularities, no excessive brush or roller marks and good **opacity**. It should show through the broken colour of the **scumble** and should add depth to the surface by being part of the colour scheme.

Colour charts can be used to check that colours are complementary

It is important therefore to be aware of the overall colour scheme of the location in which the decorative effect will be produced, to make sure that the ground coat and scumble colours complement, or match if the customer requires it, the surrounding area.

Water-borne or solvent-borne paint systems with an eggshell or low sheen finish are suitable for the ground coat, as matt or gloss finishes will adversely affect the **manipulation** process of the scumble for broken colour work. A matt finish will tend to drag on the scumble, whereas the tools used to produce the effect are likely to skid around on a gloss finish. Acrylic ground coats are more effective, as they are less porous and will allow more working time with the scumble; an emulsion ground coat will partially absorb the scumble, which will therefore set much more quickly.

Attention should be given to the compatibility of the ground coat material and the scumble type (ie whether they have the ability to be used together), and consideration should be given to the location where the decorative effects will be carried out, in relation to durability. The important aspect is the colour relationship between the ground coat and the scumble; in general there should not be too much of a difference between them, to avoid the finished appearance being too harsh and unpleasant on the eye.

Opacity

The ability of the pigment in paint to obliterate or hide the existing surface colour

Scumble

A glaze (translucent product which will retain a design) to which a colourant has been added

ACTIVITY

Using paint manufacturers' information, list three key properties of both water-borne and solvent-borne coatings.

Manipulation

Skilfull handling

INDUSTRY TIP

Sample boards are an excellent way of confirming a customer's choice. Using them may save you time and money in the long run, as customers can see what the finished decorative scheme will look like. Record the quantities of materials and the tools you use on the back so that you can **replicate** an effect. Ideally the customer should sign the back of the board to confirm their choice.

Replicate

To make an exact copy of

Dry abrade poor surfaces before you begin

ACTIVITY

Check the quality of your finished ground coat by using your fingertips and also by examining the surface from different angles, to ensure it is of a high standard.

Sinking

Reduction in the sheen of a paint film. This may occur when a section of making good has not been spot-primed and the film former has been partly absorbed by the porous filler

Impervious

Not allowing something to pass through, or penetrate

High-traffic area

An area that has many people passing through it

PREPARATION PROCESSES

Preparation processes were covered in depth in Chapter 3. It is important to prepare and make good surfaces before applying paint or paper, especially when producing specialist finishes.

To achieve the required quality of finish for the ground coat, the surface should be abraded thoroughly. Dry abrasion may be appropriate as the first stage for poor, rough surfaces, but this should be followed by wet abrading (or wet flatting) to improve the finish by completely removing any application defects.

It may be necessary to make good any imperfections or indentations, to ensure that the surface is level. The materials you use for this purpose will depend on the surface type and the imperfection, including its depth.

Areas that have been made good should be spot-primed to prevent any **sinking** of the ground coat, and de-nibbed following initial preparation.

APPLYING WALL COVERINGS BEFORE THE GROUND COAT

This section should be read in conjunction with Chapter 5. The surface should be made good and sized prior to setting out, ready to receive the wall covering. Because the textured surface is to be decorated to create a three-dimensional effect that will enhance the pattern design, attention must be given to setting out the pattern to ensure a balanced and aesthetically pleasing result.

There are different types of wallpaper paste and specialist adhesives used to apply these wall coverings; because the finished surface will be **impervious**, the paper should be allowed to dry out thoroughly before progressing, and the paste or adhesive should contain a fungicide to prevent mould growth beneath the paper.

When hanging an embossed paper, you will need to take care not to flatten the relief by applying too much pressure with the hanging/smoothing brush, or by using an inappropriate tool such as a seam roller. Although greater pressure may be applied to blown vinyl paper, it should also be considered fairly fragile because the expanded polystyrene face can be damaged easily. Lincrusta, which is a highly specialised paper with its own hanging techniques and should not be hung in the same way as the other two papers, is very robust, hard-wearing and is often specified for **high-traffic areas**. While white embossed and blown vinyl papers usually receive only an emulsion/water-borne paint as a finish, Lincrusta is designed to receive a highly decorative finish when required.

Once the wall covering has been hung, it should be inspected to ensure that there are no dry edges, blisters or adhesive on the face, which would adversely affect the next stage of decoration – the application of the ground coat. Lincrusta should be de-greased to ensure good adhesion of the ground coat. Traditionally white spirit was used for this purpose, but greater consideration for the environment and reduced use of volatile organic compounds (VOCs) has led manufacturers to develop an environmentally friendly product to prepare the surface ready to receive paint.

TOOLS AND EQUIPMENT REQUIRED FOR THE PREPARATION PROCESSES

You will have come across the tools and equipment required for the preparation processes in previous chapters. Typically you will need rubbing blocks, sponges, buckets, a dusting brush, a pasting brush, a pasting table, shears or a knife, and a hanging brush.

It is also important to remember to wear the correct PPE while preparing surfaces. This should include dust masks, disposable gloves, overalls and safety footwear as well as **barrier cream**.

THE PAINTING PROCESS

Thorough preparation should be followed by careful paint application, using clean paint, clean application tools and a clean paint kettle or roller tray. See Chapter 4 for information on preparing paint.

The number of coats required will depend on whether:

- priming is required, due to the method and extent of preparation of the surface

- a strong colour change from a previous coating is taking place

- the colour has poor opacity, eg certain yellows or blues

- the coating type is changing, eg solvent-borne to water-borne.

When the ground coat for a 'glazed and wiped' effect is applied to wallpaper, a thinned priming coat should be applied, prior to the required number of full coats of finishing paint.

Barrier cream

Barrier cream

Cream used to protect hands from contaminants such as solvents, which may cause dermatitis and irritation; some brands are also water repellent. It is advisable to use before carrying out most painting and decorating tasks

TOOLS AND EQUIPMENT

Most of the tools and equipment needed for decorative finishes will already be familiar to you from Chapter 4. Tools required include paint stirrers, strainers, paint brushes, rollers, kettles and roller trays, tack rags and hair stipple brushes.

HAIR STIPPLE BRUSH

Often known as hair stipplers or simply stipplers, these are used to remove all traces of brush marks and leave a smooth, even finish. These brushes come in different sizes (dimensions are given in inches) and particular care should be taken when using, cleaning and storing them. When not in use, they should be laid on their side or top and not left standing on the bristle ends, as this may damage and distort the bristles. The brush is effective because of the broad, flat area of bristle tips. Build-up of paint or scumble on the bristles should be avoided by frequently wiping the bristle ends with a cloth dampened with the appropriate thinner.

Hair stipple brush – 6 × 4

Hair stipple brush – 4 × 1

Stipple brush care

To maintain the condition of the brush, it should be cleaned as soon as you have finished with it, to avoid the coating drying in the bristles. Two or three trays of the thinner should be placed alongside each other with a pile of rags or cloths between each tray, to absorb excess thinner from the brush before it is placed in the next tray; when all traces of paint or scumble have been removed, wash the brush in warm, soapy water and then rinse it to finally remove any traces of thinner and keep the bristles soft. It should then be hung up to prevent damage to the bristles – ensure that it is fully dry before storing it, preferably in a box to protect it.

There are also rubber stipple brushes available, which are normally used for textured paint. However, if you require a bold effect, or the effect is to be viewed from a distance, these may be used to manipulate the scumble. It is advisable to use this type of stippler only in water-borne products, as the use of cleaning solvents will cause the brush to deteriorate.

DEFECTS

There are consequences for the ground coat if any of the following apply:

- insufficient surface preparation
- using dirty/contaminated paint, application tools and equipment
- using inappropriate application methods.

This will be evident in the appearance of the broken colour effect.

Bittiness within the ground coat is unsightly, and the scumble can collect around this, appearing as a darker colour which will spoil the finished effect.

Heavy-handed laying off by brush will result in brush marks or ropiness and, as with bittiness, the scumble can collect in the uneven paint film.

Careless laying off may lead to misses in the ground coat, and the scumble will sink.

Poor opacity or inconsistent laying off may leave an uneven ground coat colour which may be visible in the finished work.

To help reduce or avoid application defects in the ground coat, it is advisable to use either a roller with a mohair sleeve or a hair stipple brush, to provide a finish free from brush marks.

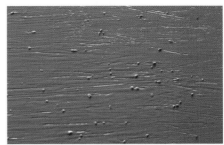

A defect such as bittiness will show up in the final effect

ENVIRONMENTAL AND HEALTH AND SAFETY CONSIDERATIONS AND REGULATIONS

Attention to safe and healthy working practices is important because you, other people and the environment are all affected by your work activities. Legislation is in place to help protect all three. Although you have looked at environmental and health and safety regulations in previous chapters, it is important to be aware of how they relate to producing specialist finishes.

CONTROL OF SUBSTANCES HAZARDOUS TO HEALTH (COSHH) REGULATIONS 2002

These regulations are intended to protect employees and others from the effects of working with substances that are hazardous to health.

When working to produce your ground coat, you may be generating:

- dust from the dry abrading process
- residue from the wet abrading process, which may, if you are working in an older building (pre-1970), contain lead
- fumes or volatile organic compounds (VOCs) when applying paints – and remember that, contrary to popular belief, water-borne coatings are not solvent free.

COSHH irritant symbol

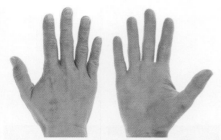

Avoid dermatitis by protecting your skin

ACTIVITY

Examine the packaging of your preparation and painting materials, and identify whether the labels use the new international symbols or the European symbols. If you do not know the difference, go to the HSE website, locate the information leaflet called 'Working with substances hazardous to health' and find the section relating to the symbols. Compare the two types to familiarise yourself with the changes.

Reasonably practicable

Sensible, taking into account the trouble, time and money involved

Check electrical equipment before use

In addition to the use of dust masks, disposable gloves and barrier cream, all of which will help to protect you while you undertake these activities, a good level of ventilation in the work area will also be required to ensure that there is no build-up of fumes or dust. All these together are termed 'control measures'.

When working with wallpaper pastes and adhesives, particularly those containing fungicides, you should wash your hands regularly to prevent ingestion, and keep containers covered to prevent children or animals coming into contact with the materials inside. Constant immersion of the hands in water while paperhanging, and the effects of the paste, will dry out the skin and this may lead to dermatitis. Use an after-work hand cream to help protect your hands and retain the skin's natural oils.

As an employee (or a self-employed person or learner), you must make use of any control measures and equipment provided, and comply with any arrangements the employer (or your place of learning) has put into effect.

WORK AT HEIGHT REGULATIONS 2005 (AS AMENDED)

The Work at Height Regulations are covered extensively in Chapter 1 and Chapter 8.

The main principle behind this piece of legislation is that everyone does all that is **reasonably practicable** to prevent anyone falling.

While undertaking the work of producing specialist finishes in your college or training centre, you may be required to work from stepladders or podiums/hop-ups. It is important to remember to always check the equipment for any defects before erecting it, then check that it is secure and on firm, level ground before starting to use it.

Electrical safety

If you are using an electrical sander to prepare the surface, it should be used in conjunction with a 110V transformer to reduce the risk of death by electrocution. Before use, check that all plugs, cables and connectors are in good condition – if there is any sign of damage, this should be reported and the equipment must not be used.

Disposal of waste

As with health and safety, there is legislation to control the safe disposal of waste products, which quite often includes coatings that are left over, used thinners, used rags and so on. The Environment Agency is responsible for this and you should ensure that you comply with its regulations (eg The Hazardous Waste (England and Wales) Regulations 2005, as amended) regarding the differing types of waste you will need to dispose of.

Your Local Authority will probably provide waste disposal services, and will give you guidance on how it should be carried out for your particular waste. However, there may be a charge for this, as it is seen as a commercial side of their business. Remember that you may have to build in the cost for waste disposal to the price you quote for any job.

If you will be using craft knives for trimming when hanging wall coverings, remember that used blades (including snap-off blades) should be safely disposed of in a sharps box. Offcuts of pasted wallpaper should frequently be placed in rubbish sacks as you work, to reduce the risk of slipping.

RISK ASSESSMENTS

In order to carry out the work and use the materials required for the job in the safest manner, it is necessary to carry out a risk assessment first. As you know from previous chapters, this is a simple but necessary look at what, in the planned work, could cause harm to people – you can then decide whether you have taken enough precautions, or whether more should be done to prevent harm.

PRODUCE BROKEN COLOUR EFFECTS USING ACRYLIC AND OIL BASED SCUMBLES

This section is about producing broken colour effects, namely sponge stippling, rag rolling (two methods – subtractive and additive), dragging, and 'glazing and wiping'.

Broken colour effects are when a **translucent**, coloured glaze (a product which will retain a design) has been applied over a different-coloured ground coat to create the desired effect. The translucency of the coloured glaze (called scumble) will allow the ground coat to be seen through it, and be part of the colour scheme.

The two methods of rag rolling used in this chapter are:

- Scumble applied as a continuous, even film to the ground coat, manipulated using a variety of materials such as crumpled lint-free fabric, paper, specialist tools and so on to break up and remove small areas of the coloured film. This is known as the 'subtractive method' because areas of colour are taken away to produce the effect.

- Scumble applied to crumpled lint-free fabric or natural sponge, then pressed onto or applied to the painted ground coat. This is known as the 'additive method' because you are adding the coloured effect.

There is more detail about the different techniques that may be used on pages 283–284.

Translucent

Allows light to pass through, but prevents images from being seen clearly. Some manufacturers refer to this as being semi-transparent

A rag-rolled effect

SUITABILITY OF THE GROUND COAT

Before starting to produce any broken colour effect, the suitability of the ground coat must first be checked. As well as producing a quality finish that has no visible defects (misses, ropiness, bits and nibs, brush marks, excessive orange peel), you also need to check that the colour is appropriate, that it has good opacity and that the paint film is **hard dry**.

The relationship between the ground coat colour and the scumble colour will influence how pleasing the final result is, and totally different effects will be produced when a pale scumble is applied over a darker ground coat (eg light blue-green scumble over a dark blue-green ground), compared with a darker scumble applied over a paler ground coat (eg red-purple scumble over a lilac ground coat). Whichever combination is used, the two colours should be of a similar tone and not too strongly contrasting. You will be learning more about colour, its use, and possible schemes in Chapter 7.

If you are producing a 'glazed and wiped' effect, check that the relief/embossed paper is soundly adhered and with a sufficient depth of relief to be effective.

MATERIALS

It is important to understand the materials that are used to create these effects, which are oil based or acrylic (water borne). Although this chapter will discuss how to use products and materials, you must always read the manufacturer's information to find out exactly how each one should be prepared and used, as there can be differences between the products.

OIL GLAZE

This is a translucent **medium** (containing linseed oil, white spirit, extenders, beeswax and driers), which has little or no opacity.

You will be aware from Chapter 4 of how coatings flow out and dry as a smooth, level film, and that this is directly related to the **viscosity** of the coating. If you are producing a broken colour finish, you do not want the scumble to flow out, however, otherwise the effect will disappear before it dries. The inclusion of beeswax in oil based glaze enables the scumble to retain its shape (or pattern) after it has been manipulated.

Because this type of glaze is based on linseed oil, it has a natural tendency to yellow. This happens over time, but is accelerated on surfaces that get hot (eg radiators), or where there is little light (eg behind pictures and furniture). Potential customers should always be advised of the possibility of this happening, so they can make an informed decision about the alternatives that are available.

Hard dry

Describing paint film that is hard enough to be worked on without damaging its finish

Medium

The liquid component that enables a glaze to be spread over a surface and dry as a film. It binds the ingredients together and provides good adhesion to the substrate

Viscosity

The ability of a liquid or coating to flow; the more viscous it is, the slower it flows

ACTIVITY

Using the internet to find manufacturers' information, find out which types of oil are used in the manufacture of paint.

Preparation

Oil glaze should always be thinned using white spirit – normally 10% – so that it can be applied as a fairly thin coat. However, take care not to over-thin it, as its ability to hold the pattern will be affected. The colourant (see pages 277–278) will then be added.

Working time

As oil glaze is based on linseed oil, it has a long 'open' or working time, which may be an advantage to the decorator, particularly when working on large areas. However, the working time of any coating will be affected by atmospheric conditions (eg heat, cold, damp) and you need to know how to adjust the material accordingly.

Raw linseed oil

■ Higher temperatures will shorten the drying time – therefore the addition of a small quantity of raw linseed oil will extend, or lengthen, the working time, meaning the drying time is slowed.

■ Lower temperatures will lengthen the drying time.

Driers

The careful addition of a very small quantity of Terebine driers will speed up the drying process, which reduces the working time. However, if you add too much, the scumble will become brittle (cracking and losing adhesion) and the lifetime of the decorative effect will be reduced.

When calculating the quantity of scumble you need for the size of area to be worked, you should always prepare more than is required, so that you have plenty to:

■ produce a sample board for the customer, from which you will match the main material supply

■ rub out and apply again if the effect is not as required, or it gets damaged while wet

■ leave with the customer on completion of the job, for any minor repairs that may be required in the future due to damage, or to enable a small area to be produced to match as closely as possible an existing finish – eg if a radiator or pipework is replaced.

However, as mentioned earlier it is difficult, if not almost impossible, to repair damage. If the scumble is oil based, yellowing may already have started and so an identical match would not be possible.

Store flammable liquids safely

Storage

Oil glaze is flammable so must be stored in cool, well ventilated conditions, with the lid of the container secured. When working indoors, glaze and thinners should ideally be stored in a metal fireproof cabinet.

ACTIVITY

Find out which type of fire extinguisher should be used on a solvent-borne or oil based coating fire.

ACRYLIC GLAZE

This is a liquid coating with small particles of acrylic resin dispersed (or scattered) in water. It is milky in appearance, but when the water evaporates, the particles merge or **coalesce** to form a continuous, translucent film with a slight sheen. You learned about this drying process in relation to emulsion paints in Chapter 5.

Manufacturers produce a range of acrylic glaze types, and the product information (technical data sheet and safety data sheet) will help you select the most suitable type for the work specification. These products have a low odour and up to one hour's working time; tools are cleaned with water and they will not yellow over time. However, they may be prone to chips or scratches and are therefore more suitable for application to walls rather than woodwork. Because acrylic scumbles dry quite quickly, a higher skill level may be required to produce a quality broken colour effect over large areas.

It is important to remember that glazes, both oil based and acrylic types, do not contain any colourant. They are not intended to be used as a clear protective film.

Preparation
The only preparation required is to add an appropriate colourant (see below) and adjust the consistency of the material to suit the atmospheric conditions and required working time.

Working time
As a water-borne product, acrylic glaze has a shorter working time than an oil based one. The challenge for the decorator is often how to extend the working time, particularly when applying it to larger areas or during warm weather.

Retarding agents
Decorators use a number of methods to extend the working time of acrylic scumbles, which are not necessarily approved of by manufacturers. These include the addition of a small quantity of glycerine, or lightly spraying the surface with water before applying the acrylic scumble. While proprietary conditioners may help to maintain a wet edge for water-borne products, they also improve the flow of the material and help to reduce application marks – this particular characteristic is not a desirable quality for broken colour work, so if you use proprietary conditioners take care not to add too much.

The use of a wet rag rather than a dry one will help to break up the scumble and will also help to extend the working time.

One manufacturer advises that, if using emulsion paint as the colourant, the working time may be altered according to the ratio of acrylic glaze to emulsion paint – eg 8:1 may give one to two hours of working time, whereas 4:1 will give about 45 minutes.

Coalesce

Particles merging to form a film, particularly in water-borne coatings – the drying process is also known as coalescence

Acrylic glaze

As time goes on, manufacturers are improving the open time of acrylic glazes, and the need to use additives to extend the working time is being reduced.

Storage

This water-borne product should be stored in cool, well ventilated, frost-free conditions.

SCUMBLE

This is glaze (either oil based or acrylic) to which colourants have been added. This new material is now a translucent *coloured* glaze.

It can be all too easy to get confused about the correct name for these different products, particularly when some manufacturers call their glaze 'scumble glaze' – the main points to remember are that:

- if the product is called 'glaze' or 'scumble glaze', it does *not* contain any colourant and is not suitable to be used on its own as a finish

- if the product is called 'scumble', it contains colourant and is ready to be used for broken colour work.

A scumble contains colourant

Consistency

The scumble should not be thick and sticky, nor should it be too thin, otherwise its effectiveness to hold an attractive decorative finish will be reduced. The decorative effects described as broken colour should provide a visual texture (a 2D texture or pattern that you can only see, because the surface of it is smooth), not a tactile texture (a 3D texture or pattern that you can both feel and see; the surface of it is **undulating** or textured).

Having clarified those two different materials, you also need to understand the difference between coatings that are translucent and those that are opaque. The meaning of translucent was explained earlier in this chapter (see page 273), as it is an important characteristic of the glazes. If something is opaque it has a solid colour finish, which **obliterates** the surface beneath – paints and some timber treatments are opaque coatings.

COLOURANTS

Good-quality colourants, which are stable, **lightfast** and compatible with the glaze (oil based, water-borne/acrylic), should be used. Because the glaze is translucent, only a small amount of colourant will appear as a strong colour; however, sufficient colour must be added so that the glaze is tinted as strongly as possible to give consistent colour when it is applied thinly over the ground coat. Even though the glaze may appear very strong in the kettle/pot, when it is brushed out across a larger area it will be less **intense**.

Undulating

Wavy or bumpy

Obliterate

To completely hide

Lightfast

Describes colours that are resistant to fading – unaffected by light

Intense

Extreme, very strong or high degree of colour

Acrylic paints can be mixed with a glaze to create a scumble

If you are using tube colour, it is helpful to place a strip of the colour onto a palette and then mix in a small quantity of the thinner (white spirit or water). This softened colour will then be easier to mix into the glaze.

Whatever type of colourant you use, make sure you fully mix and evenly disperse it throughout the glaze – if necessary, strain the scumble (using a fine mesh stocking or proprietary strainer) to ensure there are no lumps of pure colour remaining.

Before you start work, you should always test the depth of colour on a small board or piece of card coated in the ground colour – remember you can always add a little more colour, but you can never take it away.

Colourants that may be used in oil glaze

These include artist's oil colours, proprietary oil colourants, solvent-borne eggshell paint or universal stainer.

Colourants that may be used in acrylic glaze

These include artist's colours, proprietary acrylic colourants, emulsion paint or universal stainer. For training purposes, poster colours may be used. It should be noted that some manufacturers advise against using acrylic eggshell as a colourant.

If solvent-borne eggshell or emulsion paint are used to colour a glaze, remember that the pigments used in those coatings are designed to obliterate the surface, a characteristic that is not desirable in the scumble; you should therefore use them very sparingly.

ACTIVITY

Name a colourant type that may be used in both oil based and acrylic glazes.

Paper towel can be used to produce a broken colour effect

INDUSTRY TIP

Cloths that have been used with oil based scumbles pose a fire risk, as they may ignite due to spontaneous combustion. When not in use they should be laid flat on a surface to dry, allowing the solvents to evaporate, or placed in a metal bin with a cover, or immersed in a bucket of water. These precautions should be taken during lunch breaks as well as at the end of the day.

TOOLS AND EQUIPMENT

Refer to pages 190–194 for information on paint brushes, hair stipple brushes, mohair rollers, kettles and plastic pots.

LINT-FREE CLOTH

This is a cloth without fluff and loose fibres, such as cotton sheeting or mutton cloth. The texture of the cloth used will determine the effect produced.

Other products that may be used to produce broken colour effects include paper (tissue/kitchen roll), net curtain and plastic film or bags. If the cloth or alternative product is not lint free, loose fibres will stick to the wet scumble and give an unsightly effect.

CHAMOIS LEATHER

This is a specific type of leather that is soft, supple, absorbent and non-abrasive. Although imitation chamois leathers or synthetic chamois leathers are available, they do not have quite the same natural qualities as the genuine article, which is expensive to purchase.

There are some points to bear in mind when caring for chamois leather. If the chamois leather has been used for oil based scumble, clean it in white spirit first (gloves are essential for this) to remove all traces of scumble. If an acrylic scumble has been used, rinse the leather thoroughly in warm water. Using a mild bar soap (not detergent, which will cause the chamois to become dry, brittle and less absorbent) lather the chamois, rinse it out and lather again with the bar soap, but do not rinse. With the soap still in the chamois, squeeze it dry and gently stretch it out; hang the chamois in an area protected from direct heat and sunlight.

Just before you use the chamois next time, rinse it in warm water to remove the remaining soap, and squeeze out the water. Leaving the soap in the chamois between uses will help to keep it conditioned and preserve its qualities.

Chamois leathers must not be placed in a sealed plastic bag or other container while still wet, as this will cause them to break down and make them unusable.

Chamois leather

ACTIVITY

Find out from where both natural chamois leather and imitation chamois leather are sourced.

NATURAL SEA SPONGES

Sea sponges come from animals that live on the ocean floor; of the 5,000 sponge species, only seven can be harvested and used for decorative, craft and cosmetic purposes. Sea sponges are soft and pliable, and their texture enables the creation of random and unique patterns. They may be used with oil based, water-borne and acrylic coatings.

As with cleaning a chamois leather, the first stage of cleaning a sea sponge will depend on the type of scumble used – this will be followed by thorough rinsing in warm water until it runs clear. A natural sea sponge must be handled carefully. Gently squeeze it rather than wringing it out as you would a cloth, leather or synthetic sponge. Sea sponges are expensive to buy and should be dried before being stored in a location where they will not be damaged.

Natural sea sponge

DRAGGING BRUSH

This brush is used to produce specialist finishes and is usually associated with **graining**, but it may also be used to produce the broken colour effect of dragging. The filling has either two rows of natural bristle, or one row of bristle and one row of stiff nylon, which replicates the split whale bone used in the past. The filling type influences the effect produced, with nylon producing a coarser effect than bristle.

When large surface areas such as walls are to be dragged, a large wall brush or long-bristled brush such as a flogger is most appropriate.

The dragging brush is cleaned using the appropriate thinner for the material it has been used with. When all traces of the thinner have

Graining

Applying and manipulating an appropriately coloured scumble to imitate the appearance of a specific timber

Dragging brushes

Plastic palette

been removed, wash the brush in warm, soapy water and rinse it. These brushes must be allowed to dry fully before being stored, and specialist brushes (eg draggers or floggers) should be stored in a box to protect them against damage.

PALETTE

This is a rectangular timber or plastic board (sometimes with a hole to place the thumb through) on which a quantity of paint is placed.

SETTING OUT

You may be working from a scale drawing (perhaps showing panel areas on a wall), from verbal instructions, or you may be applying an effect to a specified architectural area such as a dado. If required, measure and mark out the area that is going to receive the broken colour effect, using appropriate tools such as tape measure, chinagraph pencil, spirit level for horizontal lines and plumb bob for vertical lines, and chalk and line (or self-chalking line). Check the dimensions for accuracy throughout the setting-out process, and then apply masking materials.

PROTECTING ADJACENT AREAS

When you are producing decorative effects, you need to think about the effect going right to the edge of the area and often into corners. The surrounding surfaces will need to be protected from the materials and tools you are using.

MASKING TAPE

For the protection to be effective and not cause damage, you will need to select the appropriate type of masking tape. Chapter 4 discusses the factors that must be considered.

In order to help you produce decorative effects, the tape will need the ability to:

- produce perfect, sharp edges
- hold straight lines over long stretches
- make precise curves
- be removed cleanly, without leaving residue or damaging the substrate.

Tape is rated according to how many days it may be left on without leaving a residue when removed (eg 1-, 3- or 7-day ratings). The longer-rated tapes have less adhesive and are most suitable for smooth, delicate surfaces such as those recently painted (eg the ground coat).

Masking tape

ACTIVITY

Find out which type of adhesive tape is most suitable when masking curves.

Application

If you are using separate masking tape and paper, the tape will need to be adhered to the edge of the paper, in manageable lengths. Alternatively a self-adhesive paper or pre-taped polythene sheet may be used, depending on the location and surface area of the work. First, accurately position the masking material lightly at the edge of the area to be decorated, then apply even pressure to the tape so that it firmly adheres to the surface. This will help to prevent the **creep** of scumble under the edge of the tape, which will lead to thick, blurred edges.

MASKING FILM

Masking film is available in different forms:

- It is available in sheets or rolls, eg Frisket Film. This is a self-adhesive film which has an adhesive that leaves neither residue nor surface damage when peeled from the surface after use. It is easy to cut and has a translucent backing. Some types are repositionable and, if correctly adhered, will not buckle or lift along the film edge, which would allow creep. There is a range of tack levels (eg low tack or extra tack) and finishes (gloss or matt).

- It may be applied as a liquid, by spray or roller, eg Protectapeel. This dries to form a tough, skintight, plastic film, which will protect a range of surface types. It is water based and can be sprayed over a design, which can then be cut out, providing masking for the surrounding area. It is easily peeled off and disposed of by recycling or as domestic waste.

These products are more expensive than masking tape and materials mentioned above, and are specialist in their applications. For example they may be used for airbrush work, stencilling or precise colour control.

It should also be noted that these products must be cut carefully, using minimum pressure, to prevent damage to the underlying surface from the sharp knives that are required to cut through them.

INDUSTRY TIP

Press the front of a thumbnail along the edge of the masking tape, to ensure that it is really well secured and to prevent creep.

Creep

When masking tape has not been securely fixed to a surface and some scumble seeps beneath it – this will result in there not being a sharp edge to the broken colour effect

ACTIVITY

Find out what 'frisket' means and where the word comes from.

Liquid protective film applied by roller

Liquid protective film, peeled off

REMOVAL

Masking materials should be removed as soon as is practicable after the work has been completed. When de-masking, take care to avoid the following:

- damaging the finished effect – it is almost impossible to invisibly repair and usually results in the scumble having to be rubbed out and the effect created again

- lifting the ground coat – should this occur, even shallow damaged areas will need to be filled (using fine surface filler) and spot-primed, before re-coating with the ground coat, feathering in the edges.

Take care when removing masking tape

When removing masking tape, both the surface and the adhesive tape should be dry. It should not be pulled away from the surface, but instead needs to be pulled back on itself with a careful, even pulling motion. If you do not do this, the backing material may tear and leave adhesive residue on the surface, or the ground coat could be lifted.

Disposal of waste

Removed masking materials are a slip hazard if not placed immediately in a bin liner. Potentially, if oil based scumble has been used, both masking materials and cloths are a fire risk.

APPLICATION TECHNIQUES

Having prepared your scumble (glaze plus colourant) and obtained the required consistency, you are now ready to produce a variety of broken colour effects. This section covers rag rolling (subtractive method), rag rolling (additive method), sponge stippling, dragging, and 'glazing and wiping'.

RAG ROLLING: SUBTRACTIVE METHOD

This may also be referred to as the negative technique or ragging off.

STEP 1 Apply the scumble using a well-worn brush (natural bristle may be used for oil based scumble, but synthetic filament must be used for acrylic scumble), and rub out to cover the surface evenly, being careful not to apply too much glaze.

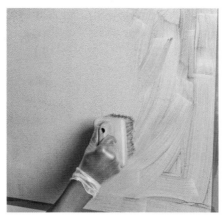

STEP 2 Remove all brush marks from the scumble and produce an evenly textured finish using a hair stippler or mohair roller. A stippler is used by firmly striking the glaze at 90° with the bristle tips, using short, sharp, clean strokes, and moving it slowly across the surface until an even texture is achieved.

STEP 3 Crumple a piece of lint-free cloth (or chamois leather), and firmly but lightly roll this across the area, working in random, snake-like moves, slightly overlapping each time to avoid unrolled areas or tramlines (this is also called banding or tracking). Repeat this process until the entire surface has been rolled and an even effect achieved, with no **discernible** pattern.

When you perform Step 2, if the pressure of the striking action is too light, it will take considerable time to remove the marks and even out the scumble; however, if too much pressure is applied there can be a tendency to drag the tool across the surface, and this will leave slip or skid marks in the scumble.

If, when you perform Step 3, a more detailed effect is required, either use a thinner type of cloth that will crumple with more broken edges, or roll the entire surface again to lift off more glaze.

Before using the stippler or roller for the first time, prime the bristle tips or roller sleeve by drawing the rubbing-in brush across them a few times; this will help satisfy the porosity of the bristles/pile and reduce the chance of scumble being absorbed by them, which would create areas of thin or removed scumble.

If you are using an acrylic scumble, dip the cloth in water and wring it out before starting. This will help to break up the scumble and extend the working time.

At regular intervals, shake out and re-crumple the cloth, taking care not to fold it, because the more broken edges there are in the ball of cloth, the more interesting the pattern. To prevent the cloth becoming overloaded with scumble, periodically rinse it out in the appropriate thinner (white spirit or water), then wring it out well.

Discernible

Able to be seen

INDUSTRY TIP

If you are working an area or section of 1m² or more, it is advisable to apply the scumble with a mohair roller, which will combine the first two stages and be more time and cost effective.

Applying scumble by roller

INDUSTRY TIP

To check that both the colour and effect are even, partly close your eyes and squint at the work – this will clearly show up any uneven patches.

When working on large areas such as walls, consider the following:

- It is advisable for one person to apply and stipple the scumble, and a second person to create the effect. As each person's work is unique to them, the film thickness and pressure used when applying and stippling the scumble, and the way of crumpling the cloth and method of manipulating it, will also be unique. Roles should not be reversed partway through the job, as the final effect will be quite different and noticeable.

- It may be necessary to replace the cloth being used. The new one must always be from the same piece of material, as the texture and pattern being produced will be unique to that product.

- Getting into corners or small areas may require using a smaller piece of cloth, yet still producing the same effect.

RAG ROLLING: ADDITIVE METHOD

This may also be called the positive technique, or ragging on.

1 Place the prepared scumble in a container, and immerse the cloth or chamois leather in it and wring it out. It is advisable to press the cloth onto a spare board or length of lining paper, to avoid applying too much scumble to the surface.

2 Roll the cloth over the surface in an irregular manner, making sure not to double-roll any areas, but also not leaving any part of the surface unrolled, otherwise tramlines or banding will result. If the amount of scumble being deposited on the surface begins to reduce, re-immerse the cloth in the scumble to re-load it, and wring it out.

SPONGE STIPPLING

This is also an additive method or positive technique. This decorative effect gives a multi-coloured, speckled appearance, with a minimum of two colours being applied to the ground coat, and three colours giving an extra dimension to the work.

An advantage of using emulsion paint for this effect is its speed of drying, particularly as two or three colours are being applied on top of one another and each colour must have dried before the next one can be applied. A large natural sponge should be used, particularly when working broad areas such as walls. Prepare it for use by immersing it in water and gently squeezing it out.

ACTIVITY

Use the internet to find out the source of the pile used for mohair rollers.

The additive method

1 Place emulsion paint or prepared scumble in a roller tray or large dish.

2 Press one side of the sponge into the paint or scumble to load it.

3 Dab the loaded sponge on a spare board or length of lining paper to avoid applying too much to the surface. Alternatively, use thinned emulsion in a container, immerse the sponge and squeeze it out, then dab off the excess paint.

4 Stipple the paint onto the wall using a light dabbing action, turning the wrist (not elbow) each time to avoid any regular pattern being created. Take care not to drag or twist the sponge on the surface, otherwise skid marks may be created. The stipples should be placed close together, but not overlap.

5 When the first colour has dried, apply the next colour(s) in the same manner, always applying the lightest colour last of all. If minor damage should occur, apply a repair using the same colour as the ground coat to disguise it.

First colour applied

Second colour applied

DRAGGING

This is a negative or subtractive technique. The decorative effect produced has an irregular striped appearance which is formed by the brush filling producing many thin lines as it is drawn (dragged) across the surface. It may be applied to small areas, for example to outline or frame panels of other decorative effects or cupboard doors, or to broad wall areas. If it is applied to broad areas, these should ideally be without obstructions or architectural features, which will cause the effect to be interrupted and therefore make it more difficult to produce. A broken or interrupted appearance may also result when working on high walls, as you will have to descend steps while trying to maintain an even pressure and parallel vertical lines.

As with all decorative finishes, the surface preparation and finish must be of a high quality, otherwise the scumble will form dark blotches in surface indentations.

If the effect is being applied to large areas, it is advisable for two people to undertake the work, as detailed for rag rolling (see facing page).

A mohair roller sleeve may be used to apply scumble to large areas

Stage 1

Apply the scumble using either a well-worn brush (natural bristle may be used for oil based scumble, but synthetic filament must be used for acrylic scumble) or, if a broad area is to be worked, apply the scumble using a medium-pile roller. Rub out to cover the surface evenly, ensuring that not too much glaze is applied, particularly at the edges, where a heavy build-up/deposit can occur. Take care when applying scumble by roller, as the ingredients make the material very likely to produce skid marks from the roller sleeve.

Scumble should only be applied to an area of a size that can be manipulated without losing the wet edge. If working alone on a large wall area, apply the scumble in vertical bands of approximately 1m and apply the effect to within 150mm of the leading edge – apply the next band and continue the process, working quickly to keep the wet edge moving.

Stage 2

Before using the dragging brush for the first time, prime the bristles or filaments lightly with scumble, as for rag rolling. The exact brush type used will depend on the size of the area and whether there are any obstructions or architectural features.

Stage 3

Holding the dragging brush at a shallow angle to the surface, pull the brush firmly across the surface in the direction required. Do this without hesitation and in a single, straight stroke if possible, to produce continuous, yet irregular stripes. Repeat this process, slightly overlapping the brush strokes and keeping them parallel.

If you are producing the effect on a broad area such as a wall or a flush door, start at the top and work to the bottom. However, if you are applying it to a panelled door/area, observe the sequence of application used to reflect the component joints – ie muntins, rails, stiles.

At regular intervals, wipe the bristles with a lint-free cloth, to remove the excess scumble which is being taken off the surface – this is necessary to produce a clean, even finish.

A dragged effect produced on a panelled door

A dragged effect being produced on a flush panel

Stage 4

When working on an area with adjacent surfaces such as ceiling, skirting boards, floor, frames, etc, care and practice are required to produce the dragged effect not only right to the edge, but also maintaining the weight of colour (quantity of scumble) and an even effect.

If little or no effect has been produced at the bottom because of the brush's proximity to the skirting board/floor, or greater pressure has been applied at the top, removing too much material, rather than rubbing out the scumble and starting again, it is possible to make it good.

At the bottom edge, reverse the brush and drag it up the wall to blend the new stripes into the existing ones, gradually lifting off the brush; continue this process along the bottom edge, ensuring that each stroke is a different length to avoid a horizontal band being created.

At the top edge, apply a small quantity of glaze just beneath the edge and carefully rub out. Angle the brush to get the bristle tips right to the internal angle and drag down to blend into the existing dragged effect, gradually lifting off the brush (as if you were laying off paint).

You will need to follow this process of achieving continuity of effect near skirtings to successfully achieve a **uniform** dragged effect.

If you are applying the effect to a small area, bear in mind that you can produce a completely different effect by pushing (rather than pulling) a dragging brush through the scumble.

Drag the brush up to correct the fault

Uniform

Always the same in shape/form, quality, quantity, etc – regular

'GLAZING AND WIPING'

This is a negative or subtractive technique.

This decorative effect is used to highlight and enhance the following:

- wall coverings that have a textured surface/relief design

- architectural room features, eg ornate covings/cornices, or a centrepiece

- surfaces produced by the application of materials that can be textured.

As with all broken colour effects, the relationship between the ground coat and scumble colours is crucial to produce an aesthetically pleasing and effective result – the use of a metallic ground coat paint can be quite effective for this process.

If the 'glazing and wiping' is being applied to large areas, it is advisable for two people to undertake the work, as for rag rolling.

Stage 1

Apply the scumble using either a well-worn brush (natural bristle may be used for oil based scumble, with synthetic filament being preferred for acrylic scumble) or, if a broad area is to be worked, a medium-pile roller. The scumble must be worked into all the recessed areas of pattern or moulding, followed by the removal of any application marks (eg careful laying off by roller, or brush marks by the hair stippler/roller).

Scumble should only be applied to a size of area that can be manipulated without losing the wet edge. If you are working alone on a large wall area, apply the scumble to sections of approximately 1m² and apply the effect to within 150mm of the leading edge, then apply the next section and continue the process, working from the edge of the area just completed.

Due to the texture of the surface being scumbled, it is considered best to apply the scumble (of either type) using a medium-pile roller. This will not only ensure that the scumble is applied as a full coat, but will also have benefits when applying acrylic scumble, which has a quicker setting time.

Stage 2

Using lint-free cloth, fold the material to form a pad with a smooth surface (no creases). For large areas such as ceilings, the wiping can be carried out using a stiff rubber squeegee, wiping off the excess scumble with a rag after each stroke; this can be returned to the pot and reused, if uncontaminated.

Stage 3

Methodically wipe over the surface to remove the scumble from the raised sections of the pattern. Do not press too hard, otherwise the scumble may also be removed from recesses, but the same amount of pressure needs to be applied over the entire area to achieve a uniform effect.

Regularly re-fold the cloth to avoid it becoming saturated, in which case it will be unable to remove the scumble. It may be necessary to replace the cloth being used – the new one must always be made of the same type of material, to ensure the same effect is achieved.

If insufficient glaze is removed, repeat the process, but at 90° to the direction of wiping used the first time, or increase the pressure you are using to wipe the surface. It is advisable to work on a test area before starting on the surface, to familiarise yourself with the material. Bear in mind that atmospheric conditions can have a great effect on surface coatings, and a material used on one day may handle differently the next if the conditions have changed.

INDUSTRY TIP

For Stage 2, you could wrap a decorator's sponge in lint-free cloth to produce a larger flat surface area.

The use of oil based scumbles means that a greater supply of lint-free rags will be required – these can be rinsed out in white spirit if required (wear gloves to protect your skin when using white spirit).

If you are using an acrylic scumble and a longer working time is required, dip the cloth pad in water and wring it out well, which will help to remove the scumble. Rags can be rinsed out and reused, which will make fewer contaminated rags that will require disposal.

Working with both the material types mentioned above to produce this decorative effect means that you will have to hold the lint-free rags in your hands. Wear gloves to protect your skin from harmful ingredients in both water-borne and solvent-borne scumble types.

'Glazed and wiped' effect on a relief texture wall covering

'Glazed and wiped' effect on a frieze

APPLICATION FAULTS

Banding/tracking
This can occur if you don't slightly overlap areas while rag rolling or check the work carefully on completion.

Slip/skid
This fault can occur if you apply too much pressure or don't take enough care when evening out the scumble or producing the effect.

Damage to decorative effect and removal of ground coat
See the instructions for removal of masking materials on page 282. Failure to properly protect the completed work while it dries, by the use of signs, tape or barriers may also lead to damage to the effect.

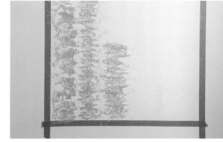

Ensure you overlap areas when rag rolling to avoid tracking

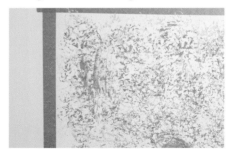

Slip/skid in a broken colour effect

PROTECTION OF THE FINISHED WORK

Broken colour finishes are delicate, and when they have been applied to areas that are subject to knocks and damage, such as doors, woodwork and certain wall areas, they need to be protected with a varnish that is compatible with the type of scumble used. An eggshell or flat varnish finish is most appropriate, as the light reflectance from any higher degree of sheen will detract from the decorative finish. The varnish should be applied as thin coats and built up, according to the durability required.

ACTIVITY

Using the internet and manufacturers' information, find a non-yellowing varnish suitable for protecting oil based and acrylic scumble work.

PERSONAL PROTECTION

The minimum precautions when producing specialist decorative finishes are as follows:

- Avoid products coming into contact with skin and eyes (wear gloves, and goggles if necessary).
- Ensure that there is good ventilation, using local exhaust ventilation (LEV) if necessary.
- Store and use products away from heat sources and flames.
- Do not eat or smoke in the vicinity of the work area.
- Wash hands before eating.

INDUSTRY TIP

For more information on PPE, refer back to Chapter 1, pages 20–23.

PREPARE STENCIL PLATES AND APPLY STENCILS

A stencil is produced when:

- a design or pattern is cut out of a thin plate of treated paper, card, acetate or metal
- the stencil plate is temporarily adhered to the surface being decorated
- colour is applied through the cut-out sections.

This produces a pattern on the surface and, by moving the stencil plate to different positions, you can produce identical versions of the pattern.

The main types of stencil plate are as follows:

- *Positive*: The actual design is cut out of the plate and is therefore applied as the colour. More intricate designs can be produced using this type.
- *Negative*: The surround or background of the design is cut out, so the design on the surface is the ground coat colour and the applied colour is the background. This often gives the design the appearance of a silhouette.
- *Border or edge*: This is a narrow band of integrated shapes, which may be either a positive or a negative plate.
- *Multi-plate*: Two or more stencil plates are used to produce the finished design, with each plate being a different part of the design and for use with a different colour. It is essential that each plate is very accurately positioned, using **registration marks**, before the paint is applied.

Registration marks

Marks (or a very small cut-out section) made on a stencil which are lined up with chalk lines on the surface, and/or part of a previously applied stencil if using a multi-plate stencil, to ensure correct positioning before applying paint

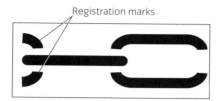

Registration marks

A positive stencil design

Registration mark

A negative stencil design

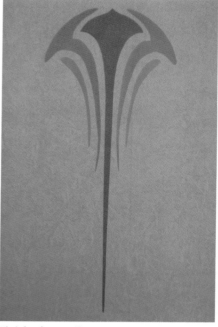

Finished stencil

Stencils may be applied in the following ways:

- *single (or spot) design*: both positive and negative types may be used

- *linear border*: eg around a room at dado rail or picture rail height

- *frame*: eg around a panelled area or on the top of a box

- *overall wall decoration*: with the designs being repeated at set distances, sometimes called a diaper pattern.

If the design for a stencil has not been carefully thought through, sections of the design will fall out when it is cut, because they are not tied to the rest of the design; these important links are called ties, and they are covered later in this chapter.

PREPARE AND MANUFACTURE STENCIL PLATES

Stencil plates are either rectangular or square, regardless of the shape of the design within.

When undertaking large jobs where the stencil plates will need to be used many times, it is advisable to produce a master plate – from this, all other working plates are produced, which will be exactly the same as the original. The master plate should be kept in a safe location so that it can be used for any future repair or maintenance work.

TRANSFERRING THE DESIGN ONTO THE STENCIL SHEET

There are several ways of doing this.

Tracing paper and pencil

1 Position the original design so it is as flat as possible, and secure it with tape. Lay tracing paper over the design and secure that with tape also.

2 Using a pencil, trace the design, or whichever part(s) of it you require.

Graphite

One form of carbon, which when used in pencils, is commonly (but incorrectly) called lead, eg 'a lead pencil'

Free brush work

The application of decorative detail or design using a signwriter's pencil and mahl stick

ACTIVITY

Find out what material is traditionally used as the filling for a signwriter's pencil, also known as a 'writer'.

Pounce wheel

A toothed wheel that perforates paper with evenly spaced fine holes – varying sizes are available to produce different-sized holes

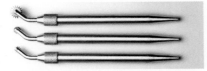

Pounce wheels

Perforate

To pierce or make holes through

Pounce bag

A small bag of coarsely woven or thin fabric (eg cheesecloth) filled with a fine powder (eg crushed chalk or charcoal) – used to transfer pounced designs

3 Remove the tracing paper and turn it face down on a smooth surface, preferably protected with paper, to prevent transfer of the **graphite** onto the surface. Moving the pencil back and forth, coat the blank side of the tracing paper with graphite; if the design has little detail, coat only the lines, not the entire surface.

4 Place the coated side of the tracing paper onto the stencil plate material and secure it to prevent any movement.

5 Using a pencil, follow the lines, which will reproduce the design on the plate material. Keep your pencil sharpened to maintain line width and accuracy.

Lining or cartridge paper and chalk

This method is more suitable for larger designs and is not necessarily associated with stencilling. It is used for **free brush work**, which you may learn in the future.

1 Using the same technique as above, and with the design already on the paper, coat the reverse side with chalk, which is quicker to apply than pencil. However, care should be taken when selecting the chalk colour, as some colours stain, leaving the work surface contaminated and messy.

2 Follow Steps 4 and 5, above.

Pounce

Pouncing is one of the oldest methods used to transfer a design or image from one surface to another.

1 With the design already traced onto paper, and using a **pounce wheel**, **perforate** the paper along the lines of the design. This should preferably be undertaken on a soft or flexible surface, such as a cutting mat (see page 295) or cardboard, to ensure that the paper is fully pierced. The reverse side may then be lightly abraded to open up the holes. Place the pounced design on the surface to which it is to be transferred, and secure it.

2 Using a **pounce bag** or pounce pad, firmly strike or wipe the surface along the perforated lines; this will push the powder through the holes, transferring the design to the new surface. Blow off any excess powder before continuing to work.

Pounce bag

Pounce pad

Photocopy or print

Ensuring that you do not infringe any copyright restrictions on the design to be copied, use a photocopying machine to replicate the object, or print it from a computer.

ENLARGING AND REDUCING

There are several possible methods of enlarging or reducing a design.

Accurate measurement

Trace or photocopy the original design and create a grid over it by drawing equally spaced horizontal and vertical lines within a box. The size of the grid squares should be appropriate for the design – there should not be too much detail in any one square. Draw another grid with the same number of squares, but at the size the design is to be enlarged to (eg, if the original is to be increased by 30%, with the original squares being 10mm, the new grid squares will be 13mm). The design in each square of the original is replicated in the new grid; for ease of referencing between the two, each horizontal and vertical line should be numbered and lettered respectively, rather than the space between them.

Grid enlargement

Illuminated projection

This may be produced by an **epidiascope** or projector. The enlarged design is traced onto paper or stencil plate material.

Photocopy

Following the photocopier manufacturer's instructions, the equipment will increase the size of the original design to your requirements.

STENCIL PLATE MATERIALS

Some common stencil plate materials are described below – paper, as well as proprietary stencil plate materials.

Paper

Cartridge paper, lining paper, Manila paper, a good-quality fairly heavyweight paper, or even card may be used – the life expectancy

Epidiascope

Epidiascope

An opaque projector which has a strong light shining onto an opaque or transparent object and, by the use of its internal mirrors/prisms and/or lenses, projects the 'enlarged' object onto a screen (or wall)

of plates made from these materials is dependent on the design, care during use, cleaning and storage methods. They will not stand up to harsh treatment and must be kept flat when not in use.

Paper must be treated to seal the porosity, to harden it and to make it 'waterproof'. The most commonly used, economical material for this process is shellac knotting. However, a few traditionalists may use thinned, boiled linseed oil, which may be over-coated with shellac knotting if desired. The exact method is down to personal preference, with most people who use paper selecting the quicker, more economical option of shellac knotting only.

The paper, having had the design applied to it, is coated on both sides with one good coat of shellac knotting, to stiffen the paper and make it easier to clean both during and after use. The shellac knotting needs to fully dry and harden before you attempt to cut and use the plate, otherwise it is likely to be quickly ruined by becoming misshapen and torn.

When manufacturing your own stencil plate, it is important to treat the whole plate, to ensure that it lies flat and does not **buckle**, or distort.

If you are using the traditional method, the paper is given a good coat of linseed oil and hung up to dry. The drying process can take a considerable length of time (many weeks) and therefore advance planning is required.

Stencil card
This is oiled Manila card which is waterproof and ready to receive a design and be cut out. It is available in varying sizes, such as 600mm × 170mm and 1000mm × 600mm.

Acetate
This thin, transparent, flexible sheet material is often referred to as plastic film. It is actually a specific type of plastic material (cellulose acetate) which is made from wood pulp or cotton fibres and whose characteristics may be desirable or otherwise, depending on its application – it has glass-like clarity and good dimensional stability, but is easily torn.

Polyester film/sheet
This material is durable, flexible and reusable – it is particularly suitable for producing detailed stencils and multi-plate stencils. It may be cut with a craft knife, a hot knife or commercially, by laser.

These products are often called Mylar – however, this name is a registered trademark owned by DuPont Teijin Films, for a specific family of plastic sheet products. Because Mylar is a high-performance plastic, it is more expensive than other types and makes of proprietary materials. It is available in sheets, or rolls of film of varying sizes.

Buckle
To bend, warp or bulge

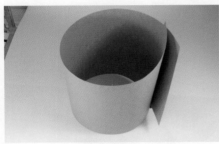
Stencil card sheets

Frisket Film

As mentioned on page 281, Frisket Film can also be used to create stencil plates.

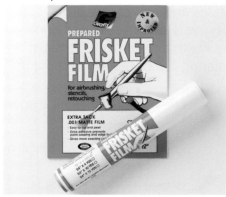

Frisket plastic film

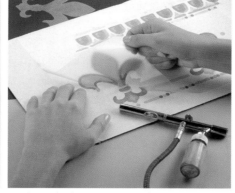

Frisket Film being removed to reveal the applied effect (a stencil produced by air brush)

Commercially manufactured plates made from metal or plastic

For companies who regularly use the same stencils (the alphabet, symbols, particular illustrations, etc) the purchase of metal or plastic stencils saves time and money as they are reusable, although the initial cost is greater. The most commonly used materials are stainless steel and plastic, but brass and zinc are also used.

Metal letter stencils

TOOLS AND MATERIALS FOR MANUFACTURING STENCIL PLATES

The base on which stencils are cut should be smooth and level, and of a material that will not be marked or damaged by the stencil knife blade. Timber surfaces are not suitable because the cutting knife will tend to follow the grain rather than the design, resulting in a rough, inaccurate design outline.

The most commonly used tools and materials for making stencils are described below.

Glass plate

This is a piece of plate glass with the edges taped to avoid injury. Sheet glass should never be used because it will break under the pressure of the knife. This surface may be used when cutting stencil plates using a stencil knife or hot pen.

Proprietary cutting mat

Sometimes referred to as a self-healing cutting mat, this provides a durable, non-slip surface for repetitive cutting without mess or harm to the knife edge or work surface. Some brands have gridlines to help with cutting straight lines, and an anti-glare surface. The mat does not actually heal, but works by being able to take a lot of cuts before wearing out and is available in a range of sizes from A4 to A1. This is not a suitable surface on which to cut stencil plates using a hot knife.

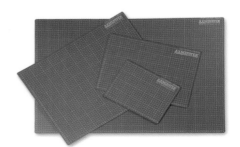

Proprietary cutting mat

ACTIVITY

Research online to find the technique used to sharpen a blade.

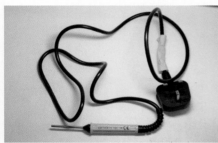

Hot knife, used to cut acetate or polyester film, eg Mylar

Steel ruler

Intricate

Very complicated or detailed

Stencil knife

This is a very sharp instrument which must be used with great care. Most have a slim aluminium handle which holds the blade still. Swivel knives, which may be used to cut circles and curves, are also available, as well as other specialist types. However, shaped and intricate areas may be cut equally well with a fixed blade; it is just a case of personal preference and acquiring the necessary technique.

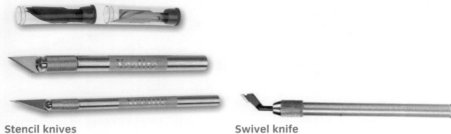

Stencil knives   Swivel knife

Hot knife

This electrical instrument is used to cut acetate or polyester film stencil plates.

Steel ruler

This will be helpful if there are a number of straight lines to be cut (eg, for lettering) and will not be damaged by the sharp knife cutting into it.

CUTTING TECHNIQUES AND CONSIDERATIONS

The quality of the finished work directly relates to the quality of this final stage of preparing the stencil plate. Any jerky cutting lines or lack of fluid curves will be evident in the applied stencil.

Place the stencil plate on a clean, smooth, level surface such as a cutting mat or sheet of glass. This surface must be free from paper cuttings or grit, which may adversely affect the cutting process, particularly when cutting **intricate** sections. There is more resistance when using a cutting mat, compared with using a glass plate, and some people prefer this greater feeling of control. Others prefer the hard surface and freer movement allowed by the plate.

The correct cutting technique should include:

- Being able to rotate the stencil plate freely, rather than twisting and turning the knife, or your body.

- Always using a sharp blade.

- Holding the knife as a pen: firmly, but not too tightly, otherwise it may cause cramp in the hand. Use the whole arm, not just the hand and wrist – this will allow flowing lines and curves to be cut and will reduce the number of jagged, uneven lines.

- Positioning your free hand so that it is *never* in line with the direction you are cutting.

- Holding the knife inclined at a low angle to use as much of the cutting edge as possible.

- Always pulling the knife towards you, not away from you.

- Leaving a 25–50mm area surrounding the design, which is known as the margin, to allow sufficient material to support/contain the design, but avoiding unnecessary excess.

- Cutting away from corners, not towards them. If any section does not fall out, do not pull it, as this will produce a rough edge which may be visible on the applied stencil.

Cutting a curve

- Holding hot knives like a pen. If you keep the tip clean, very little pressure is required to cut the plate. The cutting action should be a continuous stroke to complete the removal of a shape, before lifting it off the surface. Melted plastic may tend to build up on the tip and affect the speed of cutting and quality of finish – in this case, lightly abrade the tip to remove the build-up. With experience, a hot knife may be moved in different directions, unlike a stencil knife.

Sequence for cutting a stencil plate

1 Start with the smallest areas – if large areas are removed first, the structure of the plate will be weakened.

2 Curved areas are cut next, when you need to freely rotate the plate.

3 All vertical lines are cut before rotating the plate and cutting the horizontal lines.

Repairing broken ties

Because stencil plates can be quite fragile, you need to be able to repair them should they become damaged. It is advisable to practise this repair technique so you can undertake any required repair without delay.

1 Carefully clean and dry the stencil plate.

2 Place the damaged area face up on a cutting mat/glass sheet.

3 Re-align the damaged sections, placing masking tape over the damaged area and onto the mat/glass.

4 Cut away the excess tape beyond the design, ensuring you are very accurate in maintaining the original shape.

5 The repaired stencil plate is now ready for use.

Repairing a damaged tie

HEALTH AND SAFETY

- When using knives to cut stencils, safe working practices should be followed at all times, particularly the safe disposal of used blades in a sharps box.

- Cutting should only take place on a suitable base material such as a cutting mat or glass sheet.

- Unprotected knives should never be placed in pockets.

- Knives should not be left lying around when not in use – if the knife has a retractable blade or cover, these safety features should be used.

- A hot knife is an electrical item, and the wiring and plug should always be checked prior to use and the item turned off and disconnected at break times and on completion of the work.

- Only the handle of the hot knife should be held, as the stem and blade become hot and will burn you. Some manufacturers sell a stand to hold the knife while it is not in use.

APPLY STENCILS

MATERIALS USED FOR THE APPLICATION OF STENCILS

Paints used with stencils should have the following properties:

- little or no flow

- quick drying, particularly if a border or multi-plate stencil is being applied

- reasonably good opacity

- compatibility with the surface – for example, using emulsion paint on a solvent-borne eggshell ground coat could result in cissing.

TOOLS AND EQUIPMENT USED FOR THE APPLICATION OF STENCILS

You will have already learned about the standard stencilling tools such as tape measure, ruler and pencil (the chinagraph type to prevent permanent marks). In addition to these you will need a chalk and line, a spirit level and a plumb bob, as discussed in Chapter 5, to **set out** areas.

A palette (see page 280) should be used to hold a small quantity of paint, and a **stencil brush** is used to apply the paint. A scraper can be used to hold down the stencil plate close to where paint is being applied.

Set out

To put in a specified position or location – following a drawing, written specification or verbal instructions

Stencil brush

A round brush with a filling of short, stiff bristles set in a metal ferrule on a short handle. Stencil brushes are available in a range of sizes from 6 to 38mm

Do not allow paint to build up and dry on the bristles, which will happen quite quickly when you are using water-borne paints. Rubbing the bristle ends on a cloth dampened with the appropriate thinner will help to limit this, but do not immerse the bristles in thinner, otherwise the viscosity of the paint still to be applied will be affected. If necessary change to a clean dry brush. After use the stencil brush should be thoroughly cleaned in the appropriate thinner and then washed with soap and water. When it is completely dry, the bristles should be wrapped in paper secured with masking tape or an elastic band – this will maintain the shape of the brush filling.

SECURING METHODS

Stencils can be secured using masking tape (see page 280) or with a proprietary spray adhesive. This is an aerosol spray contact adhesive suitable for securing lightweight material. It allows the stencil plate to be peeled off, re-positioned and stuck down again for up to 12 hours. Excess adhesive can be rubbed off once it has begun to dry.

PLANNING CONSIDERATIONS

Before undertaking any stencilling work, it is essential to thoroughly plan the setting out and execution of it, taking into consideration a number of factors, to achieve a perfectly balanced end result.

If you are applying this decorative finish to a room, the dimensions, shape and location and number of doors, windows and corners can all affect the starting and finishing points and centralisation of the design, particularly on feature areas such as the chimney breast or panels. It is advisable to carefully note the dimensions of each wall and its features, to enable you to work out balanced spacing for the plates. You should note that the setting out principles for stencilling are different from those you would use for paperhanging – for example, the finishing point with wallpaper should be the least obvious internal angle in a room, while with stencilling you would aim to finish at a natural stopping point – usually a room feature such as a door or window.

If you are continuing a border stencil around an internal or external angle, the design must match on both sides, so simple designs in a single colour may be most appropriate. However, you may decide to treat each wall as a separate section and centralise the design on each wall. In this case you will need to consider the end of the stencil design and its finishing distance from the corner.

The term 'connections' relates to how many times the stencil is repeated to form a border. This is taken into account when planning out a border for a room. The gaps (connection spaces) can be changed depending on the length of the wall and the size of the stencil design, but the finished effect must be **aesthetically** pleasing and balanced.

> **INDUSTRY TIP**
>
> Do not pound the surface with a stencil brush, as this forces the bristles to spread out during use. Wrapping masking tape around the bristles of a stencil brush can stop this happening.

Spray adhesive

> **INDUSTRY TIP**
>
> Proprietary spray adhesives can sometimes lift off newly applied ground coat when removed, and are best suited to acetate stencils.

A chimney breast

Aesthetic

Visually beautiful and in good taste

ACTIVITY

List the most suitable type(s) of access equipment to use to apply a stencil at picture rail height.

Bisect

To divide into two equal parts

Feature corner stencil

The dimensions of the room will also influence the access equipment required to undertake the work – both the height at which you will be working and the length of working platform required – to enable you to achieve a comfortable workstation, as stencilling can be a slow job. See Chapter 8 for access equipment types and usage.

When you are producing a frame around an area, the stencil design should really dictate the area size, not the other way around. In these circumstances there are two ways to negotiate the corners:

- *Use a mitre joint*: **Bisect** the angle so the design will pivot on that line.

- *Stop and apply a corner feature*: While a different single stencil design may be used as the corner feature, the natural flow of the design will continue better if a part of its design has been used to create the corner stencil.

The size of the stencil design should always be relative to its location; if it is too small, a large number of repeats will have to be made and this has cost as well as possible aesthetic implications. If it is too large, it may overwhelm rather than enhance the area, and if it has large areas through which colour is to be applied, the selection of appropriate tools and materials to produce an even consistency of colour is also be a consideration.

SETTING OUT

Once you have carefully planned the positioning of the stencils, accurate measuring – including the correct use of a spirit level for horizontal lines and a plumb bob for vertical lines – is crucial. However, in (older) buildings where architectural features may not be truly horizontal or vertical, the setting out must produce an aesthetically pleasing effect, which may involve measurement only, and not the use of spirit level and/or plumb bob.

The surface should be marked out with appropriate centre, horizontal and/or vertical guide lines, using chalk and line. This is then very lightly dusted off to remove any excess chalk.

STEP 1 Place the stencil plate accurately on the surface, lining up registration marks with the chalked lines, and secure with low-tack tape or a proprietary spray adhesive. The stencil plate should be secure enough not to move while the paint is being applied (which could cause smudging), yet may be easily removed and re-positioned without damaging the surface.

STEP 2 Before applying any paint, check whether a chalk line passes through the area to be stenciled. If so, remove it with a dry cloth, otherwise it will absorb the paint and create bittiness and uneven colour.

STEP 3 Pour a small quantity of paint onto a palette board and dab the bristle ends of the stencil brush onto the paint. Remove excess paint from the brush by stippling it out on a clean area of the palette board, spare board or length of lining paper – this will also ensure the paint is evenly distributed. This action must be taken every time you re-load the brush, to avoid a number of application faults.

STEP 4 Apply the paint through the cut-out sections of the stencil plate using a stippling action, keeping the brush at 90° to the surface, and moving the brush across the area until an even colour and sharp outline has been produced.

STEP 5 Prior to removing the stencil plate, a small section of it should be lifted to check that the depth of colour is correct, as it is very difficult to replace the plate exactly once it has been completely removed, to correct any errors or deficiencies. Repeat the process of Step 1 and continue until the work has been completed. At this stage the stencil plate should be cleaned, completely dried and stored carefully, keeping it flat (if possible separated from other stencil plates with paper, to avoid them snagging each other) or hung vertically.

When the applied stencils are dry, wipe off any remaining chalk lines with a clean soft cloth or damp sponge if necessary.

Hold down the stencil with a scraper

Do:

- Regularly wipe excess paint from the stencil plate (both front and back) using the appropriate thinner. This must be done carefully to avoid damaging the plate or getting it too wet.

- Use a scraper to hold down the stencil plate close to where the paint is being applied, particularly if the stencil plate is made from treated paper.

- Regularly check that the colour application is even. This may be done by partly closing your eyes and squinting at the work, to clearly see any differences there may be between each application.

- Carefully lift part of the stencil plate to check for both even paint application and correct weight of colour, before finally removing it, as it can be difficult to re-apply the stencil plate accurately to touch up any area. If applying a border stencil, or many repetitions of a single stencil design, this check should also be to compare the weight of colour between the current stencil and those previously applied.

- Check the consistency of the paint on the palette, and replace if it is beginning to thicken or dry.

Do not:

- Be tempted to over-work the area, as this may lead to the applied paint beginning to lift off.

- Be heavy handed in applying the paint, as this will cause creep.

- Dip your stencil brush into a tin of paint – always load it from a palette.

APPLICATION FAULTS

The following are faults that you may see as a result of poor application technique.

Fault	Description and causes
Creep	This refers to paint getting beneath the stencil plate and blurring the edge of the design. It is caused by the application of too much paint or paint that is too thin, not keeping the stencil plate regularly wiped clean, heavy-handed application, or the stencil plate not being secured/held tight to the surface.
Smudging	This is caused by movement of the stencil plate on the wet paint as a result of careless removal of the stencil plate.

Fault	Description and causes
Paint lifting	This is caused by careless removal of the stencil plate or over-working an area during application.
Uneven colour	This is caused by failing to regularly check for even distribution of colour, especially over repeats.
Bittiness	This can happen when dirt and grit get into the paint film as a result of insufficient checking of the surface cleanliness prior to starting work. It can also be the result of not lightly dusting off any excess chalk deposit or using dirty tools and equipment or contaminated paint.
Undue texture	This is where excess paint has been applied to the surface, caused by not working the brush on spare board or paper immediately after re-loading it.
Buckled/curled stencil plate	This may be as a result of the method used to make the stencil, with an insufficient margin left around the design. It may also be caused by not wiping off the stencil plate frequently enough, or letting it get too wet when cleaning it off.

PRODUCE WOOD AND MARBLE EFFECTS USING BASIC TECHNIQUES

The art of graining and marbling, which is the imitation of woods and marbles using paints and scumbles, can be traced back centuries. However, it became more popular in Britain in the mid to late 1800s, as a substitute for the expensive timbers being brought into the country with the expansion of the British Empire. The rich were able to access foreign marbles to create homes that displayed their wealth, and everyone else wanted to **emulate** them.

To create a realistic imitation of woods and marbles, it is necessary to:

- understand their origins – the methods used to process them following felling and quarrying and the factors that influence the pattern structures and colours of each

- consider the location they will be used in, as they will only be aesthetically pleasing if they are used realistically and in context – for example it would be inappropriate to produce a grained door with marbled mouldings, or grained iron railings or rainwater pipes.

As with all broken colour effects and decorative work, the requirement for a high-quality ground coat of an appropriate colour is essential (involving thorough surface preparation).

The factors to check, prior to starting work on any ground coat, were covered on page 267.

Emulate

To try to equal or surpass another

INDUSTRY TIP

Many people are unclear about the difference between wood and timber. In simple terms, wood refers to the tree itself and timber refers to the wood at any stage after the tree has been cut down.

INDUSTRY TIP

This section looks at the materials, tools and processes used to produce basic graining and marbling effects. If you are interested in this specialist area there are a number of books that offer further information:
- *Holz- und Marmormalerei* (Graining and Marbling) by Ernst Oldenbruch
- *Parry's Graining and Marbling* by Brian Rhodes and John Windsor
- *The Life and Times of Ernest Dobson* by John Fleming and Terry Taylor
- *The Art of Marbling* by Stuart Spencer.

GROUND COAT COLOURS

For graining, the choice of ground coat colour often comes down to personal preference – however, that decision will be based on an understanding of colour technology (see Chapter 7), the characteristics of the wood or marble you want to imitate and the various pigments/colourants which can be used in the process. Experienced grainers often mix their own colours to obtain the required tones, particularly if they are matching existing work. Under these circumstances, the lightest colour of the existing work will be matched for the ground coat, but may still require a little adjustment when a sample board is being produced.

The **integrity** of a wood or marble imitation may be compromised by the use of an inappropriate colour for the ground coat. However, when producing fantasy (imaginary) marbles, there may be some flexibility with this.

The British Standard 4800 colours for wood and marble effects are detailed below:

- BS 4800 colours for graining:
  - Light Oak – tint of 08 C 35
  - Medium Oak – 08 C 35 (or 06 C 35). The description of 'buff' coloured' or 'biscuit' coloured is sometimes used.
  - Mahogany – 04 D 44 (or 06 C 33).
- BS 4800 colours for marbling:
  - Carrara – 00 E 55.
  - Fantasy (a black and green marble type is the example used) – 00 E 53.

INGREDIENTS IN GRAINING AND MARBLING MATERIALS

These can be divided into oil based products, colourants and pigments, and water-borne materials.

OIL BASED

Oil glaze

When graining with oil colour, a small amount is used with the pigment, to ensure that the initial rubbing in holds up (retains its shape) while being manipulated, for example by being combed or having figurework applied (see facing page).

Oil graining colour

This is the medium (known in the past as **megilp**) applied at the initial rubbing-in stage (see page 310). Traditionally it was made from one part linseed oil, two parts turpentine (derived from the resin of pine trees), liquid driers and pigment.

Integrity

Truthfulness or accurate characteristics

Medium Oak

Megilp

A variety of substances (eg soft soap, beeswax) that used to be added to graining colour to make it hold up or prevent it flowing together after it had combed or figured

Nowadays, oil glaze is used, and appropriate pigments (which are ground into oil at the manufacturing stage) are added to obtain the required colour, with white spirit added to obtain the required consistency (viscosity).

Oil based proprietary scumbles

These are ready-made oil graining colours, coloured appropriately to match the most common range of woods. They must be stirred and thinned prior to application and may have the colour adjusted by the addition of oil colourants to meet individual requirements.

Varnish

This is a solvent- or water-borne clear coating that contains film former and thinner, but no coloured pigment. It is necessary to apply varnish to protect graining and marbling effects because the materials used to produce them have little protective quality and are not very resistant to abrasion. Remember that the varnish needs to be compatible with the materials used, and should have a level of sheen appropriate for the work – for example, polished marble would require a full-gloss varnish and waxed wood, an eggshell sheen.

White spirit

This is a petroleum **distillate,** which is a volatile organic compound (VOC) or solvent, used as a thinner for coatings used in painting and decorating.

Linseed oil

Linseed oil is a pale yellowish oil made from the seeds of the flax plant, and is used as a drying oil or binder. Synthetic alkyd resins are more often used nowadays, as they do not yellow as quickly as linseed oil.

Driers

For more information about driers, see page 275.

COLOURANTS AND PIGMENTS

For information on oil and acrylic colourants, see pages 277–278.

Crayons (oil pastel/wax oil crayon)

These are sticks of pigment mixed with a non-drying oil and wax binder that are used for graining – to put in **figurework** or **figure graining**, and marbling – for fine veins.

They may be used:

- in a dry form, and once applied to the surface they can be manipulated with a brush moistened with white spirit or linseed oil

- by oiling in the surface prior to applying the detail with crayon

- with oil colour work and water colour, but should be tested before varnishing, as it may be difficult to protect.

INDUSTRY TIP

The drying time for oil based scumbles can be extended by the addition of small quantities of linseed oil. However, take care not to add too much, as this will mean the scumble will not dry properly.

INDUSTRY TIP

Eggshell and flat varnishes contain a flatting agent which reduces light reflection, and so they should be stirred before use. Gloss varnish should not be stirred, but gently shaken just before use.

Distillate

A product that has been separated from a mixture by boiling it, and then cooling the vapour, in a process known as distillation

INDUSTRY TIP

Rags soaked with linseed oil and left in a pile are a fire hazard. The linseed oil oxidises, which is an exothermic reaction (a reaction that releases energy in the form of heat) which can lead to spontaneous combustion.

Figurework/figure graining

The main design or pattern of a wood grain, which differs between tree species and according to the **method of conversion**

Method of conversion

The way a newly felled tree is sawn up into usable-sized pieces of timber, using two main methods: through-and-through, or quarter-sawn

ACTIVITY

Using your college or training centre's resources, find out more about the two methods of converting timber, and produce a drawing of each method to be inserted into your Portfolio of Knowledge.

Gouache

This is a type of paint that is similar to water colour, but modified to be opaque. It consists of pigment and binder, sometimes with an extender such as chalk added. Gouache has good reflective qualities but generally dries to a different tone than it appears when wet (lighter tones generally dry darker, while darker tones tend to dry lighter). It is available in many colours and is usually mixed with water to achieve the desired working consistency and to control the opacity when dry.

Universal stainers

These are high-strength, concentrated stainers which may be mixed with most types of paint.

WATER BASED AND ACRYLIC COLOURS

Water based graining colours are reversible when dry, which means they can be softened, or re-activated with water, or by applying more of the graining colour. For more information about acrylic glaze and acrylic colourants, see pages 276–278.

Dry (powdered) pigments

The most common pigments used are 'earth' colours and include ochres (pale yellow to deep orange/brown), siennas (yellow/brown) and umbers (brown or reddish brown). These are naturally occurring minerals, mainly iron oxides, which are found in rocks and soils. Some earth pigments are roasted in order to intensify their colour and are then known as 'burnt', as opposed to 'raw'.

Because of their good opacity, only small quantities of earth pigments should be used, to ensure that the scumble retains its translucency.

BINDERS OR FIXATIVES (FOR WATER GRAINING COLOUR)

These are used to temporarily hold together or bind dry (powdered) pigments while they are manipulated to form the grain pattern required; a varnish coat will be needed to permanently bind the dried water-borne scumble to the surface.

Fuller's earth

This is a naturally occurring sedimentary clay, used in a fine powder form:

- mixed with water, as a binder/fixative for pigments

- to prevent cissing – a damp sponge or cloth is dipped in the powder and rubbed over the surface, which is then rinsed off.

A range of powdered earth pigments

Fuller's earth

Whiting

This is powdered and washed white chalk (calcium carbonate) which is sometimes added to paint as an extender to provide body. It may also be used to prevent cissing, but not as successfully as Fuller's earth, though it is applied in the same manner.

Stale beer and malt vinegar

These were traditional binders used by grainers, as they were readily available and economical.

Glue size

This is a binder for pigments made from animal glue. The pigment colours appear matt and opaque, with reds and blues appearing quite strong, as opposed to having a translucent appearance when used in oil.

> **INDUSTRY TIP**
>
> Do not use too much glue size as the binder in water based scumble, as it will produce a brittle surface which will crack and flake off after a period of time.

RETARDING AGENTS

For more information about retarding agents, see page 276.

Glycerine

The addition of glycerine to water graining colour slows down the evaporation rate of the water, allowing an extended working time. However, if too much is added, it will stop the drying process; therefore a very small quantity should be used.

MATERIALS USED TO PREVENT CISSING

If you apply water based materials to an oil based or solvent-borne coating, you will probably experience **cissing**. The following materials work by reducing the **surface tension** (a form of de-greasing), allowing the water based material to adhere as a continuous film. Detergent (a **surfactant**, such as washing-up liquid), Fuller's earth and whiting can all be used to prevent cissing.

Cissing

This occurs when an applied material does not form a continuous film, separating to form surface globules, which leaves some areas of the surface to which it is applied uncoated

Surface tension

Simply explained, this is the tendency of the surface of a liquid/solid to resist an external force

Surfactant

This is a compound that lowers the surface tension between two liquids or between a liquid and a solid, to increase adhesion

GRAINING AND MARBLING TOOLS

Specialist tools are available that have been specifically designed for the highly skilled techniques used in graining and marbling. These are expensive, and particular attention should be given to their care and maintenance. However, it is possible to achieve a good standard of work with everyday decorating tools, and even some **improvised** items.

Improvised

Made or invented using whatever is available, based on an understanding of what is required

COMBS

These may be made from metal (steel), rubber or card (improvised) and are used mainly for oak graining. Metal combs may be fine, medium or coarse and come in four widths. Rubber combs are either triangular with fine, medium or coarse teeth, or double-ended (3-inch and 4.5-inch sides) with graduated teeth.

Metal and rubber graining combs

Check/tick roller and mottler

CHECK/TICK ROLLER

This is a small roller made of serrated zinc discs which revolve independently and take scumble off a mottler (positioned above the discs and clipped in place) and then deposit a random series of dark tick marks to simulate the dark open pores of oak grain.

MOTTLER

This is a brush consisting of a ferrule and hog hair bristle filling. It is usually used to produce the characteristic variations of light and shade seen in natural wood.

FEATHERS

Suitable types of feather to use include goose, swan and duck, with the goose feather – obtained from the wings – being the most suitable because it has the best shape, size and strength. Feathers may be used in:

Feathers – swan, goose, duck

- marbling, to produce background texture/colour, and/or veins
- graining, to produce wavy markings for woods such as walnut.

To care for feathers, regularly wipe off excess material with a lint-free rag during use. When you have completed the work, clean them using the appropriate thinner, then wash in soapy water and rinse – allow to dry fully before storing.

PALETTE KNIVES

These have carbon steel flexible blades and hardwood tang handles and come in a range of blade sizes (4-inch, 6-inch, 8-inch, etc). They are used to mix ingredients, particularly on a palette board.

See pages 278 and 279 for more information on lint-free rags and natural sponges.

Palette knife

BRUSHES

Rubbing-in brushes
These are part-worn flat paint brushes used to spread (or rub in), the scumble (or medium) over the ground coat. A separate set, consisting of 25mm and 50mm sizes, should be kept for water-borne and oil based materials.

Mixing brushes
These are part-worn brushes (25mm is ideal) used to combine ingredients ready for application.

Fitch brushes
These are long-handled, hog hair brushes, available with round or flat filling shapes of varying diameters/widths. They are normally used to produce pattern or figuring detail when undertaking marbling and graining.

Fitches – round and flat

Flogger brushes

These are brushes with less filling, but a longer length out (approximately 120mm), used to produce the pore markings seen in many hardwoods, before the main figuring is done.

Use the flat of the brush (not so much the tip) to strike or 'flog' the scumbled surface, working from the bottom upwards. They are suitable for either oil based scumbles or water based colours.

Clean flogger brushes using the appropriate thinner, then wash in soapy water and rinse – allow to dry fully before storing to prevent damage.

Softeners

These are used to blend or soften sharp edges in both graining and marbling. Use them to create an overall softened effect, by lightly stroking the glaze back and forth in one direction with the tips of the brush filling just touching the surface. When a direction of glaze appears, stroke the surface at 90° to this first direction. Continue until the desired effect is achieved.

There are two types of softener:

- *Hog hair, for use in oil based medium*: Clean regularly during use (with white spirit, and dried off on lint-free rag before reusing). On completion of work, clean with white spirit, then wash with soapy water and rinse – allow to dry fully before storing to avoid damage.

- *Badger hair, for use in water based medium*: Clean infrequently during use, but immediately wash the badger softener well in cool soapy water once finished. Rinse and hang the brush to dry on completion of work.

It is important to note that because acrylic materials dry quickly, the hair needs to be kept wet/moistened while in use. Should these materials dry in the brush clean carefully but thoroughly with methylated spirits.

Sable pencils and writers

These are often called 'writing pencils'. They are long-handled brushes, usually with sable or nylon filling held in a metal ferrule or quill (the base of a bird's feather), with a chisel (flat) or pointed end. They are available in a variety of sizes relating to their diameter and length out.

They are used in graining to produce grain markings and enhance grain characteristics, and in marbling for the application of veins or 'fractures/cracks'.

Carefully clean sable pencils in the appropriate thinner (white spirit or water), then apply a small quantity of petroleum jelly or grease to

INDUSTRY TIP

When used with water-borne scumble (not acrylic), it is advisable not to wash out the flogger brush, as any pigment adhering to the bristles will absorb water from the scumble, making it dry more quickly.

Floggers

Softeners – badger and hog hair

Signwriting pencils/writers

hold the filling together and straight. They are usually stored in an oblong box/tin or tube. Lightly swill out in white spirit to remove the grease before use.

Varnish

Varnish brushes, whether natural bristle or synthetic filament, should never be used to apply paint, but should be kept as a separate set for varnishing purposes only. It may be beneficial to work brushes into a small amount of varnish prior to application, to avoid any frothing or milkiness in the finished appearance.

Clean out varnish brushes using the appropriate thinner (white spirit or water). Wash them in detergent, rinse in clean water and allow them to dry. Alternatively, for brushes used with solvent-borne varnish, suspend them in a mixture of linseed oil and white spirit, which will help to keep the bristles supple. When required for use, rinse out in white spirit and spin well before use.

GRAINING AND MARBLING PROCESSES

RUBBING IN

This is the initial spreading of the graining colour, for example using a 25mm brush for window frames and door mouldings and a 50mm brush for larger areas. The brush is loaded **sparingly**, with just enough colour to make a thin, even coating on both flat and moulded surfaces. This process is also used in marbling.

OILING IN

This is a term that mainly applies to marbling. It is the process of moistening the ground coat using some of the medium (oil glaze or acrylic glaze) to enable the blending of colour washes.

FLOGGING

This is where thinly applied scumble or water colour is struck using a flogger brush, working upwards or away from the body, to produce the tiny pores or fine grain marks seen in most woods. This process is carried out before the main figure, or pattern of the wood, is produced.

COMBING

This is mainly used to imitate the hard and soft grain patterns of wood, particularly oak, with different comb types and sizes producing different effects. Combs should always be wiped clean after each stroke, to keep the work clean and prevent a build-up of colour into ridges. In the case of metal combs, when a piece of lint-free cloth is placed over the end of the teeth to soften or blur the effect, this should be frequently moved to present a clean edge.

INDUSTRY TIP

When using water based scumbles for graining, it is advisable to bind them down using yacht varnish. The more common polyurethane varnishes are not as resistant to water when **overgraining**.

Overgraining

The process of simulating subtle lighter and darker areas of the grain as seen in natural wood – this is carried out, usually in water colour, over completed figurework

Sparingly

Using very little

INDUSTRY TIP

Rubbing in is best done using a well-worn bristle brush, which will 'scrub' the scumble onto the surface. This will help to reduce surface tension, particularly when using water based scumble.

VEINING

This is the process of imitating the veins, fine lines and cracks that occur in marbles, using a variety of tools and materials such as feathers, writing pencils, crayons and so on.

SOFTENING

As its name implies, this process is the softening or fading out of harsh lines that may be produced when manipulating graining and marbling colour. It also enables colours to be blended together. Traditionally this has been achieved using a hog hair softener for oil colours and a badger softener for water colours. The softener is used by holding the brush at 90° to the surface and very lightly brushing the tips of it across the surface; it may be used either with a back and forth movement or in one direction only, depending on the desired effect.

GLAZING

This is the application of a thin, transparent wash of colour to give a subtle variation in the overall colour, when marbling. It is done before varnishing the completed work, and must not be carried out until the existing work is hard and dry.

CISSING OR OPENING OUT

This is achieved by flicking tiny droplets of an appropriate thinner (white spirit or water) onto wet glaze, which breaks up the glaze to reveal rings of the ground coat. This may be achieved by dipping a small fitch brush into the thinner and drawing a forefinger over the bristle tips to produce a light spray. If too much thinner is applied, lightly dab the surface with a lint-free rag to prevent it spreading further.

WIPING OUT

This is the process of lifting or removing areas of wet scumble to reveal the ground coat or underlying effect and produce figure graining and veins. This is opposed to the painting in or application of these features.

STIPPLING

For more about stippling, see page 283, Step 2.

GRAINING AND MARBLING EFFECTS

While you are learning how to produce these effects, you should be brushing out your work and repeating it a number of times, to gain sufficient practice and experiment with different materials and tools. Each of the following is just one method of producing an effect. They are provided to help you concentrate on developing the essential skills of the graining and marbling processes.

FUNCTIONAL SKILLS

Use ICT to design an advertisement for your business, which specialises in decorative finishes, to be placed in the local newspaper. The size of the advertisement is a quarter of an A4 page. Include the business name, contact details and the decorative finishes produced. Your logo and the design of the advert should reflect your specialist decorative finishes.

Work on this activity can support FICT1 (7.A1 and 7.A3).

FUNCTIONAL SKILLS

The local paper in which the advertisement is to be placed requires you to submit three 'customer reviews' of work you have produced, to cover a range of the decorative finishes you advertise. Write three reviews, by fictional customers, that you consider will support both the range of decorative finishes you advertise and also the customer service aspect of your work.

Work on this activity can support FE1 (1.3.1a).

Oak – an example of straight grain

Maritime
Related to the sea

WOOD EFFECTS

Oak (using dragging and combing techniques and check/tick roller)

Oak is a hardwood, whose natural colour varies from a rich honey colour to a yellowish brown. Its wide range of beautiful grain markings are dependent on the method of conversion. It has been widely used over the years for **maritime** and building construction purposes, as well as furniture. Oak graining is generally carried out using oil based scumbles.

Start with a surface ground out in 08 C 35 solvent-borne eggshell, or a tint of it, depending on whether you wish to produce a medium or light oak effect.

Method 1

STEP 1 Brush out thinned oak scumble glaze to evenly distribute the colour.

STEP 2 Using a dragging brush, produce firm, sharp grain markings.

STEP 3 Apply pore marks using a check/tick roller with mottler.

Method 2

STEP 1 Brush out thinned oak scumble glaze to evenly distribute the colour.

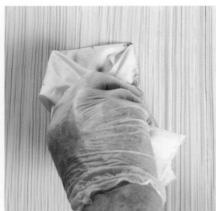

STEP 2 Using a metal comb folded into a piece of lint-free rag, produce firm, sharp grain markings.

STEP 3 With a finer metal comb, use short strokes at a slight angle to the grain marks to break up the vertical lines. (Wipe the tip of the comb regularly to remove excess scumble glaze.)

Mahogany

Mahogany is a tropical hardwood of reddish-brown colour, with a fine, silky appearance. Mahogany graining is generally carried out using water graining colour, building up the various characteristics using different processes to create the final depth of rich colour with subtle highlights – however, the process can also be successfully completed using oil based scumbles.

Mahogany – an example of straight grain

Start with a surface ground out in 04 D 44 (or 06 C 33) acrylic eggshell.

STEP 1 Prepare water graining colour using vinegar/stale beer, water and Vandyke brown.

STEP 2 De-grease the ground coat with Fuller's earth (or whiting).

STEP 3 Evenly brush out the water colour.

STEP 4 Flog the water colour, working away from your body, or upwards if on a door.

STEP 5 Leave to dry (as shown above). Then apply one coat of solvent-borne varnish, to bind the water colour to the surface, and allow to dry overnight.

STEP 6 Brush out thinned mahogany scumble over the flogged ground and apply streaks of burnt umber.

STEP 7 Use a fitch brush to spread the colour to produce broad vertical bands.

STEP 8 Using a hog hair softener, lightly soften in a horizontal direction to blur the edges of the bands.

The overall finish should be subtle, but effective enough to show some depth when varnished.

ACTIVITY

Produce an example on card/paper, by carrying out the steps above, demonstrating a mitre joint and finishing the work with one coat of acrylic eggshell varnish. The mitre joint will replicate the joints on a timber joinery component – you will have to lay off the ground coat in the appropriate directions.

MARBLE EFFECTS

A block of quarried Carrara marble

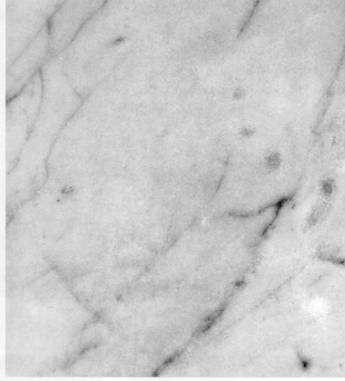

Ground and polished marble

Carrara (using softening techniques)

Carrara is a type of white or blue-grey marble, used in sculpture and building decoration. It is quarried near Carrara, in Tuscany, Italy.

Start with a surface that has been ground out in 00 E 55 acrylic eggshell.

STEP 1 Prepare a thin, pale grey acrylic scumble using acrylic glaze and white and black colourants.

STEP 2 Apply the acrylic scumble and oil or rub in the surface.

STEP 3 Slightly darken the scumble by adding a small amount of black, and apply streaks in a general diagonal direction.

STEP 4 Slightly darken the scumble again and apply darker streaks below the pale ones.

STEP 5 Using a badger softener, follow the general run of the streaks in one direction only, to produce one soft edge and one harder edge, as seen in natural marble.

STEP 6 Further variation can be achieved by applying a plastic bag or clingfilm to the surface. Wipe across the plastic with your hand in a diagonal direction, then carefully remove the plastic from the surface.

STEP 7 Soften to produce the desired effect.

STEP 8 An example of how a finished effect might look.

If the work loses shading definition, re-apply streaks of appropriate greys and work to soften them in. However, as you are working in water based materials, remember that you will have a limited working time.

The finished work should have the subtlety and depth required of many of the marble types you may imitate.

White marbles such as Carrara may have a yellow cast which can be imitated using an overglaze with raw sienna, or a blue cast for which Prussian blue may be used in an overglaze.

ACTIVITY

Produce an example on card/paper, by carrying out the steps above and finishing the work with one coat of acrylic varnish which will protect the work and maintain the colour by preventing yellowing.

Vert de Mer marble

Fantasy marble

Here marbling techniques and processes are used to produce a realistic-looking, but imaginary product.

The example shown involves ragging on or sponging (covered in earlier Outcomes) and the range of oiling in, veining (using both a feather and a signwriting pencil) and cissing techniques. Working on a black ground coat with tints and shades of green will produce a black and green 'marble', along the lines of Vert de Mer.

STEP 1 Prepare a megilp using *either* a 2:1 mix of oil based glaze and white spirit *or* a 2:1 mix of white spirit and linseed oil, and driers.

STEP 2 Oil in the surface.

STEP 3 On a palette, prepare a deep green scumble by mixing a small quantity of oil based glaze with *either* chrome yellow and Prussian blue *or* raw sienna and Prussian blue.

STEP 4 Rag on, or sponge on the green scumble to the oiled-in surface.

STEP 5 Add white to the green scumble, and rag on or sponge on between the spaces of the previous colour.

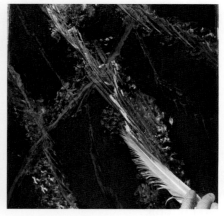

STEP 6 *Either* add more white to the mix of chrome yellow and Prussian blue *or* add Brunswick green and a little white to the raw sienna and Prussian blue. Using the new mix of green, apply a broad vein in a diagonal direction by feather, followed by further veining using various tones of green and pure white.

STEP 7 Soften as necessary.

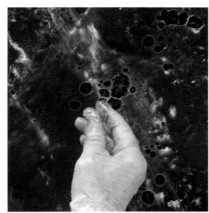

STEP 8 Ciss the surface by applying tiny splashes of white spirit.

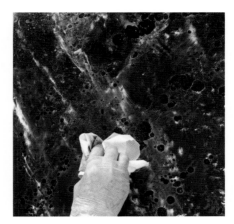

STEP 9 Dab the surface gently to remove excess solvent.

STEP 10 Soften as necessary.

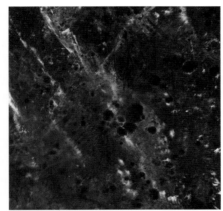

STEP 11 An example of how the finished effect might look.

To enhance the finish and give it greater depth, an overglaze of dark yellowish green (mixed from black, raw sienna, Prussian blue and oil based glaze) may be applied when the previous processes have dried.

APPLICATION PROCESSES FOR STRUCTURAL COMPONENTS

PANELLED DOORS

Follow the same sequence of working as when painting the door, ensuring that all fittings have been removed so that the grain effect is continuous, and therefore more realistic.

1 To the first top panel, rub in the graining colour to the moulding, then the panel itself, brushing the colour out as if applying paint. Remove any excess colour from the corners/moulding detail by lightly stippling with a clean brush to achieve an even distribution of colour, laid off in the direction of the constructed component parts.

2 Produce the grain detail required by flogging, brush graining (dragging) or combing.

3 Continue to apply the graining colour to the remaining panels one at a time, producing the grain effect immediately and before moving on. Keep adjacent sections (components) as clean as possible by wiping off excess colour.

4 Grain the muntins then the rails, finishing each section (component) before moving on to the next, making sure the joints (butt or mitred) are left sharp and clean.

5 Finally, grain the door edge(s) and stiles.

Any graining colour that may have been left on adjacent sections should be **worked up** if possible, when applying additional graining colour, or wiped off using a lint-free rag moistened with white spirit.

Particular attention must be given to producing clean, sharp joints which are accurately positioned. This may be achieved by carefully applying masking tape to each end of the muntins before graining them, then removing it as soon as the effect is produced. This method may also be used for the top, middle/lock and bottom rails.

However, when graining the stiles, the previously grained rails need to be protected at the joint so as not to damage the finish; this is usually achieved by holding a 'shield' (such as an oblong piece of plastic/metal/abrasive paper) over the rail, which will both protect the existing graining and produce a clean, straight joint.

Worked up

Re-activated, or made workable, by rubbing with a brush containing a small quantity of the material, or a suitable thinner

Using a shield while graining

WINDOWS

As for panelled doors, work in a methodical manner and in the same sequence that paint would be applied, with the application of graining colour to sections being immediately worked to produce the required effect.

DADO RAILS AND NARROW LINEAR RUNS (ARCHITRAVES AND SKIRTINGS)

Adjacent surfaces should be protected before work starts, to:

- prevent graining colour marking the wall

- avoid picking up any dirt/dust from the floor, which could contaminate the work.

Due to the length of some of these components, loss of wet edge could be a problem if you are working with water-borne materials. Should this occur and you are unable to adjust the consistency of the material to extend the working time, apply it to smaller sections, joining/blending the new section seamlessly in to the existing work.

Dado rail

SMALL WALL PANELS

These will be treated as the panels of the door, shown on pages 317–318, but the surrounding wall area should be protected before work starts.

Case Study: Jez and Nic

Jez completed a painting and decorating apprenticeship four years ago. Having worked for the employer for a further two years, he recently decided to become self-employed as he wished to undertake more of the decorative and specialist work that he had enjoyed learning at college. Since then he has had the opportunity to help an experienced decorator, Nic, on a few of his contracts involving stencilling and broken colour effects, including some oak brush graining.

Nic has secured a contract to re-decorate one of the council committee rooms as part of a restoration project at the local town hall, which was built in 1898. The project must be completed for the opening ceremony, which has already been booked and publicised. Nic must produce a broken colour effect, applied to the wall filling, with a border stencil of the town's logo applied at picture rail height. The existing Lincrusta wall covering on the dado needs to be 'glazed and wiped' and the dado rail and two panelled doors are to be finished in a medium oak brush grained effect.

Unfortunately Nic has recently injured his hand and is unable to undertake the work within the timescale. The council has asked if he can recommend someone with the specialist decorative skills that he has confidence in. Nic has contacted Jez, as he feels that the quality of his work is good, and because he was formally trained at a college during his apprenticeship. Nic asks Jez to produce sample boards showing the effects for the council to approve.

The council agrees to Jez undertaking the work, on the condition that Nic acts as his mentor. Jez is really pleased to have this chance but is also grateful to have Nic's support and guidance.

Work through the following questions to check your learning.

1   Which product is used to reduce the drying time of oil based scumbles?

   a   White spirit.

   b   Extender.

   c   Linseed oil.

   d   Drier.

2   Which one of the following combination of statements is correct?

   1   Paint is opaque.

   2   Glaze is opaque.

   3   Wood stain is transparent.

   4   Scumble is translucent.

   a   1 and 4.

   b   2 and 3.

   c   1 and 2.

   d   3 and 4.

3   Which one of the following is **not** a method of transferring a stencil onto plate materials?

   a   Trace.

   b   Etch.

   c   Pounce.

   d   Photocopy.

4   When manufacturing a stencil plate, which one of the following will occur if the whole plate is **not** sealed?

   a   It becomes transparent.

   b   It is difficult to cut.

   c   It buckles or curls.

   d   It lies flat.

5   Which one of the following is **not** a suitable material on which to cut stencils?

   a   Glass.

   b   Metal.

   c   Glazed tile.

   d   Timber.

6   Which one of the following pigments is yellow-brown in colour?

   a   Raw umber.

   b   Burnt umber.

   c   Raw sienna.

   d   Burnt sienna.

7   Which one of the following BS 4800 colours would be suitable to use as a ground coat for oak?

   a   08 C 35.

   b   00 E 55.

   c   00 E 53.

   d   04 D 44.

8   Which one of the following materials is **not** suitable for colouring water based glaze to produce a scumble?

   a   Universal stainers.

   b   Artist's oil.

   c   Powder pigment.

   d   Gouache.

9   When mixing a scumble to produce a straight grain mahogany effect, which one of the following pigment combinations would be appropriate?

   a   Raw sienna, raw umber, black.

   b   Burnt umber, raw umber, raw sienna.

   c   Burnt sienna, mahogany lake, black.

   d   Burnt umber, Vandyke brown, black.

10   When producing a Carrara marble effect, which one of the following colours would **most** likely be used?

   a   Raw umber, burnt sienna, ochre, white.

   b   White, black, Brunswick green.

   c   White, black, ochre, Prussian blue.

   d   Venetian red, ultramarine, ochre.

11 When making a water graining medium, which one of the following would **not** be suitable as a binder?

   a   Malt vinegar.

   b   Linseed oil.

   c   Glue size.

   d   Stale beer.

12 When producing a water graining medium, stale beer or malt vinegar may be used as which one of the following?

   a   Thinner.

   b   Pigment.

   c   Drier.

   d   Binder.

13 Which one of the following products is **best** for eliminating cissing prior to applying water graining colour?

   a   Whiting.

   b   Turpentine.

   c   Fuller's earth.

   d   White spirit.

14 Which one of the following selection of tools would **not** produce a straight grain effect for either oak or mahogany?

   a   Dragger and check roller.

   b   Sponge and softener.

   c   Flogger and softener.

   d   Comb and check roller.

15 Which one of the following selection of tools would **not** be used to produce a marble effect?

   a   Softener and feather.

   b   Softener and flogger.

   c   Sponge and lint-free rag.

   d   Softener and writer.

16 Which one of the following tools would **not** be used to produce the straight grain effect of oak?

   a   Check roller.

   b   Dragger.

   c   Flogger.

   d   Comb.

17 The tool used to soften acrylic graining scumble should have which one of the following types of filling?

   a   Badger hair.

   b   Hog hair.

   c   Squirrel hair.

   d   Ox hair.

18 Oiling in is a process used for producing which one of the following specialist decorative effects?

   a   Graining.

   b   Marbling.

   c   Stencilling.

   d   Rag rolling.

19 Which one of the following is **not** a process used when producing a marble effect?

   a   Cissing.

   b   Softening.

   c   Flogging.

   d   Veining.

20 Which one of the following is the correct sequence for producing the straight grain effect of mahogany?

   1   Apply mahogany scumble glaze with broad streaks of colour.

   2   De-grease ground coat and rub in ground colour.

   3   Drag to break up colour, then lightly soften.

   4   Flog and leave to dry.

   a   2, 3, 4, 1.

   b   1, 2, 3, 4.

   c   4, 3, 2, 1.

   d   2, 4, 1, 3.

Chapter 7
Unit 230: Creating and applying colour

What a fantastic gift, to be able to see and use colour in our everyday lives. Colour adds such positive feeling to what otherwise would be a black and white world. As a decorator you will regularly use colour in your day-to-day activities. Developing a good understanding of the theory behind colour will allow you to advise your clients on the types of decorative schemes that will enhance and suit their living space. As you will see in this chapter, colour can influence mood, creating feelings of excitement or calm, and defining space, form and texture.

All colour originates in the way light behaves when it strikes a surface, so light is the source of all colour. Pigments, dyes and other surfaces act as absorbers and reflectors of rays of light. For example a red box absorbs most of the light falling on it, reflecting only rays from the red spectrum.

By reading this chapter, you will:

1 Understand the colours required to create a colour wheel.

2 Be able to create a colour wheel on a broad surface.

3 Understand colour organisational systems and terminology used in industry.

4 Understand the effects that artificial light has on colour.

5 Be able to produce colour schemes for internal and external areas.

THE SPECTRUM

The English physicist Sir Isaac Newton made a scientific study of light rays and their relationship with colour. He discovered that sunlight is composed of all the colours in the **visible spectrum**. He used a triangular prism to bend the light rays, and after passing through the prism the rays split into seven colours when projected onto white paper. You will no doubt have noticed these colours in the form of a rainbow on a rainy day, which is formed by the sun's rays passing through the rain droplets.

Sir Isaac Newton arranged this set of colours into a circular shape, which became the model for many future colour systems.

Visible spectrum

The colours of a rainbow: red, orange, yellow, green, blue, indigo and violet

A rainbow is formed by sunlight passing through rain droplets

INDUSTRY TIP

It is said that the human eye can distinguish over 10 million different colours, but every colour is based on the colours of the light spectrum.

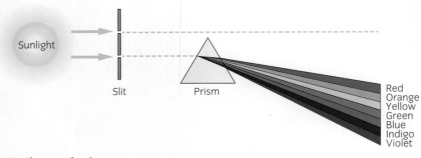

Newton's theory of colour

THE COLOUR WHEEL

In most colour wheels or circles the layout will be based on six of the seven spectrum colours, as follows: red, orange, yellow, green, blue and violet. Dark blue, or indigo (as this colour is sometimes called), is usually omitted in modern colour theory. The colour wheel can take various forms and may include numbers depending on what it is being used to show.

A colour wheel enables us to express our understanding of colour, and also helps us to develop colour schemes. The wheel allows us to see how colours work together, and develop theories connected with them. The way we see colours and our psychological responses to them have inspired scientists and colourists to define terms to describe them and impose some kind of order on all the possibilities.

A large section of this chapter deals with the theory of colour. It is from this theoretical standpoint that paint manufacturers make sense of how colours go together. Later in the chapter you will look at how colour theory can be put to practical use when related to modern colour schemes and paint charts.

MAKING COLOUR

From prehistoric times colour has been used to provide decoration. The colour from plants and the earth allowed early cave dwellers to produce their art.

In more modern times, artists and decorators have continued to use natural products to make their paint colours. Paint manufacturers have adapted the ideas in order to mass produce paints, and still use naturally derived reds, blues and yellows along with manufactured pigments. Earth pigments such as ochre, umber, iron oxide and others are used to this day to provide some of the colours for paints. However, pigments are increasingly entirely artificially manufactured, with some using metals as their starting point and others produced from scratch by chemical processes.

Cave dwellers used natural pigments to create colour paints

PRIMARY COLOURS

The simplest form of colour wheel is made up of only three colours – red, yellow and blue – and these are termed **primary** colours.

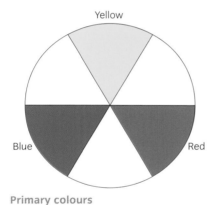

Primary colours

Primary

First in a sequence. In the case of primary colours, red, yellow and blue are deemed primary as from these first colours many others can be mixed

With the addition of black and white, these three primary colours can in theory be used to mix any colour. In traditional colour theory (as used in paint and pigments), the primary colours are the three pigment colours that cannot be mixed or formed by any combination of other colours.

SECONDARY COLOURS

The second stage in building the colour wheel is to mix the primary colours with each other to form **secondary** colours.

- If red and yellow are mixed together in equal amounts, the colour orange will be formed.

- If red and blue are mixed together in equal amounts, the colour purple (or violet) will be formed.

Secondary

Second, or the second stage (after primary)

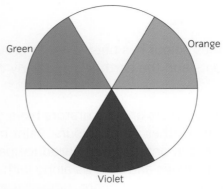

Secondary colours

- If yellow and blue are mixed in equal amounts, the colour green is formed.

If the mixes do not use equal amounts the intensity of each of the colours will be altered.

TERTIARY COLOURS

Tertiary

Third, or the third stage (after secondary)

The third stage of extending the colour wheel is the development of a **tertiary** group of colours.

A tertiary colour results from mixing a primary colour with an adjoining secondary colour, as shown in this illustration. You will see why they are also referred to as intermediate colours. Red added to orange makes red-orange, yellow added to orange makes yellow-orange, and so on.

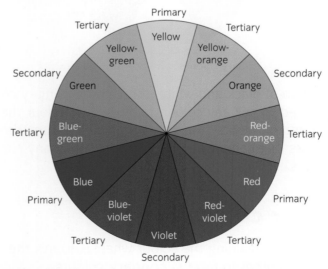

Full circle showing primaries, secondaries and tertiary intermediaries

Three more tertiary colours can be made by the admixture of the secondary colours with each other, as shown in the illustration.

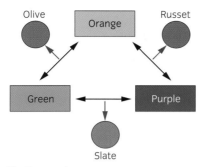

Olive   Orange   Russet

Green   Purple

Slate

Tertiary colours

- Purple and orange mixed in equal amounts will produce a brown or russet colour.

- Orange and green mixed in equal amounts will produce an olive colour.

- Green and purple mixed in equal amounts will produce a slate colour.

COLOUR SCHEMES

Using a colour wheel makes it possible to visually arrange colours to form schemes such as analogous, complementary and monochromatic. Understanding the ideas behind these schemes will allow you to apply them to interiors and exteriors for the benefit of your clients. In most cases you will find it possible to assemble colours that are pleasing to the eye and work well together.

ANALOGOUS COLOURS

These are colours that are directly beside, or adjacent, to each other on the colour wheel. For example, a scheme using colours from the range of yellow, yellow-orange and orange would be described as analogous. One colour is usually used as a dominant colour, while others are used to enrich the scheme. The use of tints and shades of the pure **hues** will create a **tonal balance** and a harmonious overall effect.

COMPLEMENTARY COLOURS

Colours that are directly opposite each other on the colour wheel are known as complementary. The illustration shows that yellow and violet complement each other. Later in the chapter you will see how you can use this knowledge to good effect in colour schemes.

Complementary colours are **contrasting** and give off a sense of energy, vigour and excitement.

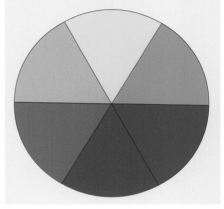

Hue

A pure colour such as red or yellow

Tonal balance

You can achieve tonal balance by manipulating your use of colour. For example, a small amount of colour can offset the visual weight of a large area of neutral values. Similarly, a small area of warm colour can balance a large area of cool colour

Contrast/contrasting

In colour terminology this usually relates to colours opposite on the colour wheel. They will naturally go well together – you can use one to **accentuate** the other

Accent/accentuate

In colour terminology, using a small amount of contrast colour will enhance the other colour(s) and add excitement to a scheme

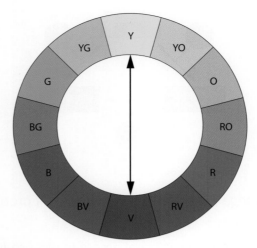

Complementary colours

MONOCHROMATIC COLOURS

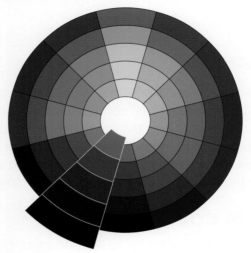

Monochromatic colours

Here you can see all the hues (variations) of one colour segment on the colour wheel, showing the dark, medium and light values of that colour. In this illustration, using the blue-violet hue at the outside of the circle, the term monochromatic is demonstrated by the addition of white. All or some of these colours, when used together, will provide a pleasing and **harmonious** scheme.

Harmony/harmonious

Terms often used in the description of colour schemes to express that something is pleasing to look at

CREATE A COLOUR WHEEL ON A BROAD SURFACE

As part of your practical work, you will be required to set out, draw and apply the correct primary and secondary colours to a colour wheel on a broad surface such as a panel or wall.

EQUIPMENT

You will need the following equipment:

- pencils
- compass
- trammel
- ruler
- chalk line
- spirit level
- masking tape.

You will have come across most of this equipment before, except perhaps for the compass and trammel. These will allow you to draw circular shapes. The size of the circle will be limited only by how far the legs of the compass can be opened, or by how long the beam or trammel bar is.

Large board compass

Large beam compass or trammel

DRAW A COLOUR WHEEL TO INCORPORATE PRIMARY AND SECONDARY COLOURS

Follow your tutor's instructions on the exact size and position of the wheel on the wall or board. You may use a large compass, trammel/beam compass or string and pencil.

INDUSTRY TIP

Stick a piece of putty or tack under the point of the compass to stop it slipping and also to protect the wall.

Drawing a circle with a large compass

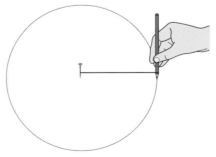

Drawing a circle using a pencil and string

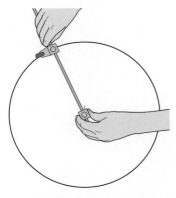

STEP 1 Once you have decided on the diameter and position of your circle, draw a circle using the board compass, trammel, or string and pencil.

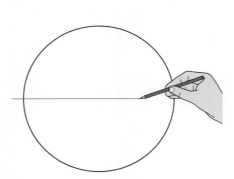

STEP 2 Once the circle has been drawn to the correct size, draw a line horizontally through your centre point as in the illustration, using a spirit level to check that it is perfectly level. You now have two perfect halves to your circle and the line you have drawn is known as the diameter.

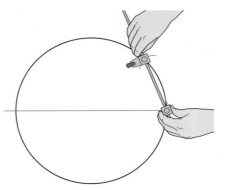

STEP 3 With your equipment still set to the same radius, place the point end on the outer edge of the diameter and make a mark on the edge of the circle with the pencil end. Move the compass point to that mark and make another mark further around the edge of the circle. Continue doing this until you have six marks, three to the top of the diameter and three to the bottom.

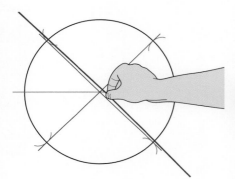

STEP 4 Using a line and chalk, join these marks diagonally as shown. Your drawn circle should now have six segments.

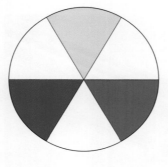

STEP 5 Apply the primary colours.

STEP 6 Using equal amounts, mix the correct primary colours to produce the secondary colours. Apply the secondary colours.

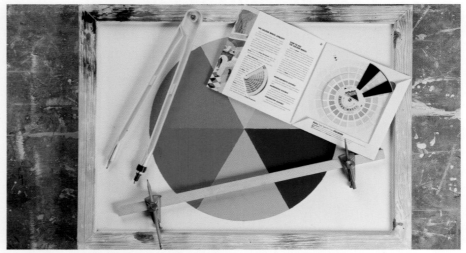

A colour wheel can be set out using a trammel, board compass or string and pencil

Your tutors will advise you on the best methods of painting curves and straight lines. They may ask you to paint using straight edges, masking tape or other templates, or freehand. Each method has its benefits, but with lots of practice you will be able to produce a clean, sharp colour wheel.

COLOUR ORGANISATIONAL SYSTEMS AND TERMINOLOGY

The use of colour in the paint industry has led to the need to organise colour into systems. This helps with referencing and selection and ensures that colours conform to certain standards. Many paint scientists and colour theorists have also developed their own referencing systems.

COLOUR THEORIES

As explained earlier, most of what we understand about colour was developed from the initial concepts of Isaac Newton and his interpretation of the colour spectrum. Early theorists studied colour but did not really put forward a system that could be followed. It was not until the twentieth century that major advances in colour systems were proposed. Many of the tutors of the Bauhaus School of design in Germany, such as Wassily Kandinsky, Johannes Itten, Faber Birren, Paul Klee and Josef Albers, developed their concepts into something that could be studied and utilised in their artistic teachings.

However, it has primarily been the following theories that have been taken, followed and further developed for use in our industry today.

THE MUNSELL SYSTEM

In 1915, Albert Munsell published his *Munsell Book of Colour*. He was an artist and an art teacher, and he developed the basic principles of his system mainly for the purpose of bringing order to the study of colour. His system was based on the three-dimensional attributes of hue, **value** and **chroma**.

The illustration on the following page shows how Munsell saw colour in a three-dimensional way.

The Munsell colour system is set up as a numerical scale with visually uniform steps for each of the three colour attributes – in Munsell colour **notation**, each colour has a logical and visual relationship to all other colours. The central column is ranged white to dark at the bottom and each leaf of the model depicts how the main colour is gradually mixed with white, black, grey, and shown within the varying levels and leaves of the model.

Value

In the Munsell system, colour's relative lightness or darkness

Chroma

The degree of intensity, saturation, purity and brilliance of a colour

Notation

Text or numerical references that indicate the groups or categories of colours

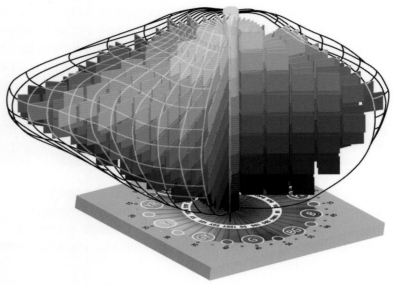

Munsell solid

The Munsell system is based on the following principles, which are utilised by the BS 4800 system:

- *Hue*: Each colour is described with a letter and there are ten principle hues. For example, 5Y represents a mid yellow, and so on.

- *Value*: This represents the lightness (added white) or darkness (added black) of a colour, and is identified by a number from 0 to 10.

- *Chroma*: This represents the greyness of a colour and is identified by a number from 0 to 14.

In simple terms the hue defines the colour, against the value on the central column and its chroma will be determined by its relative closeness to the value column. The closer a colour is to the outside of the model, the more intense it will be.

Specifying a colour using the Munsell system

A colour is fully specified by listing the three numbers for hue, value and chroma, in that order. For instance, a purple of medium lightness that is fairly saturated would be 5P 5/10, with 5P meaning the colour in the middle of the purple hue band, 5/ meaning medium value (lightness), and a chroma of 10, meaning it is quite intense (see the sample to the right).

5P 5/10

In industry terms the number of colours that could be produced using this system was too great – it was felt that a smaller number of colours would more easily be accepted by manufacturers, as the cost of reproduction would be limited. Stockists would only need to stock a smaller range of colours and there would be less to show to clients when deciding on specifications. This is why the British Standards Institute developed colour standards for the paint industry, as described later in this chapter.

Exploring value

The image shows how the value of a colour can be changed by the addition of the colour white. The squares within each column (1–9) have a red, green or blue hue, and in each column the same amount of white has been used, therefore the value of each of the column of colours is the same. This illustration demonstrates a range of colours that are monochromatic as well as demonstrating the term 'value'.

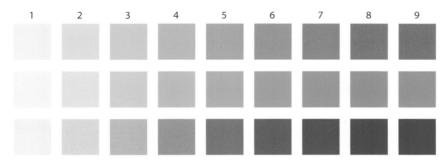

The value of a colour is changed by the addition of white

INDUSTRIAL COLOUR REFERENCING

The major colour systems described below are the standards set by industry and/or the British Standards Institute.

BS 5252:1976 FRAMEWORK FOR COLOUR CO-ORDINATION FOR BUILDING PURPOSES

BS 5252 is the British Standard that establishes a framework for co-ordinating the colours for all building products. There are 237 colours selected to enable standardisation between products such as paints, ceramics, plastics and tile flooring. It may also now be possible to obtain matches to any material using the paint manufacturers' hand scanners. This range incorporates the BS 4800 colours but does not include the BS 381C standard range of colours.

BS 4800

BS 4800 is a selection of colours for building purposes taken from the BS 5252 Framework for colour co-ordination. BS 4800 colours are widely specified in the UK.

BS 381C

BS 381C is a specification for colours for identification, coding and special purposes. These paint colours are technical colours used in industry and engineering including transport. Colours from this range are used particularly by the Ministry of Defence for vehicles, buildings and signage. Camouflage colours are included in this range.

BS 1710:1984 SPECIFICATION FOR IDENTIFICATION OF PIPELINES AND SERVICES

Colours from this particular standard are used for identification of pipelines and services to enable engineers and users to recognise which pipes carry water, steam, gas and other chemicals or substances. Being able to identify certain services by colour standard allows engineers to carry out repairs safely. The table shows the colours used for pipeline Identification in line with this standard.

Basic identification colours – BS 1710:1984			
12 D 45	Water	22 C 37	Acids or alkalis
10 A 03	Steam	20 E 51	Air
06 C 39	Oils	00 E 53	Other fluids
08 C 35	Gas	06 E 51	Electrical services

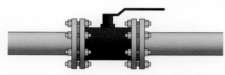

Pipe contents	RAL code
Gas	RAL 1004
Fire fighting	RAL 3000
Air	RAL 5012
Combustible liquids	RAL 8001
Acids and alkalis	RAL 4001
Water	RAL 6010
Other liquids	RAL 9005
Steam	RAL 9006

RAL codes are used in pipeline identification

RAL COLOURS

In 1927 the German Imperial Commission for Delivery Terms and Quality Assurance devised a colour range of 40 colours under the name RAL 480. In the 1930s the original notation system was changed to four digits and the collection was renamed to RAL 840 R (R for revised). Colours were continually added to the range and it was revised again in 1961 with the RAL Classic range now consisting of 213 colours.

RAL is the most popular European colour standard in use today. The colours are standard in architecture, construction, industry and road safety.

The illustration in the margin shows the colours used for pipeline identification using RAL four-digit numbers as a comparison with BS 1710, shown above.

NATURAL COLOUR SYSTEM OR NCS

This is an international colour standard that can be used to specify all types of surfaces. It is used by the majority of paint manufacturers and paint suppliers for their colour mixing machines to enable them to accurately match paints to a variety of materials.

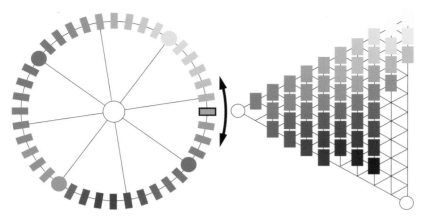

The Natural Colour System colour wheel and a page of tints, shades and tones developed from the main hue

S 2570-Y60R

The colour outlined above is shown here with its notation.

Each manufacturer will often use its own referencing system for its colour range. A number of paint manufacturers now use hand scanners to try to match samples to their colour mix systems. It may therefore be possible to accurately match co-ordinating fabrics with paint colours.

For the purpose of this chapter we will explore BS 4800 further, as it is the industry standard colour system most used by the trade, although it is fair to say that many decorators will also select from manufacturers' colour mixing systems, as they provide a much larger selection.

MORE ABOUT BS 4800:2011

BS 4800 specifies 122 colours of paint for building and construction work. This is an essential reference for anyone who needs a particular paint colour to use in the refurbishment of buildings – especially at Local Authority level or for major works such as office blocks, airports, schools and hospitals. This standard includes 22 additional colours that are mostly brighter to reflect the latest trends for putting finishes on public buildings. These paint colours are widely recognised throughout the UK and are often used to meet safety, legal or contractual requirements.

The standard was primarily developed to enable there to be a system of colour notation ordered by numerical reference that would be adhered to by the major paint manufacturers. The individual colour notations would enable colours to be mixed and sold to a standard, and each manufacturer would follow the same formula for colour mixing. The BS 4800 colour system uses the Munsell principles of hue, value and chroma, but refers to them as hue, greyness and weight.

The illustration shows how the colours from the BS 4800 may be arranged to form a colour wheel. It shows them in their brightest and most saturated form.

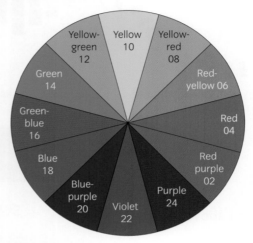

12-colour wheel based on BS 4800

The table below shows the greys plus the 12 hues used by BS 4800. Each colour selected will start with the hue reference number from this table. For example a colour selected from the yellow range will begin with the number 10.

00 Grey plus black and white			
02 Red-purple		14 Green	
04 Red		16 Green-blue	
06 Red-yellow		18 Blue	
08 Yellow-red		20 Blue-purple	
10 Yellow		22 Violet	
12 Yellow-green		24 Purple	

The colours used are for reference only, and manufacturers' colour cards should be used to define exact colours.

Each BS 4800 colour for building purposes has a unique code – a combination of numbers and a letter, for example: 10 B 15.

This is what the code means:

- The first part of the code is an even number, from 00 to 24, which indicates the hue. In this case it is 10, and if you look at the table above, it shows that 10 is from the yellow hue range.

- The second part of the code is a letter from A to E, and it indicates the greyness. Group A has a lot of grey content, while group E has little or no grey content. The letter here is B and the colour is in the yellow range (see photo on the right).

- The last part of the code is an odd number from 01 to 55. It indicates the weight – the higher the number, the brighter and stronger the colour.

All of this is a very precise way of describing a colour from the yellow range that contains a lot of grey and is not very intense, or in other words, off white.

This way of describing a colour means that it will be the same no matter which manufacturer produces it, even if they give it a more descriptive name such as 'Gardenia', 'Soft white' or 'Ivory'. The name may be different but the code will always be the same, if it follows the British Standard.

In some cases manufacturers will use the same name to describe a colour. For example 'Magnolia' is used by many, but unless the BS 4800 code is specified it is likely there will be some variation in colour.

OTHER COLOUR TERMS

There are some other terms you may come across that are useful when describing colour.

NATURAL ORDER OF COLOUR

This helps us to make sense of colour, for example using a spectrum. A reversal of the natural order is known as discord. The natural order starts with yellow being the lightest colour on the colour wheel and ends with purple as the darkest. Used in this order they are pleasing to the eye. If a reversal of the system takes place and the purple becomes the lightest colour and yellow the darkest, discordant colours are created.

SATURATION

Many terms are used to describe saturation – this relates to the chroma, or weight, of the colour. The following terms are often used to denote the intensity, brightness or purity of a colour.

ACTIVITY

Select a colour card from a paint manufacturer's range – preferably one that uses British Standard numbering. You may need to check with your tutor to make sure that the card uses this form of referencing. You will be able to use this colour card for other exercises later in this chapter.

10 B 15 is used on the walls in this room, making a fairly neutral colour scheme

ACTIVITY

Here are three BS 4800 codes:

- 10 E 55
- 00 A 13
- 04 D 44

Find the codes on your colour cards and describe them using the BS 4800 terms of hue, greyness and weight in a similar way to the example given earlier.

In most cases colours that appear fully saturated will seem to be very intense and will probably be used to provide accents. These fully saturated colours are also often used for the front doors of properties, as they stand out from the (often) white painted frame.

ACHROMATIC TONES

Achromatic tones are not technically classed as colours, as they are without a hue. These range from black through to white and are sometimes referred to as sensations.

The most popular achromatic colour scheme is black and white, often used in kitchens and bathrooms but shown here in a living room.

Achromatic colour scheme

NEUTRALS

Neutrals are perhaps the easiest group of colours, or rather non-colours, to work with. They don't appear on the colour wheel and include black, grey, white and sometimes browns and beiges. They all go together and can be layered and mixed and matched. No neutral colour will try to dominate another. It is quite easy to add bolder colours to provide accents or excitement to the overall scheme.

Warm colour scheme

WARM COLOURS

In the most general terms, warm colours are associated with the yellow/red side of the colour wheel. They attract attention and are generally perceived as energetic or exciting. Warm colours are also sometimes referred to as advancing colours – they give the appearance of being closer to the eye.

COOL COLOURS

These typically sit on the blue/green side of the colour wheel opposite the warm colours, and they are generally perceived as soothing and calm. Cool colours are sometimes referred to as receding, creating the appearance of space and appearing to move further into the distance.

Cool colour scheme

TINTS AND SHADES

A tint is a colour plus white. The addition of white makes the colour paler and less intense.

A shade is a colour plus black. A dark blue shade, in other words, is blue that has been darkened by adding black.

ARTIFICIAL LIGHT AND COLOUR

Colour can be greatly affected by both natural and artificial lighting. Therefore when selecting colours you should view them in the appropriate setting. Choosing paint colours in natural sunlight is ideal. Natural sunlight provides the neutral balance between the warm and cool ends of the light spectrum (with more yellow and blue, respectively). Northern light is the coolest, while southern exposure is the most intense. If you paint two rooms with the same paint – one with a northern exposure and one with a southern exposure – the wall colour will look different in each room.

Even natural sunlight isn't consistent. It changes throughout the day and varies depending on whether it is cloudy or clear. The shadows created by an overcast day will impact on how the wall colour looks, as well.

Furthermore, a bedroom that faces east and receives strong sunlight in the early morning will look very different when seen at night under artificial lighting. Most interior types of lighting cast a yellow aspect over colours and will alter their appearance accordingly. As long as this has been taken into account, there should be no disappointment about the appearance of a colour.

It is worth considering choosing a warm colour when decorating a room with a northern aspect, as it will not receive much sunlight and may therefore appear dark and cold.

Colours look very different in direct sunlight and in shadows

TYPES OF LIGHTING

Different lighting types will have various effects and you need to consider this when selecting colours for interiors. This changing appearance of colour under different light sources is known as the metameric effect. If you try to match a colour under a particular lighting condition and then change the light source, the colour will generally no longer match.

Metameric effect

Table lamps will make painted walls appear differently

Incandescent lighting

This is used to refer to tungsten lighting in particular. A wire filament is heated by electricity which then glows white hot and emits light

Eco-friendly

'Eco' is short for 'ecology', so eco-friendly literally means 'Earth-friendly' or 'not harmful to the environment'

Fluorescent lighting provides an overall general brightness

The photo on the previous page shows how different colours appear when seen in fluorescent light and daylight. You can see from this that it is extremely important to ensure that when colours are selected that they are viewed in the types of light to which they will be subjected.

For example, tungsten and halogen lights enhance reds and yellows, and mute blues and greens. Fluorescent lights enhance blues and greens, and mute reds and yellows. To further complicate things, wall colour lit from above is going to look somewhat different from wall colour lit by floor and table lamps.

TUNGSTEN

Tungsten lighting was the traditional form of lighting for many years, until recently. It is also referred to as **incandescent lighting**. It is likely to cast a yellowing, warm light which will dull down cool colours, and enhance warmer colours.

The requirement to provide more **eco-friendly** types of lighting has led to the eco bulb, which tends to use a form of fluorescent, LED or halogen technology. These bulbs last longer than tungsten bulbs and are therefore a more sustainable option.

FLUORESCENT

This type of lighting has a green tinge, which can dull warm colours. Some give off a pink tinge, which is more colour-friendly and can even enhance warm colours. Fluorescent lighting tends to be used in offices or areas where general lighting is required. It provides an overall general brightness in an area but is no substitute for natural light.

LPS (LOW PRESSURE SODIUM)

This kind of lighting is most often used for street lamps and security lights. It gives off a soft, luminous glow with little glare. LPS is also sometimes used in cafes and restaurants, as it helps to create a warm, welcoming atmosphere. It is not typically used in domestic situations.

Sodium lighting makes the red building appear more brown in colour

HALOGEN AND LEDS (LIGHT-EMITTING DIODES)

These types of lighting are now commonly used in domestic situations, having migrated from more industrial or commercial settings. They are often used for accent lighting, spotlights and other general area lighting. **Halogen** and **LED** lights come closest to daylight in terms of how colours are affected – however, because bright light is cast on specific areas there may well be areas of deep shadow where colours will look less bright.

The LED lighting used in this picture demonstrates how different areas can be accentuated

COLOUR ASSOCIATION

In very simple terms, colour association relates to how a person perceives various colours and how they affect the senses.

Scientific tests have been carried out, for example, which show that red excites the senses and provokes feelings of warmth, while blue and green have been shown to invoke a sense of coolness. Purple is considered regal by some but may also be associated with death.

Psychological tests have also shown that there are some colour effects that have universal meaning. Colours in the red area of the colour spectrum are generally accepted as warm colours, though they encourage feelings of anger and hostility as well as warmth and comfort.

Colours on the blue side of the spectrum are generally seen as cool colours. These colours are often described as calm, but they also call to mind feelings of sadness or indifference.

The perception of colour and colour preferences may also be affected by cultural associations. For example those living in particularly warm climates will be used to very strong sunlight and they may be more likely to favour vibrant colours.

Halogen

A halogen lamp, also known as a tungsten halogen lamp or quartz iodine lamp, is an incandescent lamp that has a small amount of a halogen gas combined with a tungsten filament producing a very bright white light

LED (light-emitting diode)

An LED is an electronic device that emits light when an electrical current is passed through it

Orange paint can provoke feelings of warmth

Blue paint can produce a calming effect

COLOUR SCHEMES FOR INTERNAL AND EXTERNAL AREAS

In this section you will look at how to select colours and produce colour schemes for interior and external areas. Monochromatic, analogous and complementary colour schemes are the main focus, and you should be able to draw on knowledge gained earlier in the chapter.

Paint manufacturers and various websites will provide you with many ideas and choices when it comes to colour selection. However, if you apply the simple principles covered in this chapter you should be able to provide sound, accurate advice to your clients and hopefully meet their requirements.

Some manufacturers have developed 'heritage' or 'historical' ranges of colours specifically for organisations such as English Heritage and the National Trust. It has become increasingly desirable to be able to closely match Georgian, Victorian or other historical colours particularly when recreating or refurbishing these types of property.

This illustration shows a Georgian interior with typical use of calm green colours appropriate to the period.

A Georgian style room painted with heritage colours

A strong feature wall

White radiators stand out. Paint the radiator the same shade as the wall to make it less obvious

SELECTING COLOURS FOR INTERIORS

If your client has not selected colours for their interiors, first consider the following key points:

- Which way does the room face – north, south, east or west?
- Is the room naturally light or dark?
- What is the room to be used for?
- Will the room be used mainly in artificial light?
- Are there items already in the scheme that could be used as a starting point?

Other points that could be considered may include the following:

- Provide a feature wall in a strong colour to contrast with neutral colours alongside.
- Paint out objects such as radiators in the same colour as the walls to make them less obvious.
- Look at colours from the swatch individually. Do not have them surrounded by lots of other colours from the colour swatch or chart.

CREATING A SPECIFICATION

Before starting it is desirable to set out the scheme (eg, monochrome, analogous or complementary) in the form of a specification or schedule, as shown below. Using a table or system such as this will enable you to select your colour and also to put a colour chip representing that colour alongside the description. This will enhance the communication and minimise confusion.

EXAMPLE SPECIFICATION FOR DECORATION

Ceiling	The ceiling is to be prepared and finished with two full coats of vinyl silk emulsion in BS 08 C 31	
Wall filling	The wall filling is to be prepared and coated with BS 08 C 31	
Dado rail	To be prepared, primed with a water-borne primer/undercoat and brought to a two-coat acrylic gloss finish in BS 10 A 11	
Dado	The dado is to be prepared and coated with a ground colour of acrylic eggshell BS 10 A 03	
Skirting, door frames and architraves **Window frames and architraves**	To be prepared, primed with acrylic primer/undercoat and brought to a two coat acrylic gloss finish in BS 10 A 11	

As part of the activities for this section, you will be required to illustrate monochromatic, analogous and complementary colour schemes. Below and on the next page are example illustrations for each.

A monochromatic colour scheme, using green as the main hue is shown below. A pastel green tint has been used on the back wall and stronger green colour has been used for the sofa to make a feature of it.

Monochromatic colour scheme

Hint: Remember, monochromatic means bringing together colours using tints and shades of one hue.

An analogous colour scheme, using red, yellow and orange in various tones is shown below.

Analogous colour scheme

Hint: Remember, analogous means bringing together colours that are adjacent or side by side on the colour wheel.

A complementary colour scheme, using predominantly orange and blue in various tones is shown below.

Complementary colour scheme

Hint: Remember, complementary colour schemes bring together colours that are opposite each other on the colour wheel.

ACTIVITY

Using the example specification on the previous page, produce a colour scheme for each of the following:

- monochromatic
- analogous
- complementary.

Use colour cards to help you make your choices. As well as using colour names and reference numbers, also stick the colour chip to the specification sheet. Make sure you clearly label each with the type of scheme, your name and the date.

Case Study: John and Razz

John and Razz have been asked to make recommendations for the colours at a house they are currently working on. The client, Mrs Brown, has asked for a colour scheme to go with a predominantly green carpet. The picture shows how it turned out. Using the client's choice of carpet colour has helped them to put together a very pleasant scheme and the client was extremely pleased with the outcome. Using specific furnishing items to put a scheme together can be a very good starting point.

Monochrome scheme using green

FUNCTIONAL SKILLS

Write a letter to the client in the case study, putting forward recommendations for the colour scheme. Remember to describe the scheme by name and enclose a colour specification to complete the recommendation.

Work on this activity can support FE1 (3.1b).

Work through the following questions to check your learning.

1 Which one of the following is a primary colour?

   a   Blue.

   b   Slate.

   c   Purple.

   d   Orange.

2 Which one of the following is a secondary colour?

   a   Red.

   b   Green.

   c   Blue.

   d   Olive.

3 Which one of the following is a tertiary colour?

   a   Orange.

   b   Purple.

   c   Russet.

   d   Blue.

4 Which one of the following descriptions relates to the term 'monochromatic'?

   a   Colours that are next to each other on the colour wheel.

   b   Colours that are opposite each other on the colour wheel.

   c   Colours that use tints and shades from the colour wheel.

   d   Colours from the cool side of the colour wheel.

5 Which one of the following descriptions relates to the term 'analogous'?

   a   Colours that are next to each other on the colour wheel.

   b   Colours that are opposite each other on the colour wheel.

   c   Colours that use tints and shades from the colour wheel.

   d   Colours from the warm side of the colour wheel.

6 Which one of the following colours is complementary to blue on the colour wheel?

   a   Orange.

   b   Green.

   c   Purple.

   d   Red.

7 Which one of the following descriptions relates to the term 'value'?

   a   Lightness.

   b   Intensity.

   c   Cool.

   d   Tinted.

8 Which one of the following words describes 'chroma'?

   a   Warm.

   b   Intensity.

   c   Cool.

   d   Neutral.

9 Which one of the following is a cool colour?

   a   Red.

   b   Blue.

   c   Yellow.

   d   Orange.

10 Which one of the following colours illustrates 'shade'?

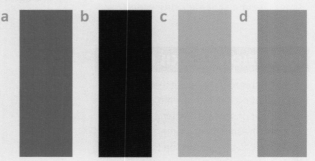

11 Which one of the following colours illustrates 'tint'?

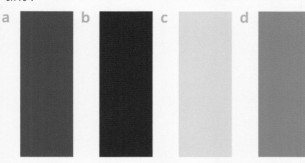

a   b   c   d

12 Which one of the following British Standard references relates to the use of colour for building surfaces?

a   BS 1336.

b   BS 4800.

c   BS 2992.

d   BS 7956.

13 Hue and value are terms used by the Munsell system. Which of the following is **also** specifically used as a reference code in this system?

a   Tint.

b   Discord.

c   Chroma.

d   Shade.

14 Which one of the following terms relates to the reversal of the natural order of colour?

a   Neutral.

b   Achromatic.

c   Discord.

d   Saturation.

15 Which one of the following descriptions relates to the term 'achromatic'?

a   Uses blue, green and grey.

b   Uses yellow, red and grey.

c   Uses black, white and grey.

d   Uses green, yellow and grey.

16 What happens to colours when viewed in tungsten light?

a   They appear lightish.

b   They appear yellowish.

c   They appear blueish.

d   They appear greenish.

17 Which one of the following describes the metameric effect under various lighting conditions?

a   Colours appear brighter.

b   Colours appear duller.

c   Colours appear different.

d   Colours appear warmer.

18 Which one of the following is sodium lighting mostly used for?

a   Street lighting.

b   Task lighting.

c   General lighting.

d   Spot lighting.

19 Which one of the following colour combinations could be used in an analogous colour scheme?

a

b

c

d

20 Which one of the following colour combinations could be used in a complementary colour scheme?

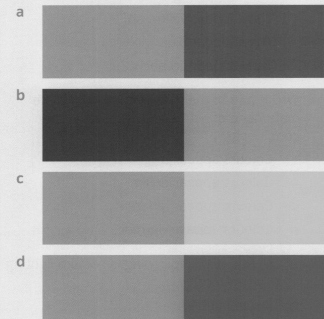

a

b

c

d

Chapter 8
Unit 220: Erecting and dismantling access equipment and working platforms

Working at height is something that most decorators will need to become experienced at doing, and it is essential to be properly trained in order to be competent and able to work safely. Accidents can happen to anybody, and a fall can cause serious injury and even death. The Health and Safety Executive (HSE) website is an excellent resource to help you get up to speed in this area, and it is highly recommended that you become as familiar as you can with its contents.

This chapter covers the following types of access equipment and working platforms: ladders, stepladders/platform steps, proprietary towers, trestle platforms, proprietary staging and podiums, independent scaffolds and scaffold boards, and mobile elevating work platforms (MEWPs).

By reading this chapter, you will understand:

1 The preparation required for using access equipment and working platforms.

2 How to check access equipment and identify faults.

3 How to erect access equipment and working platforms.

4 How to dismantle and store components.

PREPARE TO USE ACCESS EQUIPMENT AND WORKING PLATFORMS

PREPARE TO USE ACCESS EQUIPMENT AND WORKING PLATFORMS

As you can see from the HSE statistics that follow, falls from height account for a number of fatalities each year in the UK, so it is essential to get this aspect of working right.

INJURY AND FATALITY STATISTICS

The construction sector accounts for the greatest number of fatal injuries of all industries. In 2011/2012, 28% of all fatal injuries to workers happened in construction. The most frequent causes of injury are manual handling, slips and trips, and falls from height. There were 49 fatalities as a result of construction workers falling in 2011/2012, and 23 of these fatalities were self-employed workers. This compares with an average of 59 over the previous five years, with an average of 19 being self-employed. These figures show how vital it is to be aware of the risks, and to make sure safety is always a priority when working at height.

The table shows the main causes of worker fatalities in the UK over the past five years, in the construction industry compared with other industries.

Cause of fatality	Proportion of fatalities 2007–2012	
	Construction	All industries
Fall	47%	24%
Struck by a falling or moving object	12%	16%
Collapse	12%	10%
Hit by a moving vehicle	11%	16%
Electricity	6%	4%
Other	12%	30%

In the year 2011/2012, more than half of all fatalities in the UK construction industry were caused by falls. (This is shown by the pie chart in Chapter 1, page 2.)

INDUSTRY TIP

Don't become one of these statistics. Ensure that you properly assess the risks and always take the safest approach.

FUNCTIONAL SKILLS

Using a word processing program, represent the information in the pie chart on page 2 relating to construction fatalities for the year 2011/2012 as a bar chart.

Work on this activity can support FICT1 (1.7 and 1.8).

FUNCTIONAL SKILLS

Using the information in the table opposite, answer the following questions:

1 In 2007–2012, what was the percentage difference between fall fatalities in the construction industry and fall fatalities in all industries?

2 Roughly, what is the **proportion** of construction fall fatalities to fall fatalities across all other industries during the period 2007–2012?

Work on this activity can support FM1 Cl.11.

Answers: 1. 47 − 24 = 23%, 2. Roughly 200%, or twice as many.

SELECTING ACCESS EQUIPMENT AND WORKING PLATFORMS

There are a number of factors to consider when you are selecting access equipment. In the first instance it is worth considering the simple rules for working at height as set out in the Work at Height Regulations 2005 (as amended). They apply to all work at height where it is likely someone will be injured if they fall.

The Work at Height Regulations set out the following three rules, which should be considered in the order shown:

1 *Avoid* work at height if you can – If you don't need to go up there, don't!

2 *Prevent* falls by selecting and using the right access equipment, if work at height cannot be avoided.

3 *Minimise* the impact of any fall. Where you cannot eliminate the risk of a fall, use work equipment or other means to minimise the distance and consequences of a fall, should one occur.

Having checked these three rules, the next step is to select the correct equipment for the job at hand. Factors to consider will include:

- ground conditions
- height, type and duration of work
- weather conditions
- internal/external locations
- **access** and **egress**.

A very useful aid to thinking about these factors can be found on the HSE website in the form of 'WAIT' – the **W**ork at height **A**ccess equipment **I**nformation **T**oolkit – which gives some possible solutions.

The toolkit suggests solutions and possible equipment to use, bearing in mind the following:

- height of working platform
- work duration
- time between equipment movements
- restricted job access
- type of work activity
- whether access equipment needs to be freestanding.

INDUSTRY TIP

Always be aware that any height above ground is deemed to be working at height.

Access

The means to enter or gain entry to a place

Egress

The means to leave or exit a place

ACTIVITY

Visit the HSE website and navigate to the WAIT page: http://www.hse.gov.uk/falls/wait/wait-tool.htm. Explore the different types of equipment it suggests.

Mobile scaffold

For example, entering the following information will result in the suggestion of a mobile scaffold.

Height	1.5 to 6m
Work duration	Over 30 minutes
Is access to the job restricted?	No
Time between equipment movements	More than 30 minutes
Work activity	Light (painting and decorating is classed as light activity)
Does the access equipment need to be freestanding?	No

Select 'Mobile scaffold' to find out more, and download the HSE guidance on tower scaffolds.

Now answer the following questions:

1 What guidance points does it suggest with regard to moving the tower?

2 In the section on inspection, who does it say should carry out the inspection?

3 What guidance is given on protecting the public?

4 The guidance document talks about two methods of tower erection. What are they?

5 Why is it important to use the right equipment for the job?

FACTORS TO CONSIDER WHEN SELECTING ACCESS EQUIPMENT AND WORKING PLATFORMS

A range of factors need to be taken into account before the final selection of access equipment. When considering these factors, think about the need to prevent falls by selecting the right equipment, and also the need to minimise the impact of a fall. These aspects will need to be included in the **risk assessment**.

GROUND CONDITIONS AND INTERNAL/ EXTERNAL LOCATIONS

Whether the work is to be carried out inside or outside, ground conditions need to be level, firm and preferably clean and dry. Adequate steps and additional accessories may need to be used to

Risk assessment

An assessment of the hazards and risks associated with an activity and the reduction and monitoring of them

achieve some of these key points, particularly when working externally. Whatever steps are taken to achieve these perfect conditions, the method must be safe.

Internal locations

Make sure areas are clear from any potential trip hazards or obstructions. If working on sloping areas or stairs, make sure that the equipment chosen is fit for purpose.

External locations

Soft ground, rough or uneven ground, or unstable ground conditions will all need to be considered, as will ensuring that the site area is clear and tidy and that any likely obstructions or restrictions on full use are noted.

Ensure that any form of ground support used under any of the selected equipment will not sink into soft ground. For example, when levelling a ladder on a slope, ensure that the wedges or blocks used cannot slip when in use. Of course the ladder must always be secured, preferably at the top, should anything occur to further affect stability.

Equally, ensure that stability is not compromised when working on rough ground conditions. This will be particularly important if using tower scaffolds, and you will need to check that the structure is level and re-levelled after every move.

> **INDUSTRY TIP**
>
> Always check that the surface conditions under your access equipment are level, firm, stable and – as appropriate – clean and dry.

HEIGHT, TYPE AND DURATION OF WORK

An assessment relative to the height of the project needs to be carried out irrespective of the actual height. Remember, any height from which a person may fall is deemed to be 'working at height'. You also need to consider the type and duration of work.

WEATHER CONDITIONS

All types of equipment can be affected by weather conditions, particularly when used externally. Major problems can arise from using access equipment in very windy conditions, in particular if items are not securely tied or materials that might be dislodged are stored on the platform.

Safe working practice is described by the manufacturer or is stipulated by regulations such as the Work at Height Regulations 2005 (as amended) or the Provision and Use of Work Equipment Regulations 1998 (PUWER).

Take care when using access equipment in adverse weather conditions

ACCESS AND EGRESS

Being able to access and egress the equipment should be planned before erection. Trying to work around obstructions can lead to hazardous working conditions, so it is best to try and clear working space for the equipment. Make sure that there are clear indicators at the base of access equipment to stop vehicles striking it – traffic cones or barriers work best.

Consideration should also be given to the general public – it is extremely important to ensure that they are protected. Scaffolds and access equipment should have barriers erected around them to prevent people colliding with the equipment or having objects fall on them. If this cannot be fully achieved then, in the case of scaffold, you will need to provide adequate walkways through with highly visible standards and debris netting, as shown in this illustration of a scaffold erected in a busy street. This structure will require a temporary structure licence from the Local Authority. The licence will set out how long the scaffold will be in place and what arrangements must be made for any pedestrian diversions.

Safe walkways should be set up in busy public areas

ACCESS EQUIPMENT AND WORKING PLATFORMS FOR INTERNAL AND EXTERNAL WORK

There are many kinds of access equipment available, and your choice will depend on factors such as the type and duration of work as well as the location.

STEPS, TRESTLES, PODIUM STEPS, HOP-UPS AND WORKING PLATFORMS

A podium with guard rails on all sides

Steps can be used for low-level work

These will usually be limited to not much more than standard internal heights of around 2.5m and may also be used externally within these limitations. Activities will be relatively short-term and will include painting/papering ceilings or other areas at single-storey height, such as fascias, windows and other parts of the building structure. Podium steps provide low-level height access, offering a firm platform with adjustable height and a guard rail. They may be tubular self-erecting or folded prior to erection, so as to pass through standard doors and corridors.

TIMBER AND ALUMINIUM ALLOY TRESTLES AND WORKING PLATFORMS

When you are using a working platform, your risk assessment will determine whether you need to use guard rails and a toe board. Access to the platform is by an additional ladder. Never use trestles as steps, because the space between supports is designed to allow variation in platform height and is too far apart for stepping.

ADJUSTABLE-HEIGHT STEEL TRESTLES

These are more commonly used by bricklayers and plasterers in conjunction with scaffold boards to provide a low-level platform, although they may be used by painters for low-level ceiling work. They are best used with handrail attachment to reduce the risk of falling. They are sometimes locally referred to as bandstands.

Adjustable-height steel trestles are designed to be used with four standard 225mm-wide scaffold boards or two 450mm-wide lightweight stagings.

Adjustable-height steel trestles

Trestles in use

To erect, position each scaffold board on the trestles, with help, then adjust the boards to centralise them on the trestle. Each scaffold board must be supported every 1.2m or less. The board must lie flat on the trestle without the possibility of rocking and with a minimum of four times the board thickness overhang on each end.

Ensure that you do not attempt to stand on the overhang areas, as this will increase the likelihood of the board tipping. This risk can be reduced by the use of a handrail system, which will prevent you from stepping into this area. In many cases it will be desirable to use a purpose-made handrail system to fully comply with the Work at Height Regulations 2005 (as amended), but this can be determined by the risk assessment for the particular task at hand.

A number of manufacturers have designed purpose-made handrail and toe board systems that can be attached either to the steel trestles themselves or to the working platform.

LIGHTWEIGHT STAGING

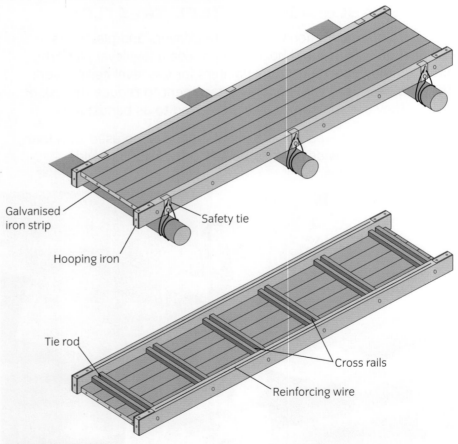

Lightweight staging

Lightweight staging is a specially constructed timber and aluminium platform for spanning greater widths than scaffold boards. Stagings can be used without intermediate supports when used on trestles and placed directly on roof trusses.

Sizes of stagings vary from 450mm wide, with lengths of 1.8–7.3m. Stiles are reinforced with high tensile steel wire. Cross supports are every 380mm or 450mm along the length of the staging and are reinforced with steel ties.

SCAFFOLD BOARDS

Scaffold boards (planks) are used to provide a working platform on trestles and tubular scaffolds. If you are using scaffold boards as a working platform you should always consider whether a safer mode of scaffolding could be used instead. Painters in particular tend to use one or two boards, but this is only suitable in certain situations.

LADDERS

Ladders are intended to be used only for short-term light activities of no more than 30 minutes' duration, unless they are being used to access or egress working platforms. They may be used up to 6m high but must be securely tied or secured top and bottom. Remember that during any activity, the user must always maintain three points of contact with the ladder. That is both feet and one hand, which therefore leaves only one hand free to carry out the activity. For this reason you should use an attachable tray support for the paint kettle and any other small tools you may be using. The illustration shows this incorporated into the ladder stand-off.

Scaffold boards

An attachable tray support and paint kettle

Labels on ladders will indicate which standards the equipment conforms to

British/European Standards for classifications of ladders

Check that the ladder you are using conforms to the relevant standards:

- BS 2037:1994 – aluminium ladders
- BS 1129:1990 wooden ladders
- BS EN/131 (or EN/131) – applies to both.

It is recommended that you use one of the following:

- Class 1 (industrial) – maximum static load 175kg (27.5 stone)
- BS EN/131 (or EN/131) – maximum static load 150kg (23.5 stone).

The ladder should be marked with the class number, maximum weight and instructions on how to use it safely – follow these at all times.

ROOF LADDERS

Working on roofs of any type will present an additional challenge to the decorator, but it is quite common to have to carry out maintenance to such items as wooden skylights, or indeed to decorate whole sections of corrugated iron roof cladding.

Properly designed roof ladders or crawling boards are an essential aid for any work on sloping roofs. This type of equipment will also be essential for gaining access over fragile roof surfaces to reach other items that require decoration. They should be long enough to span the supports (at least three rafters) and securely placed. Roof ladder anchorages should bear on the opposite slope of the roof and not rely on the ridge tiles for support, as these can easily break away. Do not use gutters to support any ladder. It is advisable to use a safety harness and lanyard attached to the ladder when working from a roof.

A typical roof ladder

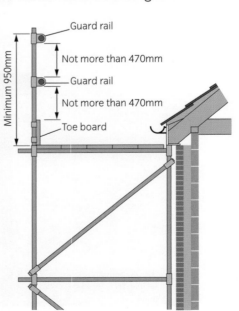

Edge protection on a roof

It is also preferable to have edge protection on the edges of the roof area from which you are working.

TOWER SCAFFOLDS

These should be erected and used only on ground suitable for the purpose – generally with a surface of concrete, tarmac or similar. Where towers are built on soft, uneven or sloping ground, they should be set on boards or other rigid packing, which will provide a firm foundation.

Specific tower instructions would normally be provided in the manufacturer's instructions, which usually include a detailed set of erection and dismantling procedures. You can also refer to the Level 1 book for more detailed guidance.

Tower scaffold

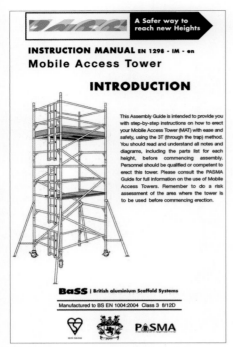

Always follow the manufacturer's instructions

Points to remember

Manufacturers' instructions should always be adhered to, but the following are some useful general points:

■ Always climb a tower on the inside, using the ladder rungs within the frame, and gain access to the platform through the trapdoor platform. Never climb on the outside of a tower.

■ Each time a mobile tower is relocated it should be re-levelled by adjusting the legs. Each castor should be re-locked. When adjustable outriggers are fitted, check that their footings are sound after each move.

■ Working platforms should be fully and closely boarded.

■ Use guard rails and toe boards on all working platforms. The boards must be at least 150mm above platform level. Safety rails should be positioned at between 950mm and 1140mm above the platform, and a mid rail should also be positioned so as not to allow a gap of more than 470mm.

Tower height

The height of a mobile tower should not exceed three times the length of the shortest side, and a static freestanding tower should not exceed three-and-a-half times the dimension of the shortest side (see below). Towers in excess of 10m should be tied to the building, and towers over 12m should be specially designed to enable checks to be carried out on stability and safe loading limits.

Interior use:
Static tower length of shortest side × 3.5
Mobile tower length of shortest side × 3

Exterior use
Static tower length of shortest side × 3
Mobile tower length of shortest side × 2.5

Outriggers or stabilisers

Outriggers or stabilisers increase the effective base dimensions of the tower and must always be fitted to higher towers.

INDEPENDENT SCAFFOLDS AND OTHER TUBULAR SCAFFOLDS

Decorators often use tubular scaffolding for access to work at height that is to be carried out over a long period of time or on large structures such as tall offices, cinemas and bridges.

The illustration shows a typical independent scaffold (without boards, toe boards or guard rails) that will allow access at various floor levels and provides a good working platform around all sides of a building to a considerable height. Generally, though, when the height exceeds standard domestic-type properties, the structure should be properly designed to withstand wind and use loading. This will be essential in the case of scaffold types such as birdcage, slung, suspended, truss out and cantilevered, as well as many other specialist structures.

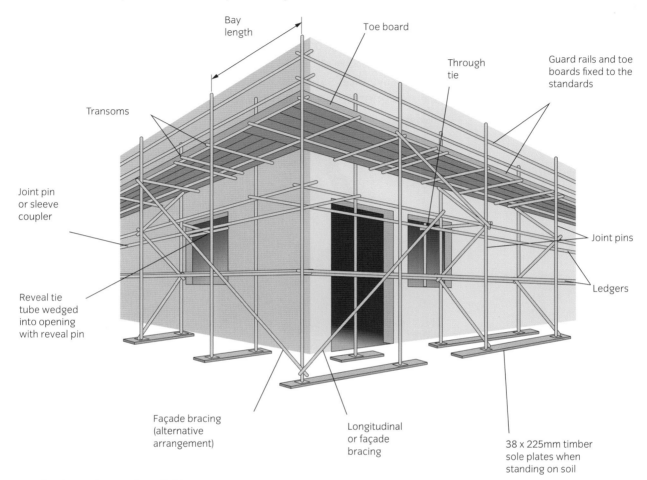

Bay length

Toe board

Through tie

Guard rails and toe boards fixed to the standards

Transoms

Joint pin or sleeve coupler

Joint pins

Ledgers

Reveal tie tube wedged into opening with reveal pin

Façade bracing (alternative arrangement)

Longitudinal or façade bracing

38 x 225mm timber sole plates when standing on soil

Example of independent tied scaffold

Certified scaffolders

All forms of tubular and system scaffold may be erected, altered and dismantled only by trained and competent scaffolders. They should hold a Construction Industry Scaffolders Record Scheme (CISRS) card. Trainee scaffolders must be properly supervised while carrying out any work.

Scaffolding licences

It is the responsibility of the main contractor or scaffolding hire company to get a licence for any scaffolding that is put up on the highway (this includes the pavement). However it's the responsibility of the user or contractor to check they have this legal document and that it does not run out before the work is finished.

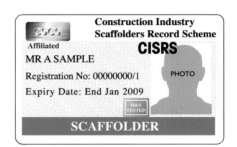

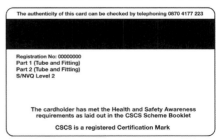

Scaffolders Record Scheme card

MOBILE ELEVATING WORK PLATFORMS (MEWPS)

These are specialist pieces of equipment and should be used only by trained and certificated operators, as there are many safety aspects that must be considered before, during and after use.

MEWPs include cherry pickers, scissor lifts, and vehicle-mounted booms and self-propelled booms. They can be used both indoors and outdoors, and can allow the worker to reach the task quickly and easily. Vital safety features are guard rails and toe boards, which are designed to prevent a person from falling.

Cherry picker

Scissor lift

Vehicle-mounted boom

Self-propelled boom

Operator training and certification

All MEWP operators should have attended a recognised operator training course. On successful completion of the course they will receive a certificate, card or 'licence', eg IPAF's Powered Access Licence (PAL) or Construction Skills' Construction Plant Competence Scheme (CPCS) card, which clearly identifies the bearer and lists the categories of MEWP they are trained to operate. This document can be updated as the operator undergoes further training, and has an expiry date, which should be checked.

Before using a MEWP, it is important to think about the following questions:

- *Height*: How high is the job from the ground?

- *Application*: Do you have the appropriate MEWP for the job? If you are not sure, check with the hirer or manufacturer.

- *Conditions*: What are the ground conditions like? Is there a risk of the MEWP becoming unstable or overturning?

- *Operators*: Are the people using the MEWP trained, competent and fit to do so?

- *Obstructions*: Could the MEWP be caught on any protruding features or overhead hazards, eg steelwork, tree branches or power lines?

- *Is there passing traffic?* If so, what do you need to do to prevent collisions?

- *Restraint*: Do you need to use either **work restraint** (to prevent people climbing out of the MEWP) or a **fall arrest** system (which will stop a person hitting the ground if they fall out)?

- *Allowing people to climb out of the basket is not normally recommended*: Do you need to do this as part of the job?

- *Checks*: Has the MEWP been examined, inspected and maintained as required by the manufacturer's instructions, and daily checks carried out?

RISK ASSESSMENTS FOR ACCESS EQUIPMENT AND WORKING PLATFORMS

You will have looked at the topic of risk assessments in Chapter 1, but in this chapter you will look at how to apply them in the context of working at height.

The Construction, Design and Management (CDM) Regulations 2007 require employers to make a suitable and sufficient assessment of the health and safety risks to employees and non-employees arising

Work restraint

A device used to prevent people climbing out of a MEWP

Fall arrest

A system of restraint that stops a person from hitting the ground

Ensure you wear the correct PPE when using a MEWP

All employers will be responsible for producing the risk assessment, and if they employ five or more employees, a written form must be provided. Each risk assessment should be written in clear, understandable language and should be explained to workers before the task or process is commenced. Work at height is a particular area for which risk assessments should be undertaken.

HAZARD IDENTIFICATION

The following points may be considered when identifying **hazards**:

- falls from heights (people/materials)

- slips, trips, cuts and abrasions

- faulty equipment

- altered/removed parts

- control measures.

Hazard

Something that may cause people harm or ill-health

ACTIVITY

Download or make reference to the risk assessment document on the HSE website and list the Five Steps to Risk Assessment.

Using the information from the HSE guidance document you will see how this been applied in the examples shown in the table.

Task	Hazard	Risk	Control
Using ladders as a means of access from one level to another.	Falling from the ladder. Displacement of the ladder. Failure of the ladder.	Major or lost-time injury to head, legs, arms or internal organs.	Inspect the ladder for visible defects before use. Ensure that the ladder is secured to the landing point and if necessary at the base. Use both hands when climbing up or coming down the ladder.
Working at or adjacent to a leading edge.	A person or persons falling from one level to another. Materials falling from heights.	Fatal, major or lost-time injury. Fatal, major or lost-time injury due to being struck by falling material(s).	Check the work location prior to commencement. Confirm the positioning, integrity and suitability of the barrier. If considered unsuitable, stop and have the assembly upgraded.

Task	Hazard	Risk	Control
Working from bandstand scaffolds or hop-ups.	A person or persons falling from the work platform. Structural failure of the assembly.	Major or lost-time injury.	Authorisation for the use of bandstand scaffolds or hop-ups to be recorded in the Safety Method Statement. The platform height must not exceed 1.2m. Overloading must be prohibited. Safe ladder access point must be established.
Working from tubular steel or proprietary system scaffolds.	Structural failure or displacement of the scaffold. Failure of scaffold boards. Personnel falling from the scaffold. Materials falling from the scaffold.	Fatal, major or lost-time injury. Fatal, major or lost-time injury due to being struck by falling material(s).	Scaffold or section of the scaffold to be inspected by an authorised person to confirm suitability and structural integrity prior to use. Inspection sequence and method to be in accordance with company health and safety procedures. Work from incomplete or suspect scaffolding prohibited.
Working from steps or ladders.	Failure of the steps/ladder. Falling from the steps/ladder. Over-reaching from the steps/ladder.	Fatal, major or lost-time injury.	Task to be subject to a specific risk assessment. If authorised, for short duration, light-duty tasks only. Ladder to be footed and secured. Lone working prohibited.
Working from steps in the vicinity of energised electrical apparatus or apparatus capable of being energised.	Making contact with or causing an arc from the apparatus to the steps.	Electric shock or flashover fatal or major injury. Damage to equipment.	Steps made from non-conductive material only may be used in such locations.

Task	Hazard	Risk	Control
Working from or resting ladders/steps against cable trays or in-situ pipework.	Failure of the tray suspension system. Failure of or damage to in-situ pipework.	Fall from height – fatal or major injury. Uncontrolled release of liquid, gas or other substance being piped. Major injury and/or damage.	Working from suspended cable trays prohibited. Resting ladders/steps against in-situ services prohibited unless authorised by the service owner.
Issuing or using safety harnesses for the purpose of arresting the fall of a person.	Use of untrained personnel. Failure to inspect the system before issue/ use. Attaching the system to an unapproved fixing point.	Fatal, major or lost-time injury in the event of a malfunction of the system or the anchorage point.	Safety harnesses to be issued to and used by trained personnel only. The task and location shall be subject to a specific risk assessment. The system shall be subject to a record-keeping regime as prescribed by the manufacturer.

For further information and to view sample risk assessments go to www.hse.gov.uk/risk/casestudies and view the example assessment for a plastering company.

METHOD STATEMENTS

Method statements are further examples of essential documentation related to work activities. They are set out in concise terms and include the following aspects:

- *Personal Protective Equipment*: Outlines in detail any PPE required for the task.

- *Planning*: To include a description of potential hazards; information that can be used to make safe decisions before beginning the task. It includes topics such as site assessments, correct equipment choices, time and resource planning, obtaining information from qualified persons, obtaining permits, notifying authorities, etc.

- *Preparation*: Provides more site-specific information. While the planning section looks at the bigger picture, the preparation section focuses on what is needed locally at the time.

- *Pre-operational inspection*: Includes checks that all equipment to be used is in a safe condition. Includes machinery, tools, lifting equipment and associated slings, or other such necessary items.

Method statement

A description of the intended method of carrying out a task, often linked to a risk assessment

■ *Operation*: Outlines the task in sequence. All risks are to be identified.

■ *Maintenance*: Highlights maintenance regimes or inspection requirements where they are legislated.

■ *Emergency procedures*: Highlight essential emergency information. This can include specific first-aid procedures if relevant.

A method statement is a useful way of recording the hazards involved in specific work at height tasks and communicating the risk and precautions required to all those involved in the work. The statement need be no longer than necessary to achieve these objectives effectively. It should be clear and illustrated by simple sketches where necessary. Avoid ambiguities or generalisations, which could lead to confusion. Statements are for the benefit of those carrying out the work and their immediate supervisors, and should not be over-complicated. Equipment needed for safe working should be clearly identified and available before work starts. Workers should know what to do if the work method needs to be changed.

Planning that is linked to risk assessments and method statements will go a long way to ensure that a safe preventative approach is taken to all work that you are doing, and this is of paramount importance when using access equipment.

CHECK ACCESS EQUIPMENT AND IDENTIFY FAULTS

Your employer will ultimately be responsible for ensuring that the equipment supplied to you is safe and fit for purpose, but remember that as the user you are responsible for your own safety; it is important that visual checks are carried out on a regular basis to ensure that the equipment you are using is still fit for use.

This section follows on from the Level 1 textbook, particularly with regard to ladders, steps, podiums, trestles, hop-ups and tower scaffolds. As a recap, some of the points are repeated here to ensure a complete understanding of the range of equipment available to the decorator.

Some of the information given in this section will help you carry out systemised checks and inspections in line with the regulations, but be sure to report any defects found during your daily checks so that remedial action may be taken.

Ladder tag inspection record

INSPECTION TIME PERIODS

Access equipment should be checked:

- pre-erection

- post-erection

- before handing over

- if there are inclement weather conditions

- if major alterations have been made

- every seven days

- post-accident and -incident, as the condition of the equipment may have altered.

You need to know when to inspect access equipment

PROCEDURE FOR CARRYING OUT VISUAL CHECKS ON ACCESS EQUIPMENT PRIOR TO USE

To complete a safety check, the correct paperwork must be completed. While you are training, you should be overseen by a competent person who can provide you with the correct guidance to complete these simple documents, while identifying any potential hazards.

Schedule 7 of the Work at Height Regulations 2005 (as amended) requires the following particulars to be recorded:

- the name and address of the person for whom the inspection was carried out

- the location of the work equipment inspected

- a description of the work equipment inspected

- the date and time of the inspection

- details of any matter identified that could give rise to a risk to the health or safety of any person

- details of any action taken as a result of any matter identified in paragraph 5

- details of any further action considered necessary

- the name and position of the person making the report.

CHECKS AND INSPECTIONS OF LADDERS, STEPS AND TRESTLES

Typical areas to be checked with regard to ladders relate to the items that are included in the inspection records provided to help with recording this information. This involves, on a daily basis, ensuring that the equipment is being safely used and at the correct angles, on safe ground and using the correct PPE when required. This will go a long way towards ensuring that there are no areas for concern.

For example, is the ladder being used at the correct angle of 75°, or a ratio of one out to four up?

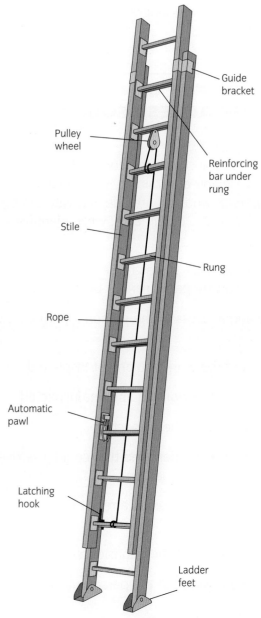

Guide bracket

Pulley wheel

Reinforcing bar under rung

Stile

Rung

Rope

Automatic pawl

Latching hook

Ladder feet

Labelled ladder

Basic pre-use checklist

Employers and employees and all users of ladders should be able to answer 'Yes' to each of the following questions, or to the alternative given, before a job is started:

(a) Is a ladder, stepladder, etc the right equipment for the work?   YES [   ] NO [   ]

(b) If so, is the equipment in good condition and free from slippery substances?   YES [   ] NO [   ]

(c) Can the leaning ladder be secured at the top?   YES [   ] NO [   ]

(d) If not, can it be secured at the bottom?   YES [   ] NO [   ]

(e) If a ladder has to be used and cannot be secured, will a second person stationed at the base provide sufficient safety?   YES [   ] NO [   ]

(f) Does the ladder project above the platform by 1m?   YES [   ] NO [   ]

(g) Is there an adequate handhold at the place of landing?   YES [   ] NO [   ]

(h) Are there platforms at 9m maximum intervals?   YES [   ] NO [   ]

(i) Is the ladder angle correct?   YES [   ] NO [   ]

(j) Is the support for the ladder adequate at both the upper point of rest and the foot?   YES [   ] NO [   ]

(k) Is the ladder properly positioned?   YES [   ] NO [   ]

(l) If it is necessary to carry tools and equipment, has provision been made for carrying them so that the user can keep their hands free for climbing?   YES [   ] NO [   ]

(m) If an extension ladder is used, is there sufficient overlap between sections?   YES [   ] NO [   ]

(n) On the stepladder, are the locking bars or support ropes in good condition?   YES [   ] NO [   ]

(o) Can the stepladder be placed sufficiently near the work on a firm level surface?   YES [   ] NO [   ]

(p) Is the ladder clear of overhead electric cables?   YES [   ] NO [   ]

ACTIVITY

In the list, there are a number of questions that need to be answered as part of the pre-use check:

- When would ladders be suggested as the right equipment for the job?
- What is the correct angle for the ladder?
- What are the dangers of using ladders near electric cables?

The following illustrations indicate the parts that will require checking on steps and trestles. The condition can be recorded on the inspection records.

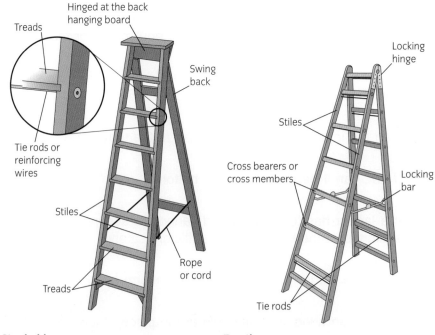

Stepladder   Trestle

An inspection log is attached to the side of a piece of equipment confirming that it has been inspected, and that it is either safe or unsafe to use. The green log denotes that it has passed the inspection and is safe, while the red log indicates that it has not passed and is not safe.

Inspection labels

Below is an example inspection checklist for ladders, steps and trestles.

LADDERS		
(6-MONTHLY INSPECTION)		
Department/Location: Ladder No:		TICK OK
Inspected by:		
NO: ITEM:	**Condition**	☑
STRAIGHT LADDER		
1.1 Loose rungs (move by hand)		
1.2 Loose nails, screws, bolts, etc		
1.3 Loose mounting brackets, etc		
1.4 Cracked, broken, split stays		
1.5 Splinters on stays or rungs		
1.6 Cracks in metal stays		
1.7 Bent metal stays or rungs		
1.8 Damaged/worn non-slip devices		
1.9 Wobbly		
STEPLADDER		
1.10 Wobbly		
1.11 Loose/bent hinge spreaders		
1.12 Stop on spreaders broken		
1.13 Loose hinges		
EXTENSION LADDER		
1.14 Defective extension locks		
1.15 Defective rope pulley		
1.16 Deterioration of rope		
TRESTLE LADDER		
1.17 Wobbly		
1.18 Defective hinges		
1.19 Defective hinge-spreaders		
1.20 Stop on spreads defective		
1.21 Defective centre guide for extension		
1.22 Defective extension locks		
FIXED LADDER		
1.23 Ladder cage		
1.24 Deterioration in all metal parts		
GENERAL		
1.25 Painting of wooden ladders		
1.26 Identification		
1.27 Storage		

CHECKS AND INSPECTIONS ON LEANING LADDERS

SET-UP

- Do a daily pre-use check (include ladder feet).

- Secure it.

- Ground should be firm and level.

- Maximum safe ground side slope 16° (level the rungs with a suitable device).

- Maximum safe ground back slope 6°.

- Have a strong upper resting point (not plastic guttering).

- Floors should be clean, not slippery.

IN USE

- Short-duration work (maximum 30 minutes).

- Light work (up to 10kg).

- Ladder angle 75° – one in four rule (one unit out for every four units up).

- Always grip the ladder when climbing.

- Do not overreach – make sure your belt buckle (navel) stays within the stiles and keep both feet on the same rung or step throughout the task.

- Do not work off the top three rungs – this provides a handhold.

- Always maintain three points of contact with the ladder, preferably both feet and at least one hand.

CHECKS AND INSPECTIONS ON STEPLADDERS

SET-UP

- Do a daily pre-use check (include stepladder feet).

- Ensure there is space to fully open the stepladder.

- Use any locking devices.

- Ground should be firm and level.

- Floors should be clean, not slippery.

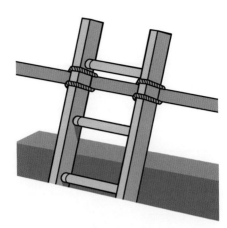

The top of a ladder secured by lashing

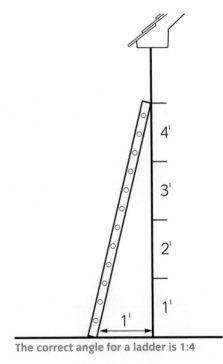

The correct angle for a ladder is 1:4

IN USE

- Short duration work (maximum 30 minutes).

- Light work (up to 10kg).

- Do not work off the top two steps (top three steps for swing-back/ double-sided stepladders) unless you have a safe handhold on the steps.

- Avoid side-on working.

- Do not over-reach – make sure your belt buckle (navel) stays within the stiles and keep both feet on the same rung or step throughout the task.

ACTIVITY

Visit the ladderassociation.org.uk website and download the *Ladder Book*. From the information provided write down what is described as the STEP methodology.

CHECKS AND INSPECTIONS ON TUBULAR SCAFFOLDING

There are strict regulations that dictate the regularity of checking, recording and monitoring of scaffolds on site. A scaffold should not be used unless it has been inspected by a **competent** person:

- within the immediately preceding seven days

- after exposure to weather conditions likely to have affected its strength or stability or to have displaced any part.

A report must been made of the results of every such inspection, and entered in the site register, and signed by the person making the inspection.

Competent

Someone who is properly trained or has sufficient skill and knowledge to carry out a task

FUNCTION AND IDENTIFICATION OF TUBULAR SCAFFOLD COMPONENTS

As decorators making use of such scaffolds it will be important to look out for the scaffold inspection log and to further note that there are no tags indicating areas unfit for use.

Tubular scaffolds

The following illustrations indicate the parts that make up a tubular scaffold. The key areas to check as a user will include the following aspects:

- Ensure that guard rails and toe boards are in place.

- Ensure that the working platform is close boarded with no gaps through which a person could fall.

- Ensure that there are no trip hazards.

- Ensure that all access ladders are properly secured and provide an adequate handhold when stepping onto a platform.

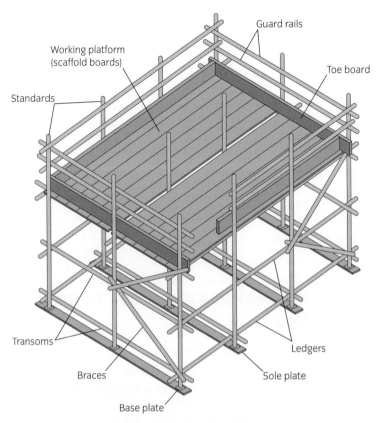

Birdcage scaffold: often used by decorators when completing large-scale, long-duration work such as on cinemas, churches and other large buildings

Scaffold part	Description
Tubular steel or aluminium poles 	These are poles in various sizes that are used to perform the role of standards, ledgers, transoms, diagonal braces, guard rails, ties and rakers.
Standards 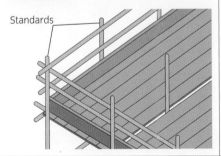	These are vertical or upright tubes that carry the main weight of the structure.

Scaffold part	Description
Ledgers Ledgers	These are horizontal tubes that stretch the length of the scaffold, making internal and external frames with the standards to support the transoms.
Transoms Transoms	These are cross members that span across the ledgers to support the working platform, ie scaffold boards.
Diagonal or cross braces Braces	These triangulate the scaffold frame to provide greater rigidity.
Guard rails Guard rails	These are safety rails, with one positioned at between 950mm and 1140mm above the platform and also a mid rail positioned so as not to allow a gap of more than 470mm.
Ties Ties	These are tubes used to connect the scaffold to the building to provide stability.

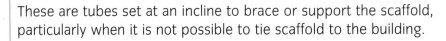

Scaffold part	Description
Rakers 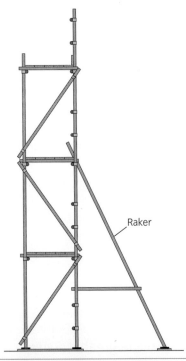	These are tubes set at an incline to brace or support the scaffold, particularly when it is not possible to tie scaffold to the building.
Double coupler 	Double couplers are used to connect ledgers to standards at 90°. They are load bearing and carry the main weight of the scaffold platform.
Swivel coupler 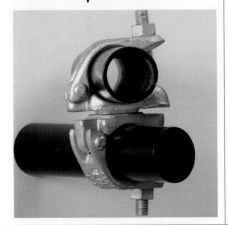	Swivel couplers enable two scaffold tubes to be connected together at any angle. They are used mainly for diagonal bracing.

Scaffold part	Description
Single coupler or putlog coupler 	A single or putlog coupler typically connects guard rails to standards. It should not be used as a load-bearing coupler.
Toe board 	This is a scaffold board on edge, fixed to the standards along the edge of the working platform to stop objects being kicked off or falling over the edge.
Base plate 	This is used to provide a flat bearing surface for even load distribution of scaffold standards. It should be used in conjunction with a sole plate. As an alternative to a base plate, a base jack can be used. This has a threaded adjustment that can be used to level scaffold on sloping or uneven ground.
Sole plate 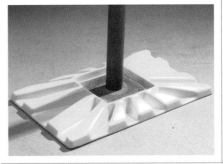	This is for use with a base plate or base jack where there are soft ground conditions. Timber sole plates are commonly used.

Scaffold part	Description
Scaffold board 	This is used to provide a working platform. The minimum width of a working platform is two boards wide (450mm). The maximum overhang is four times the thickness of the board, but not less than 50mm. Scaffold boards should normally be supported at least every 1.2m.
Scaffolding inspection equipment 	This is used to record inspections and/or to prohibit the use of scaffold when undergoing changes that make sections unsafe.

ACTIVITY

Visit www.scafftag.co.uk and find the following information:

■ the cost of the Scafftag safety system
■ the cost of the Laddertag safety system.

Add the cost of these items together and then add VAT at 20%.

INDUSTRY TIP

Under no circumstances should you attempt to alter any part of a tubular scaffold. This kind of alteration must be carried out by a trained scaffolder.

The scaffolding structure is always subjected to a handover inspection between the scaffolding contractor and the main building contractor before use and after every alteration carried out by the scaffolding contractor. During the weekly inspections, the contractor will be checking to make sure that the scaffolding has not deteriorated or been interfered with.

Guard rails

There are specific requirements within Schedule 2 of the Work at Height Regulations 2005 (as amended). The most important of these relate to guard rail locations and dimensions, and the illustration below highlights the key dimensions. The regulations also state that the minimum height of a guard rail should be no less than 950mm from the working platform.

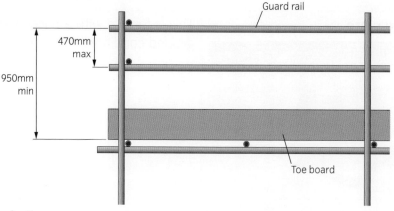

Guard rail

Further regulations governing dimensions relate to maximum working heights for non-designed structures and also relate to the widths of working platforms. This is covered in Schedule 1, but in addition it is advised that a working platform should not be less than 600mm wide.

PASMA Tower Inspection Record

CHECKS AND INSPECTIONS ON MOBILE TOWERS

The Work at Height Regulations 2005 (as amended) require that mobile access scaffold towers are inspected after assembly and before use by a competent person, and that a written report of that inspection is completed before going off duty, and that a copy is given to the person for whom the report was completed within 24 hours.

PASMA, in consultation with the HSE, has developed the PASMA Tower Inspection Record for this purpose. As well as providing a visual indicator of the tower's inspection status, it acts as a written report, and by affixing the record to the tower, you satisfy the requirement to give it to the person for whom it was completed within 24 hours.

PASMA

The Prefabricated Access Suppliers' & Manufacturers' Association – the lead trade association for the mobile access tower industry

TIME PERIODS

All towers must be inspected following assembly and then at suitable regular intervals. In addition, if the tower is used for construction work and a person could fall 2m or more from the working platform, it must be inspected following assembly and then every seven days. Stop work if the inspection shows that it is not safe to continue, and put right any faults.

The HSE guidance indicates, in addition to the seven-day frequency of inspections, that a tower should be inspected after any event likely to have affected its stability or structural integrity, such as adverse weather conditions. You may be able to think of other events that could have such an effect. It is important to note that the regulations do not require a written report each time a tower is moved or relocated to the same site. However, if guard rails or other components have to be removed to enable the tower to be moved past an obstruction, a pre-use check should be undertaken by a trained and competent user to make sure the tower has been reinstated correctly.

COMPLETION OF RECORD

When the record is full, it is removed from the tower (if the tower is still being used, a new Tower Inspection Record is commenced), and the previous one is retained as a record of the inspections until the work is completed, and thereafter at your office for a further three months, as required by the regulations.

INDICATING DANGER

As well as being suitable for recording inspections, the reverse of the PASMA Tower Inspection Record can also be used as a visual indicator and record that the tower is not to be used, because it is incomplete, damaged, or otherwise unsafe. If your tower is incomplete or is in a dangerous condition, you must let other people know. You should affix a 'Tower incomplete', 'Tower damaged' or 'Tower unsafe' sign in a prominent position or adjacent to an access point, so that any potential users are aware of its condition and do not attempt to use it. Always keep up to date with any changes in the regulations.

INSPECTION

PUWER (Provision and Use of Work Equipment Regulations) 1998 and the Work at Height Regulations 2005 (as amended) make it a legal requirement to ensure that all commercial scaffold towers are safe to use. The image in the margin shows such a system in use so that it complies with the regulations. The scaffold should be inspected on a regular and systematic basis.

REQUIREMENTS

The requirement for inspection is different for small towers under 2m, and for towers of 2m and above.

If the tower is under 2m in height, the tower must be inspected:

- after assembly in any position

- after any event liable to have affected its stability, and

- at suitable intervals depending on frequency and conditions of use.

If the tower is over 2m in height, the tower must be inspected:

- after assembly in any position

- after any event liable to have affected its stability, and

- at intervals not exceeding seven days.

SAFETY CHECKLIST

- Ensure all brace claws operate and lock correctly prior to erection.

- Inspect components prior to erection.

- Inspect tower prior to use.

- Ensure tower is upright and level.

- Ensure that **castors** are locked and legs correctly adjusted.

Equipment inspection

Castors

The swivelling wheels fixed to a scaffold frame

■ Diagonal braces fitted?

■ Stabilisers/outriggers fitted as specified?

■ Platforms located and windlocks on?

■ Toe boards located?

■ Check that guard rails are fitted correctly.

The illustration below shows the various parts of a tower scaffold to provide a visual check for the inspection process.

It is very important to ensure that any defective equipment is taken out of use and its condition reported to your line manager or supervisor. Make sure that others who may be likely to use the faulty equipment are informed of its condition.

If items are missing, such as toe boards from tower scaffolds for example, it may be possible to collect these and put them in place. Once again, remember that you need to have been trained to ensure they are correctly fixed.

INDUSTRY TIP

Under no circumstances should you attempt to carry out any makeshift repairs.

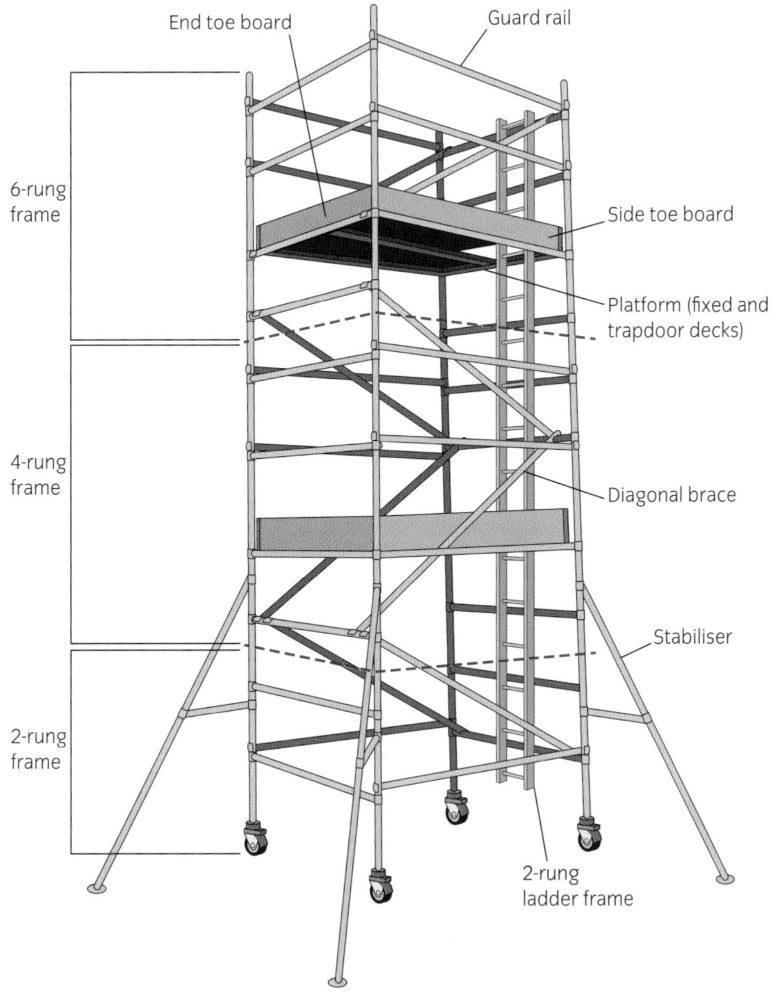

Example of a tower scaffold

Falling from a ladder can be fatal

HAZARDS ASSOCIATED WITH ACCESS EQUIPMENT AND WORKING PLATFORMS

As well as being aware of the need to check and inspect access equipment, it is important to be able to understand typical hazards associated with the work to prevent accidents happening and help you identify faulty equipment.

FALLS

The key factor is avoiding falls. The HSE has identified the top ten safety risks that lead to fatal accidents. They can be viewed at www.hse.gov.uk/construction/lwit/risk-behaviours-tool.htm. This interactive tool has been developed to prevent accidents through a better understanding of the risks. Note that falls from ladders are the number one killer, and that five of the top ten are related to working at height.

OTHER HAZARDS

As well as the main hazard of falls, there are also other hazards relating to not ensuring clear and tidy work areas, including working platforms. Slips and trips account for high numbers of accidents, and these can become even more serious when working at height. When working from platforms, whether from simple trestle platforms, tower scaffold platforms or tubular scaffolding, it is important to ensure that any spillage is avoided or wiped up. Further slips can also occur when recommencing work after rain or other inclement weather. It is essential to take extra precautions to remove weather-related hazards from the platform, such as rain or snow.

Sharp edges, splinters and rough surfaces can potentially cause cuts and abrasions, and to avoid or reduce the likelihood of them occurring, PPE such as gloves, overalls, hard hats and boots should be worn.

ERECT ACCESS EQUIPMENT AND WORKING PLATFORMS

When we come to consider and plan the erection of the access equipment chosen, we will have carried out a risk assessment to ensure that the work will proceed safely.

BENEFITS OF RISK ASSESSMENTS

The following are key benefits of risk assessments:

- The job will be well organised and planned.
- Hazards are identified.
- Risks are evaluated and precautions taken.

These aspects should enable the types of activity described in the risk assessment to be carried out time and time again without accident. However, it is important to review them each time to ensure they are still adequate for the activity.

PERSONAL PROTECTIVE EQUIPMENT (PPE)

Remember that where the work requires it, and in particular when on construction sites, there will be a requirement to wear the correct PPE. Typically this will be gloves, safety boots, hard hat, overalls and high-visibility jacket. In addition to the basic safety equipment you may also be required to wear goggles and specialist equipment such as safety harnesses with attached lanyards or fall arrest devices. This will have been highlighted within the method statement and will be specific to the task.

MANUAL HANDLING

When erecting, dismantling or handling access equipment you should ensure that the correct manual handling techniques are employed to minimise injury.

The information and illustration below demonstrate aspects related to lifting items from the floor, and could apply to lifting ladders, frames or other access equipment from the floor. The correct technique is known as kinetic lifting, which means always lifting with your back straight, elbows in, knees bent and your feet slightly apart.

The safe kinetic lifting technique applies to ladders, frames and other access equipment used by painters and decorators

This lifting technique can also be used when lifting materials onto the work platform, but generally decorators do not deposit any materials of great weight when working at height. It is important to consider safe working load limits on the scaffold structure or working platform. Do not, for example, overload a tower scaffold with more people than it is designed for. This information will normally be included in the manufacturer's guidance leaflet.

You may need to lift items that are awkwardly shaped, and you will need to ensure that they are correctly balanced. Make an assessment as to whether you are strong enough to support, carry and handle all the equipment you need to use.

The photographs below demonstrate techniques for handling some items that may not fit the standard categories. However, it is also extremely important to be properly trained and to have had the various methods of manual handling demonstrated before you put them into practice.

Carrying a scaffold board

Two people carrying a ladder over distance

Carrying steps safely

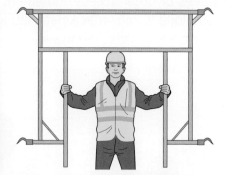

Carrying a tower scaffold frame

DISMANTLE AND STORE COMPONENTS

The illustrations below demonstrate the erection of ladders and scaffold towers, but the principles can be applied to all types of access equipment. Ensure that there is a fall protection device or procedure in place at all times when dismantling such equipment.

DISMANTLING OF LADDERS

The sequence of erecting and moving ladders is shown opposite.

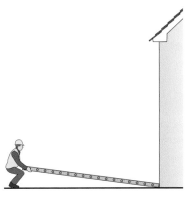

STEP 1 When setting up the ladder for use, push the base of the ladder into the bottom of the wall and start lifting as shown. Ensure that your back is kept straight, and bend from the knees.

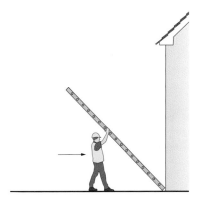

STEP 2 Continue to push the ladder into an upright position. Ensure that you only lift a weight that you are able to hold.

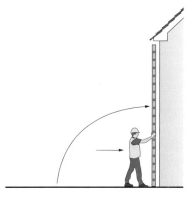

STEP 3 Continue lifting until the ladder is in a near-vertical position, and start to pull the bottom of the ladder out while the ladder is resting on the wall.

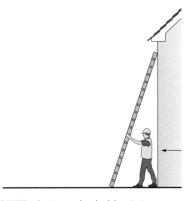

STEP 4 Once the ladder is in an inclined position it may be easier to move to the back of the ladder to set the correct angle.

STEP 5 Once you have finished using the ladder in one position, you may wish to move the ladder a short distance to another position. This can be achieved by holding the ladder against your shoulder to achieve balance. Your hands will be placed one higher and one lower to enable lifting and to maintain balance. This method should only be used when moving short distances.

If possible, you should take the ladder down and carry it horizontally, at your side. This will help you to keep your balance, and make the ladder easier to handle. Lowering the ladder will be a reverse procedure of the method for putting it up.

INDUSTRY TIP

If you can't comfortably carry the ladder by yourself, don't risk an accident. Get help.

DISMANTLING OF TOWER SCAFFOLDS

The step-by-step series on the next page shows a shortened sequence extracted from a manufacturer's guidance leaflet of the erection of a tower scaffold. As in every case it is a good idea to have attended a training course run on behalf of PASMA, at the end of which a certificate of competence will be issued. Whether equipment is hired or owned, it is important to follow the manufacturer's instructions.

In each illustration, the parts coloured red are the parts covered in the instructions. You may require an assistant to hand you the various parts of the tower as it gets taller.

STEP 1 Push the wheels into position, and lock.

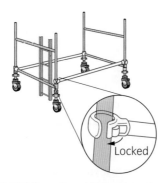

STEP 2 Holding the frame upright, attach the horizontal cross brace. Ensure that this is locked in position. Note how the brace locks onto the inside of the frame. Repeat this activity by locking the brace onto the other side of the frame. Note that this is locked onto the rung of the frame. Attach the brace from one frame to the other to form a solid base for the tower.

STEP 3 Attach the first set of frames to each side. Attach diagonal braces as shown in the diagram. Ensure that interlock clips are locked in place.

STEP 4 Level the tower using a spirit level. You may need to adjust the legs to obtain the correct level. Attach outriggers/stabilisers to each side of the tower.

STEP 5 Attach the bottom platform first, then attach the platform with the trapdoor. Climb up the internal ladder, push open the trapdoor and attach guard rails to both sides before stepping through the trapdoor and standing on the platform.

STEP 6 Attach two more diagonal braces as shown, and insert the next two tower frames while standing on the platform.

STEP 7 Attach two more diagonal braces as shown, to stabilise the upper frames. Attach the next trapdoor platform above your head, and add in a further diagonal brace.

STEP 8 As before, climb up the internal ladder, push open the trapdoor and attach guard rails on both sides before stepping through the trapdoor and standing on the platform.

STEP 9 Attach toe boards around the top platform. Position the tower in its working position and lock the brakes before re-checking the tower is level.

Dismantling is the reverse of the sequence shown.

STORAGE REQUIREMENTS FOR ACCESS EQUIPMENT AND WORKING PLATFORMS

In general terms, with regard to storing all access equipment, it is important that the area is well ventilated, dry and secured or protected from theft or damage. It is recommended to use properly designed racks to enable ladders, scaffold boards and stagings to be stored flat, horizontally and adequately supported along their length to prevent bowing, warping and twisting. All materials are affected by damp in particular, but heat can also cause problems, particularly where timber-based products are concerned.

Metal items may require hinges, joints and so on to be regularly oiled to keep them in good working order.

Always store ladders in a covered and well ventilated area. Ladders must be protected from the weather and kept away from too much damp or heat.

REPAIRS

You should not attempt to repair a ladder unless you are qualified to do so. You should seek advice from the manufacturer about repair or replacement.

SAFETY WHEN NOT IN USE

When ladders are not in use, such as at night or on weekends, it will be necessary to prevent anyone climbing the scaffold. This is not just for security purposes, but also to ensure safety. If ladders are left 'open' during non-working periods and someone does have an accident on or around the scaffold, the company would be liable for not making the site safe.

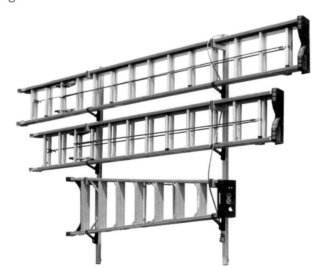

Storage solution: horizontal storage rack

Store equipment correctly and safely

INDUSTRY TIP

Oiling items after use and before storage is a good maintenance tip, as well as checking for damage or decay.

Case Study: Armand and Geri

Armand and Geri are experienced decorators and have been sent to decorate a staircase. Their main task will be hanging wallpaper on the walls. They have carried out this task quite often in the past but are a bit concerned that their work methods may be out of date.

The access method they have always used is a ladder and a plank or scaffold board resting on a stair at one end and a rung of the ladder at the other. This method has allowed them to reach everything within the confined space of a stairwell.

Are Armand and Geri right to continue to use this method? What is the recommended procedure now for decorators to wallpaper the walls adjacent to the staircases in houses, bearing in mind that they need access to brush the wallpaper so it sticks smoothly to the wall?

Geri and Armand's method is incorrect. Although possibly used widely, this method is not good practice. This is because:

- the rung of the ladder has not been designed for this practice

- standard scaffold boards must be supported at regular (1.2m) intervals, and are therefore at risk of failure when being used in this manner.

The solution is to use a narrow stair scaffold that will provide all-round access as well as providing a safe working platform.

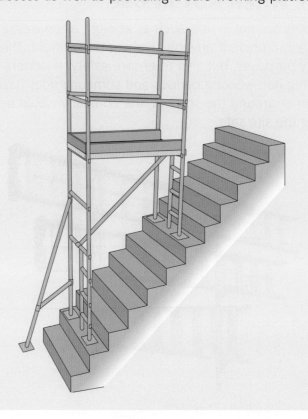

Work through the following questions to check your learning.

1 Which one of the following items would provide the most protection against cuts and abrasions?

  a Safety gloves.

  b Hi-viz jacket.

  c Safety goggles.

  d Dust mask.

2 Working at height is

  a 1m above ground

  b 2m above ground

  c any height above ground

  d 3m above ground.

3 A ladder should **not** be painted because

  a this will make it slippery

  b the paint may hide defects

  c the paint will come off on you

  d it will need repainting.

4 Tower scaffolds are suitable for use for

  a interior use only, with stabilisers

  b exterior use only, with stabilisers

  c neither interior nor exterior use

  d both interior and exterior use.

5 When using a tower scaffold, it is found that the wheel brakes do not work. What should be done?

  a Only use the tower if the floor is level.

  b Get someone to hold the tower while it is in use.

  c Do not use the tower until the brakes are fixed.

  d Wedge the wheels so they do not move.

6 To reach the working platform of a tower scaffold it is necessary to climb up

  a a ladder on the outside of the tower

  b the ladder built inside the tower

  c a ladder leant against the side

  d the outside of the bracing.

7 The gap between the intermediate and top guard rail should **not** exceed

  a 950mm

  b 400mm

  c 470mm

  d 520mm.

8 The **minimum** height of the top guard rail on scaffolding is

  a 950mm

  b 900mm

  c 850mm

  d 800mm.

9 What is the **maximum** base ratio when using mobile tower scaffolds internally?

  a Length of shortest side × 2.5.

  b Length of shortest side × 3.

  c Length of shortest side × 3.5.

  d Length of shortest side × 4.

10 The tubular scaffold being worked on requires some adjustment to the working platform. Who should carry out the adjustment?

  a Someone who thinks they can do it.

  b Someone who has the tools.

  c Someone trained and authorised.

  d Someone who is a supervisor.

11 Which one of the following descriptions describes a standard?

  a A horizontal tube that runs the length of the scaffold.

  b A vertical tube that bears the weight of the scaffold.

  c A tube that spans across the ledgers to support the working platform.

  d A tube that diagonally braces the scaffold.

12 Which one of the following descriptions describes a double coupler?

  a They enable two scaffold tubes to be connected together at any angle.

  b They typically connect diagonal braces to standards.

  c They are used for joining two scaffold tubes together.

  d They are used to connect ledgers to standards at 90°.

13 Which one of the following describes a base plate?

  a For use with base jacks on soft ground conditions.

  b A scaffold board on edge to prevent objects falling off.

  c Used to provide a flat bearing surface for even load distribution of scaffold standards.

  d For fixing a toe board to a standard on a working platform.

14 What are toe boards used for?

  a To stop things falling off the working platform.

  b To support a scaffold working platform.

  c To support standards at the base.

  d To stop things being placed on the working platform.

15 The Work at Height Regulations 2005 (as amended) are quite specific when it comes to inspecting working platforms. Which one of the following is true?

  a Records of inspections do not need to be kept.

  b Records of inspections need to be kept.

  c HSE keep records of inspections.

  d Records of inspections are about using PPE.

16 Which one of the following is a benefit of using a risk assessment for access equipment?

  a It identifies where to store materials.

  b It identifies the hazards.

  c It identifies how to do the work.

  d It identifies who should do the work.

17 Which one of the following is the **correct** manual handling procedure when lifting materials or equipment?

  a Back bent, legs bent, feet together.

  b Back straight, legs bent, feet slightly apart.

  c Back straight, legs straight, feet together.

  d Back bent, legs bent, feet slightly apart.

18 Which one of the following provides good practice guidance and certification for training in the use of mobile scaffolds?

  a Ladder Association.

  b COSHH.

  c NASC.

  d PASMA.

19 The main purpose of the Work at Height Regulations 2005 (as amended) is to

  a prohibit the use of ladders

  b stop people working at height

  c prevent deaths and injuries

  d make people wear PPE.

20 Which one of the following sets of conditions is best for storing scaffold components?

  a Cool and dry.

  b Warm and moist.

  c Warm and dry.

  d Cool and damp.

TEST YOUR KNOWLEDGE ANSWERS

Chapter 1: Unit 201

1   c   Risk assessment.
2   d   Blue circle.
3   b   Oxygen.
4   a CO_2.
5   b   Control of Substances Hazardous to Health (COSHH) Regulations 2002.
6   c   75°.
7   c   Glasses, hearing protection and dust mask.
8   d   Respirator.
9   a   400V.
10 b   80 dB(A).

Chapter 2: Unit 202

1   a   Specification.
2   a   1:5.
3   a   Door.
4   b   Insulation.
5   a   A point of a known height used for setting out.
6   c   Trench.
7   b   Raft.
8   c   Coarse aggregate.
9   a   Insulation.
10 b   English.

Chapter 3: Unit 215

1   b   Spruce.
2   c   Urea formaldehyde.
3   d   Hardwood.
4   d   Rafters.
5   c   Raking out.
6   b   Removing paint from metal surfaces.
7   a   Sugar soap.
8   d   Ceiling rose.
9   b   Iron.
10 b   Aluminium primer.
11 d   growth of moss and lichen.
12 b   Pencil marks.
13 d   Runs.
14 b   Efflorescence.
15 b   Respirator mask.
16 b   weaken the metal
17 d   reduce slipping hazard.
18 c   Liquid paint remover.
19 d   flaking.
20 a   bleeding

Chapter 4: Unit 216

1   d   Computer.
2   c   Filament.
3   a   the texture would be too heavy
4   c   fading
5   c   White spirit.
6   b   Water.
7   d   Skirting boards.
8   b   Grinning.
9   c   Laid flat in a dry place.
10 b   To ensure that older stock is used first.
11 b   To prevent dust transferring through.
12 c   Plastic sheet.
13 d   Skid marks.
14 d   The brush marks are less visible.
15 b   To stop the paint being lifted off.
16 d   Micro-porous paint.
17 b   Thixotropic.
18 a   rapid drying
19 d   mouldings.
20 b   At specific temperatures.

Chapter 5: Unit 217

1   d   Heat expansion.
2   b   Wet embossing.
3   c   Heat expansion.
4   d

5 b 2.

6 c Embossed.

7 b Every second length is hung upside down.

8 b

9 c Starch paste.

10 c Applying paste to paper by pasting machine.

11 d Over-stretching.

12 b Skin irritation.

13 c Plain fibre lining.

14 c By the window.

15 a Shading.

16 a To make sure the paper is plumb.

17 c Ceiling rose.

18 a Over-brushing.

19 b Patterned papers.

20 b prevent damage to the edges

Chapter 6: Unit 218

1 d Drier.

2 a 1 and 4.

3 b Etch.

4 c It buckles or curls.

5 d Timber.

6 c Raw sienna.

7 a 08 C 35.

8 b Artist's oil.

9 d Burnt umber, Vandyke brown, black.

10 c White, black, ochre, Prussian blue.

11 b Linseed oil.

12 d Binder.

13 c Fuller's earth.

14 b Sponge and softener.

15 b Softener and flogger.

16 c Flogger.

17 a Badger hair.

18 b Marbling.

19 c Flogging.

20 d 2, 4, 1, 3.

Chapter 7: Unit 230

1 a Blue.

2 b Green.

3 c Russet.

4 c Colours that use tints and shades from the colour wheel.

5 a Colours that are next to each other on the colour wheel.

6 a Orange.

7 a Lightness.

8 b Intensity.

9 b Blue.

10 b

11 c

12 b BS 4800.

13 c Chroma.

14 c Discord.

15 c Uses black, white and grey.

16 b They appear yellowish.

17 c Colours appear different.

18 a Street lighting.

19 a

20 b

Chapter 8: Unit 220

1 a Safety gloves.

2 c any height above ground

3 b the paint may hide defects

4 d both interior and exterior use.

5 c Do not use the tower until the brakes are fixed.

6 b the ladder built inside the tower

7 c 470mm.

8 a 950mm.

9 b Length of shortest side × 3.

10 c Someone trained and authorised.

11 b A vertical tube that bears the weight of the scaffold.

12 d They are used to connect ledgers to standards at 90°.

13 c Used to provide a flat bearing surface for even load distribution of scaffold standards.

14 a To stop things falling off the working platform.

15 b Records of inspections need to be kept.

16 b It identifies the hazards.

17 b Back straight, legs bent, feet slightly apart.

18 d PASMA.

19 c prevent deaths and injuries

20 a Cool and dry.

INDEX

PICTURE CREDITS

Every effort has been made to acknowledge all copyright holders as below and the publishers will, if notified, correct any errors in future editions.

3M: p299; **A&S Stencil Marking Company LTD:** p295; **Acclaimed Building Consultancy:** © Eamonn Donnellan p138; **AkzoNobel group:** pp 152 - The image of the Dulux Trade Stain Block Plus product sold in the United Kingdom is used by kind permission of the AkzoNobel group, 342; **Alamo Hardwoods:** p120; **Alamy:** © Andy Dean Photography p357; © Angela Hampton pp xi, 262; **Alan Stockdale:** p145; **Anaglypta:** p266; **Ann Cook:** pp xxxvii, 193, 279, 286, 291, 299, 308, 309; **Anstey Wallpaper Company:** pp 221, 222, 223, 224, 225, 239; **APL:** pp 25, 354, 358; **Arnold Laver:** p113; **Australian Scaffolds:** p386; **Axminster Tool Centre Ltd:** pp xvi, xvii, xviii, xxi, xxiii, xxiv, xxvi, xxvii, xxix, xxx, xxxi, xxxii, xxxiv, xxxvi, xxxix, xl, xl, xli, xlii, xliii, xliv, xlv, 20, 22, 23, 34, 36, 109, 114, 115, 116, 117, 118, 123, 128, 132, 133, 134, 135, 146, 148, 151, 162, 163, 164, 172, 174, 175, 176, 191, 192, 193, 194, 197, 242, 249, 269, 272, 275, 280, 295, 296, 298, 302, 329, 354; **BaSS:** p360; **Buildershop (UK) Ltd:** p113; **Capital Safety:** pxxii; **Cebu Belmont Inc:** pp xxxviii, 132; **Celotex:** p100; **Charleston Crafted:** p121; **Chase Manufacturing Ltd:** pp xxvi, 241; **CICRS:** p361; **Clow Group Ltd:** pp xi, xiv, xxviii, 241; **Concreteideas.com:** p139; **Construction Photography:** © Adrian Greeman pp xxxiv, 21, 56; © Adrian Sherratt p89; © CJP p89; © BuildPix pp xlv, 11, 33, 145, 172; © Chris Henderson p34; © Damian Gillie p85; © David Burrows p85; © David Potter p92; © David Stewart-Smith p91; © Grant Smith p13; © Imagebroker p89; © Image Source pp 15, 16, 85, 97; © Jean-Francois Cardella pp xxi, 47, 153; © MakeStock p43; © QA Photos/Jim Byrne p85; © Xavier de Canto p1; **CORAL Tools Ltd:** pp xxxiii, 193, 250; **Coveryourwall.co.uk:** p227; **CWV Ltd:** p266; **Everbuild Building Products Ltd:** p152; **Fall Protection Solutions:** pxxii; **Fibrehand Plastering Supplies Ltd:** p227; **Fotolia:** © Alan Stockdale p39; **Getty Images:** © Andreas Kindler p216; **Go Wallpaper Ltd:** p226; **Grafix:** p295; **Grŵp Llandrillo Menai:** pxxvii; **Hackney Community College:** pp xi, xiv, xv, xvii, xviii, xix, xx, xxvii, xxviii, xxx, xxxv, xxxvi, xxxvii, xxxviii, xli, xliv, xlv, xlvi, 34, 107, 108, 118, 119, 127, 139, 140, 141, 142, 144, 147, 148, 149, 150, 154, 161, 162, 166, 171, 172, 175, 177, 179, 180, 191, 192, 197, 200, 201, 202, 203, 207, 208, 210, 211, 219, 231, 233, 237, 238, 250, 251, 254, 255, 256, 261, 265, 268, 279, 283, 284, 285, 286, 287, 289, 301, 306, 307, 308, 309, 312, 314, 315, 316, 318, 319, 349, 355, 358, 364, 368, 379, 386, 389; **Handover.co.uk:** pp xxv, xxxii, xxxv, xli, 270, 276, 278, 280, 292, 294, 296, 297, 323, 330; **Hawes Plant Hire:** p18; **Health and Safety Executive:** pp xv, 9, 212; **Hire Station:** p355; **Huntco:** pp 130, 115; **If Images:** © Michael Grant p47; **iStock:** © Ajphoto p369; © Banks Photos p95; © Deepblue4you p210; © Ictor pxxxviii; © JasonDoiy p195; **JSP Ltd:** pxxvi; **Mad Supplies Ltd:** pxlv; **Malmesbury Reclamation:** pp xxii, 130; **Mediscan:** p23; **Merlwood Timber:** p86; **Meteor Electrical:** pp 35, 90; **Munsell Color, a division of X-Rite Incorporated:** p332; **Oxford Plastics:** p379; **PASMA:** pp xxxii, 381; **PAT Labels Online:** p372; **PAT Training Services Ltd:** p37; **Philip Kearney:** p273; **Photographers Direct:** © Robert Clare p271; **Pinewood Structures:** p120; **Power Tools Direct:** pp xxiv, 129; **ppconstructionsafety.com:** p52; **Prominent Paints:** p153; **Protectapeel by Spraylat International:** p281; **PureSafety™:** p275; **reliablesource.co.uk:** p142; **Ronseal Ltd:** p120; **RIBA Product Selector:** p78; **Sandtex Trade:** pp xviii, 156; **Scaffolding Supplies Limited:** p379; **Science Photo Library:** © Dr P. Marazzi/Science Photo Library p23; **ShurTech Brands:** pp 175, 282; **Shutterstock:** ©3drenderings pp xxxi, 352; ©501room p362; © Abimages p342; © Agnieszka Guzowska p199; © Alena Brozova p95; © Alessandro0770 p93; © Alessandro Colle p314; © Alexander Erdbeer p13; © Alexey V Smirnov p120; © Alina G pxl; © Amnarj Tanongrattana p174; © Amy Johansson pxxx; © Andrey_Popov p390; © Andy Lidstone pp xix, 272; © Anette Andersen p340; © Anne Kitzman p110; © Anteromite pxliv; © Aragami12345s p18; © Archideaphoto pp 343, 345; © Arigato p111; © Artazum and Iriana Shiyan p178; © Artter p150; © Auremar pp 18, 45, 65, 75, 168, 230,